MW00395917

THE
PARENT'S GUIDE

TO

ATTENTION DEFICIT DISORDERS

Intervention Strategies for the Home

Stephen B. McCarney, Ed.D.
Angela Marie Bauer, M.Ed.

SECOND EDITION

Copyright © 1995 by Hawthorne Educational Services Inc.

Printed in the United States of America

H A W T H O R N E
Educational Services Inc.
800 Gray Oak Drive
Columbia, MO 65201
Telephone: (314) 874-1710

Table of Contents

C. Hyperactive

III. Supplemental Behaviors and Solutions

D. Memory, Organization, Following Directions/Rules

E. Self-Control

I. Dishonest

J. Selfish

K. Defiant

L. Careless with Appearance and Possessions

M. General Academics

N. Reading

O. Written/Expressive Language or Speech

P. Math

I. Introduction

The **Parent's Guide to Attention Deficit Disorders** was developed to provide parents with specific, practical strategies to use in helping their child be more successful in the home environment. The intervention strategies have been tried and tested by teachers and parents of children with Attention-deficit Disorders and are presented in the most convenient and practical manner possible.

The format chosen for the guide was designed for ease of use in identifying the problem the child exhibits and providing a selection of strategies parents may implement to successfully deal with that problem. This format reduces the need for lengthy reading exercises, indecision over how or exactly what to do, and indecision over whether the intervention strategies are appropriate for the child.

Because of differences in situations and the kinds of behaviors associated with Attention-deficit Disorders, the interventions take several forms. Some interventions are appropriate for the prevention of problems, while others reduce problem behavior, increase the child's self-control of his/her behavior, or help the child learn more appropriate behavior. A variety of intervention strategies is presented for each behavior problem associated with Attention-deficit Disorders so that **parents** will be able to choose the interventions best suited to **their child**, in **their home**. We chose to produce a collection of strategies parents can practice in the home, without the need for a therapist or counselor to explain how to "implement" those strategies. We also chose to develop a reference guide that parents can keep available in their homes to answer that primary question, "What do you do when your child...?" rather than a text parents read one time and then shelve without further use. And, lastly, we chose the most logical and common sense approaches because they are the ones that work best with children.

We believe it is extremely important that the intervention strategies employed to help a child succeed are those with which parents are most comfortable. Parents are likely to be more successful implementing those interventions they think are best for themselves and their child rather than attempting to implement interventions suggested by a third party who would not have the same insight the parents have relative to their child's behavior.

The **Parent's Guide to Attention Deficit Disorders** was written for all parents who are genuinely concerned about their child's success and are willing to do all they can personally to make that success possible. We also wrote **The Parent's Guide to Attention Deficit Disorders** for a little boy who came to live in my home a few years ago. He came with nothing but a trash bag containing a few mismatched pieces of clothing that were too small for him. He also brought all the love a little boy's heart can hold and an optimism and zest for life that would seem to negate his past. He has been my teacher for these past few years and he has taught me far more than I had accumulated in all the years prior to his coming. Some days have not been easy, with problems at school and some educational personnel who have been reluctant to be understanding. But, at night, after his bath, when he's in his pajamas and robe, wearing his slippers and smelling really good, and I put him in bed and pull up the covers and he wraps those little arms around my neck and booms out in that little boy voice, "I love you, Daddy!" I know the answer to all his problems. The answer is, "We will get up tomorrow and do all this again because we are all he has. And he is all we have."

We dedicate **The Parent's Guide to Attention Deficit Disorders** to you, Billy. You made it possible. May God bless you and watch over you always.

S.B.M.
A.M.B.

II. Behaviors and Interventions

1 Is easily distracted by other things in the home

1. Carefully consider if your child is capable of performing the responsibilities expected of him/her. Do not give your child too many chores to do at once; make sure he/she gets up early enough to get to school on time; provide more than enough time to perform a responsibility, etc.; and do not expect perfection.

2. Establish rules for performing everyday expectations (e.g., get up on time for school, do your chores right after you get home from school, finish your homework before you watch TV, etc.). These rules should be consistent and followed by everyone in the home. Talk about the rules often.

3. Establish a routine for your child to follow when getting ready for school, performing chores, doing homework, etc. This will help your child remember what is expected.

4. Reward your child for getting things done without being distracted. Possible rewards include verbal praise (e.g., "You're on time for school. Good for you!" "Thank you for remembering to finish your homework before you turned on the TV." etc.), a kiss on the cheek, a hug, having a friend over to play, staying up late, watching a favorite TV show, and playing a game with a parent. (See Appendix for Reward Menu.)

5. If there are other children or adolescents in the home, reward them for getting things done without becoming distracted.

6. Model for your child the appropriate ways to get things done without becoming distracted. Show your child how to follow a routine by following one yourself and getting things done on time.

7. Make certain that your child sees the relationship between behavior and the consequences which follow (e.g., failing to feed the dog will cause the dog to go hungry).

8. When your child does not get something done because he/she was distracted, explain exactly what he/she did wrong, what should have been done and why.

For example: Your child is supposed to catch the school bus at 7:45 a.m. but is still getting dressed when the bus arrives. Go to your child and explain that the bus was missed because he/she was not ready on time. Explain that it is unacceptable to miss the bus because you don't have time to take him/her to school.

9. Write a contract with your child.

For example: I, William, will be ready and waiting for the school bus at 7:40 a.m. for three days in a row. When I accomplish this, I can watch 30 extra minutes of TV.

The contract should be written within the ability level of your child and should focus on only one behavior at a time. (See Appendix for an example of a Behavior Contract.)

10. Allow natural consequences to occur due to your child becoming distracted and not getting things done (e.g., a pet goes hungry if not fed, possessions are lost if not put away, etc.).

11. Along with a directive, provide an incentive statement (e.g., "After you get ready for bed, you may watch TV.").

12. Provide your child with written reminders (e.g., a list posted in the bathroom, indicating what his/her chores are and when they need to be done). (See Appendix for List of Chores.)

13. Tell your child when it is time to set the table, feed the dog, etc.

14. Limit the number of chores for which your child is responsible and gradually increase the number of chores as your child demonstrates the ability to get them done on time without becoming distracted.

15. Allow your child to help decide what his/her routine responsibilities will be.

16. Have your child perform the same responsibilities each day, week, etc.

17. Show your child how to perform a new responsibility (e.g., setting the table) several times before expecting your child to do it on his/her own.

18. Make sure your child has all the necessary materials needed in order to get responsibilities done on time.

19. Explain to your child that responsibilities not done on time will have to be done at other times (e.g., playtime, TV time, weekends, etc.).

20. Reduce distracting activities which interfere with your child performing responsibilities (e.g., turn off the TV when it is time to set the table, do not allow friends to come over when it is time to do homework, etc.).

21. Have your child put a star or check mark beside each responsibility performed on time, and allow your child to trade in the stars or check marks for rewards.

22. Set aside time each week for your child to straighten his/her room, put toys away, etc.

23. Set aside time each day for everyone in your home to complete his/her responsibilities (e.g., after dinner, everyone does those chores assigned to him/her).

24. Do not accept your child's excuse of "forgetting" responsibilities. Have your child make up the chores forgotten during free time, TV time, etc.

25. Provide an atmosphere where everyone works together to get things done around the house.

26. Have your child do those things that need to be done when it is discussed instead of later (e.g., put swimsuits in the car now so that when you go to the pool later this afternoon, they will not be forgotten, etc.)

27. Help your child begin a chore (e.g., cleaning up his/her room) in order to get your child started on the chore.

28. Do not punish your child for becoming distracted during chores, responsibilities, homework, etc.

29. Make certain that the responsibilities given to your child are appropriate for his/her level of development and ability.

30. Provide your child with a "Chores Checklist" and have your child "check off" chores as they are completed.

2 Does not listen to what others are saying

1. Establish rules for listening (e.g., listen when others are talking, ask questions if you do not understand, etc.). These rules should be consistent and followed by everyone in the home. Talk about the rules often.

2. Reward your child for listening. Possible rewards include verbal praise (e.g., "You did a great job of listening!" "I like the way you listen!" etc.), a kiss on the cheek, a hug, having a friend over to play, staying up late, watching a favorite TV show, and playing a game with a parent. (See Appendix for Reward Menu.)

3. If there are other children or adolescents in the home, reward them for listening.

4. Carefully consider your child's age and experience when expecting him/her to be a good listener.

5. Demonstrate the appropriate way to listen by listening to your child when he/she talks.

6. When your child does not listen to what others are saying, explain exactly what he/she did wrong, what should have been done and why.

7. Write a contract with your child.

For example: I, William, for three days in a row, will listen to what others are saying without having to be reminded. When I accomplish this, I can watch 30 extra minutes of TV.

The contract should be written within the ability level of your child and should focus on only one behavior at a time. (See Appendix for an example of a Behavior Contract.)

8. Make certain that your child sees the relationship between behavior and the consequences which follow (e.g., failing to listen to what others are saying may result in missing directions, instructions, etc.).

9. In order to help your child be able to listen to what others are saying, turn off the TV, give directions in a room away from friends, etc.

10. Allow natural consequences to occur due to your child's failing to listen to others (e.g., missing assignments, missing a ride, etc.).

11. Along with a directive, provide an incentive statement (e.g., "When you listen to what I am saying, you may watch TV.").

12. When your child has difficulty listening to others (e.g., at the grocery store, in the mall, playing a game with family members, etc.), remove your child from the situation until he/she can demonstrate self-control and listen to what others are saying.

13. In order to determine if your child heard what was said, have your child repeat it.

14. Deliver directions in a supportive rather than a threatening manner (e.g., "Please take out the trash." rather than "You had better take out the trash or else!").

15. Do not criticize. When correcting your child, be honest yet supportive. Never cause your child to feel bad about himself/herself.

16. Be consistent when expecting your child to listen to what others are saying. Do not allow your child to fail to listen one time and expect appropriate behavior the next time.

17. Make a written list of directions you want your child to follow (e.g., feed the dog, take out the trash, etc.). (See Appendix for List of Chores.)

18. Talk to your child before going into a public place and remind your child of the importance of listening to what others are saying.

19. Make sure your child is paying attention to you when you tell him/her to do something. Have your child look directly at you when you are speaking and have your child repeat the directions to check for understanding.

20. Have your child's hearing checked if you have not done so in the past year.

21. Do not talk to your child from another room. Go to your child, get his/her undivided attention, and tell your child what to do.

22. Make certain to give directions in a very simple manner and be specific as to what you want your child to do.

23. Do not ignore your child when he/she wants to tell you something. When you ignore your child, your child learns that it is acceptable to ignore people.

24. When your child does not listen to what others are saying, let your child know that he/she is not listening and that he/she needs to listen to what others are saying.

25. Treat your child with respect. Talk to your child in an objective manner at all times.

26. Provide your child with a list of written directions, instructions, etc.

3 Does not direct or fails to maintain attention

1. Establish rules for listening (e.g., listen to conversations and instructions, ask questions if you do not understand, follow the instructions, etc.). These rules should be consistent and followed by everyone in the home. Talk about the rules often.

2. Reward your child for listening. Possible rewards include verbal praise (e.g., "You did a great job of listening today!" "I like the way you listen!" etc.), a kiss on the cheek, a hug, having a friend over to play, staying up late, watching a favorite TV show, and playing a game with a parent. (See Appendix for Reward Menu.)

3. If there are other children or adolescents in the home, reward them for directing attention to important sounds in the environment.

4. Carefully consider your child's age and experience when expecting him/her to maintain attention to important sounds in the environment.

5. Demonstrate the appropriate way to direct attention to important sounds (e.g., pay attention to conversations, ask questions, etc.).

6. When your child does not listen, explain exactly what he/she did wrong, what should have been done and why.

7. Write a contract with your child.

For example: I, William, for three days in a row, will listen without having to be told more than once. When I accomplish this, I can watch 30 extra minutes of TV.

The contract should be written within the ability level of your child and should focus on only one behavior at a time. (See Appendix for an example of a Behavior Contract.)

8. When your child has difficulty directing attention in the presence of others (e.g., at the grocery store, in the mall, playing a game with family members, etc.), remove your child from the situation until he/she can demonstrate self-control and follow directions.

9. Make certain that your child sees the relationship between behavior and the consequences which follow (e.g., failing to listen to instructions to bring in a bike at night may result in the bike being stolen).

10. Along with a directive, provide an incentive statement (e.g., "When you eat your peas, you may have dessert." "You may watch TV after you get ready for bed." etc.).

11. Do not give your child directions to follow with more than two or three steps. Directions that involve several steps can be confusing and cause your child to have difficulty following them. An example of a two-step direction is: "Please turn off your light and go to bed."

12. In order to determine if your child heard what was said, have your child repeat it.

13. Deliver directions in a supportive rather than a threatening manner (e.g., "Please take out the trash." rather than "You had better take out the trash or else!").

14. Do not criticize. When correcting your child, be honest yet supportive. Never cause your child to feel bad about himself/herself.

15. Be consistent when expecting your child to direct his/her attention to what is said. Do not allow your child to fail to listen one time and expect appropriate behavior the next time.

16. Make a written list of directions you want your child to follow (e.g., feed the dog, take out the trash, etc.). (See Appendix for List of Chores.)

17. Talk to your child before going into a public place and remind your child of the importance of listening to what is said.

18. Make sure your child is paying attention to you when you tell him/her to do something. Have your child look directly at you to know he/she is listening and have your child repeat the direction to check for understanding.

19. Do not talk to your child from another room. Go to your child, get his/her undivided attention, and talk to your child.

20. Do not punish your child for accidently forgetting, for accidents that interfere with following directions, etc.

21. Make certain to give instructions in a very simple manner and be specific as to what you want your child to do.

22. Have your child do those things that need to be done when it is discussed instead of later (e.g., put swimsuits in the car now so that when you go to the pool later this afternoon, they will not be forgotten, etc.).

23. Make certain that the responsibilities given to your child are appropriate for his/her level of development and ability.

24. Let your child know that directions will only be given once and that you will not remind him/her to follow directions.

25. In order to help your child listen to what is going on around him/her, reduce distractions (e.g., turn off the TV, talk to him/her in a room away from friends, etc.).

26. Have your child's hearing checked if you have not done so in the past year.

27. Do not allow your child to go to public places, friends' homes, etc., if your child cannot listen to what others are saying.

28. Allow natural consequences to occur due to your child's inability to direct his/her attention to what others are saying (e.g. having to "sit out" at the pool for not listening, losing pool privileges, etc.).

29. Make certain you direct your attention to others when they are talking to you in order to demonstrate for your child how to listen to others.

4 Is unsuccessful in activities requiring listening

1. Establish rules for listening (e.g., listen to directions, ask questions about directions if you do not understand, follow the directions, etc.). These rules should be consistent and followed by everyone in the home. Talk about the rules often.

2. Reward your child for listening. Possible rewards include verbal praise (e.g., "You did a great job picking up your clothes!" "I like the way your follow directions!" etc.), a kiss on the cheek, a hug, having a friend over to play, staying up late, watching a favorite TV show, and playing a game with a parent. (See Appendix for Reward Menu.)

3. If there are other children or adolescents in the home, reward them for listening.

4. Carefully consider your child's age and experience before expecting your child to be successful in activities that require listening.

5. Demonstrate the appropriate way to follow directions (e.g., give your child directions to feed the dog and then you feed the dog with him/her).

6. When your child does not listen, explain exactly what he/she did wrong, what should have been done and why.

7. Write a contract with your child.

For example: I, William, for three days in a row, will listen without having to be told more than once. When I accomplish this, I can watch 30 extra minutes of TV.

The contract should be written within the ability level of your child and should focus on only one behavior at a time. (See Appendix for an example of a Behavior Contract.)

8. Make certain that your child sees the relationship between behavior and the consequences which follow (e.g., failing to follow the direction to bring in a bike at night may result in the bike being stolen).

9. In order to determine if your child heard what was said, have your child repeat it.

10. Allow natural consequences to occur due to your child's failing to follow directions (e.g., a pet goes hungry if not fed, possessions are lost if not put away, etc.).

11. Along with a directive, provide an incentive statement (e.g., "When you eat your peas, you may have dessert." "You may watch TV after you get ready for bed.").

12. When your child has difficulty listening and following directions in the presence of others (e.g., at the grocery store, in the mall, playing a game with family members, etc.), remove your child from the situation until he/she can demonstrate self-control and follow directions.

13. In order to help your child be able to listen to directions, reduce distractions (e.g., turn off the TV, give directions in a room away from friends, etc.).

14. Do not give your child directions to follow with more than two or three steps. Directions that involve several steps can be confusing and cause your child to have difficulty following them. An example of a two-step direction is: "Please turn off your light and go to bed."

15. Deliver directions in a supportive rather than a threatening manner (e.g., "Please take out the trash." rather than "You had better take out the trash or else!").

16. Give your child a special responsibility (e.g., answering the door, serving food, cleaning, etc.) in order to teach your child to follow directions.

17. Do not criticize. When correcting your child, be honest yet supportive. Never cause your child to feel bad about himself/herself.

18. Be consistent when expecting your child to follow directions. Do not allow your child to neglect to follow directions one time and expect appropriate behavior the next time.

19. Use a timer to help your child know how much time he/she has to follow directions.

20. Make a written list of directions you want your child to follow (e.g., feed the dog, take out the trash, etc.). (See Appendix for List of Chores.)

21. Talk to your child before going into a public place and remind your child of the importance of following directions.

22. Establish a regular routine for your child to follow on a daily basis in order to help him/her ''remember'' to take care of responsibilities. (See Appendix for Weekday or Saturday Schedule.)

23. Make sure your child is paying attention to you when you tell him/her to do something. Have your child look directly at you to know he/she is listening and have your child repeat the direction to check for understanding.

24. Do not give directions to your child from another room. Go to your child, get his/her undivided attention, and tell your child what to do.

25. Do not punish your child for forgetting, for accidents that interfere with following directions, etc.

26. Make certain to give directions in a very simple manner and be specific as to what you want your child to do.

27. Have your child do those things that need to be done when it is discussed instead of later (e.g., put swimsuits in the car now so that when you go to the pool later this afternoon, they will not be forgotten, etc.).

28. Make certain that the responsibilities given to your child are appropriate for his/her level of development and ability.

29. Let your child know that directions will only be given once and that you will not remind him/her to follow the directions.

30. In order to help your child remember directions, reduce distractions (e.g., turn off the TV, give directions in a room away from friends, etc.).

31. Make certain that games, activities, etc., in which your child participates are appropriate to his/her level of development.

32. Make certain your child understands that if he/she does not follow directions when playing games, activities, etc., others will not want to play with him/her.

33. Play games with your child to help him/her follow directions, rules, etc.

34. Provide your child with written directions, chores, rules, etc. (See Appendix for List of Chores and Posted Rules.)

5 Needs questions and directions repeated

1. Establish rules for listening (e.g., listen to directions, ask questions about directions if you do not understand, follow the directions, etc.). These rules should be consistent and followed by everyone in the home. Talk about the rules often.

2. Reward your child for listening. Possible rewards include verbal praise (e.g., "You did a great job picking up your clothes!" "I like the way you follow directions!" etc.), a kiss on the cheek, a hug, having a friend over to play, staying up late, watching a favorite TV show, and playing a game with a parent. (See Appendix for Reward Menu.)

3. If there are other children or adolescents in the home, reward them for listening.

4. Carefully consider your child's age and experience when expecting him/her to respond to oral questions and directions.

5. Demonstrate the appropriate way to listen to oral questions and directions (e.g., look at the person who is talking to you, ask questions, etc.).

6. When your child does not listen, explain exactly what he/she did wrong, what should have been done and why.

For example: You tell your child to clean up his/her room before 5:00. At 5:00, go to your child and say that he/she has not cleaned up the room and that he/she needs to follow the direction to clean the room now.

7. Write a contract with your child.

For example: I, William, for three days in a row, will listen without having to be told more than once. When I accomplish this, I can watch 30 extra minutes of TV.

The contract should be written within the ability level of your child and should focus on only one behavior at a time. (See Appendix for an example of a Behavior Contract.)

8. In order to determine if your child heard what was said, have your child repeat it.

9. Make certain that your child sees the relationship between behavior and the consequences which follow (e.g., failing to follow the direction to bring in a bike at night may result in the bike being stolen).

10. Allow natural consequences to occur due to your child's failing to follow directions (e.g., a pet goes hungry if not fed, possessions are lost if not put away, etc.).

11. Along with a directive, provide an incentive statement (e.g., "When you eat your peas, you may have dessert." "You may watch TV after you get ready for bed.").

12. When your child has difficulty listening to directions in front of others (e.g., at the grocery store, in the mall, playing a game with family members, etc.), remove your child from the situation until he/she can demonstrate self-control and follow directions.

13. In order to help your child be able to listen and follow directions, reduce distractions (e.g., turn off the TV, give directions in a room away from friends, etc.).

14. Do not give your child directions to follow with more than two or three steps. Directions that involve several steps can be confusing and cause your child to have difficulty following them. An example of a two-step direction is: "Please turn off your light and go to bed."

15. Deliver directions and requests in a supportive rather than a threatening manner (e.g., "Please take out the trash." rather than "You had better take out the trash or else!").

16. Give your child a special responsibility (e.g., answering the door, serving food, cleaning, etc.) in order to teach your child to follow directions.

17. Be consistent when expecting your child to listen and follow directions. Do not allow your child to fail to follow directions one time and expect appropriate behavior the next time.

18. Do not criticize. When correcting your child, be honest yet supportive. Never cause your child to feel bad about himself/herself.

19. Use a timer to help your child know how much time he/she has to follow through with directions.

20. Make a written list of directions you want your child to follow (e.g., feed the dog, take out the trash, etc.). (See Appendix for Sample List.)

21. Talk to your child before going into a public place and remind your child of the importance of following directions and listening to what is being said.

22. Make sure your child is paying attention to you when you tell him/her to do something. Have your child look directly at you to know he/she is listening and have your child repeat the direction to check for understanding.

23. Do not talk to your child from another room. Go to your child, get his/her undivided attention, and tell your child what to do.

24. Do not punish your child for accidently forgetting, for accidents that interfere with following directions, for asking questions, etc.

25. Make certain to give directions in a very simple manner and be specific as to what you want your child to do.

26. Have your child do those things that need to be done when it is discussed instead of later (e.g., put swimsuits in the car now so that when you go to the pool later this afternoon, they will not be forgotten; etc.).

27. Make certain that the responsibilities given to your child are appropriate for his/her level of development and ability.

28. Assist your child in performing responsibilities. Gradually require your child to independently assume responsibility as he/she demonstrates success.

29. Write down information for your child (e.g., take the dog outside at 3:00, clean your room, etc.).

30. Encourage teachers, school officials, etc., to offer your child a written list of directions along with oral directions.

31. Make certain to be specific when telling your child what you want him/her to do.

32. Do not accept your child's excuse of "forgetting" to complete responsibilities. Have your child make up the chores that were forgotten during free time, TV time, etc.

33. Limit the number of responsibilities for your child and gradually increase the number of chores as your child demonstrates the ability to get them done on time.

6 Has difficulty concentrating

1. Make certain the responsibilities assigned to your child are appropriate for his/her level of development and ability.

2. Do not assign your child too many things to do at once, provide more than enough time to get things done, and do not expect perfection.

3. Help your child begin things (e.g., help to open the dog food can, empty a trash can with your child, etc.).

4. Establish rules for getting things done (e.g., complete responsibilities right after school, before you watch TV, before you go out with friends, etc.). These rules should be consistent and followed by everyone in the home. Talk about the rules often.

5. Establish a routine for your child to follow for completing responsibilities, homework, etc. This will help your child remember what is expected.

6. Reward your child for staying on task. Possible rewards include verbal praise (e.g., "Thank you for setting the table!"), a kiss on the cheek, a hug, having a friend over to play, staying up late, watching a favorite TV show, and playing a game with a parent. (See Appendix for a Reward Menu.)

7. If there are other children or adolescents in the home, reward them for staying on task, following a conversation, etc.

8. Model appropriate behavior for your child by staying on task, following a conversation, etc.

9. When your child does not stay on task, attend to a conversation, etc., explain exactly what he/she did wrong, what should have been done and why.

10. Along with a directive, provide an incentive statement (e.g., "You can watch TV after you set the table.").

11. Write a contract with your child.

For example: I, William, for four days in a row, will set the table before watching TV. When I accomplish this, I can skip one night of setting the table.

The contract should be written within the ability level of your child and should focus on only one behavior at a time. (See Appendix for an example of a Behavior Contract).

12. Make certain that your child sees the relationship between behavior and the consequences which follow (e.g., failing to concentrate on homework will result in low grades or incomplete work).

13. Allow natural consequences to occur as a result of your child's failing to stay on task, follow a conversation, etc. (e.g., not knowing what to do, not knowing where to go, etc.).

14. Provide your child with written reminders (e.g., a list posted in his/her room) indicating what chores are to be done and when they need to be completed. (See Appendix for List of Chores.)

15. Tell your child when it is time to complete homework, listen to others, etc.

16. Limit the number of responsibilities for your child and gradually increase the number of responsibilities as your child demonstrates the ability to complete his/her current chores, responsibilities, etc.

17. Have your child complete the same chores and responsibilities each day, week, etc.

18. Show your child how to perform a new chore or responsibility, such as setting the table, several times before expecting the child to do it on his/her own.

19. Make sure your child has all the necessary materials in order to take care of responsibilities.

20. Explain to your child that chores, homework, responsibilities, etc., not completed will have to be completed at other times (e.g., playtime, TV time, weekends, etc.).

21. Have everyone in the family perform chores and responsibilities at the same time in order to help your child remember to complete chores.

22. Reduce distracting activities which interfere with your child's ability to stay on task, follow a conversation, etc. (e.g., turn off the TV when it is time to set the table, do not allow friends to come over when it is time to do homework, etc.).

23. Have your child earn money or privileges for staying on task, following a conversation, etc.

24. Have your child put a star or check mark beside each responsibility completed and allow your child to trade in the stars or check marks for rewards.

25. Set a timer for your child indicating a limited amount of time to finish a chore, homework, etc.

26. When giving your child a chore to do, discuss when it needs to be done and how long you think it will take to do the chore.

27. Make certain to give directions in a very simple manner and be specific as to what you want your child to do.

28. Have your child do those things that need to be done when it is discussed instead of later (e.g., put swimsuits in the car now so that when you go to the pool later this afternoon, they will not be forgotten; etc.).

29. Vary your child's chores from time to time so that he/she does not get tired of doing the same chore.

30. Make certain that the responsibilities given to your child are appropriate for his/her level of development and ability.

31. Assist your child in performing responsibilities. Gradually require your child to independently assume more responsibilities as he/she demonstrates success.

7 Is disorganized with possessions

1. Establish a rule for putting things back where they belong so they can be easily found the next time they are needed. This rule should be consistent and followed by everyone in the home. Talk about the rule often.

2. Reward your child for putting things back where they belong. Possible rewards include verbal praise (e.g., "Thank you for putting your toys in the toy box!"), a kiss on the cheek, a hug, having a friend over to play, staying up late, watching a favorite TV show, and playing a game with a parent. (See Appendix for Reward Menu.)

3. If there are other children or adolescents in the home, reward them for being organized.

4. Carefully consider your child's age before expecting your child to be organized. Help your child put away toys, clothes, etc.

5. Teach your child to put things back where they belong by returning things to their places after you use them.

6. When your child forgets to put things back where they belong, explain exactly what he/she did wrong, what should have been done, and why.

For example: Your child forgets to put a toy back where it belongs. Go to your child and say that he/she forgot to put away the toy and that it needs to be put back where it belongs so it can be found later.

7. Write a contract with your child.

For example: I, William, for five days in a row, will put my toys back where they belong after I'm finished with them. When I accomplish this, I can watch a favorite TV show.

The contract should be written within the ability level of your child and should focus on only one behavior at a time. (See Appendix for an example of a Behavior Contract.)

8. Along with a directive, provide an incentive statement (e.g., "You may watch TV after you put your clothes back where they belong.").

9. Make certain that your child sees the relationship between behavior and the consequences which follow (e.g., not putting away toys will result in not being able to find them and possibly losing them).

10. Allow natural consequences to occur as a result of your child's failing to put things back where they belong (e.g., not being able to find them, the items being damaged and possibly lost, etc.).

11. Make certain there is a designated place for all items in and around the home.

12. Require your child to put his/her coat, gloves, hat, etc., in a designated place upon entering the home.

13. Set aside time each week for your child to straighten his/her room, clothes, toys, etc.

14. Make a list of your child's most frequently used items and/or materials and have your child make sure that each item and/or material is put in its designated place each day.

15. Identify a place for all members of the household to keep frequently used items (e.g., coats, boots, gloves, hats, keys, pens and pencils, purses, etc.).

16. Set aside time each evening when all family members put things in their proper places and organize their possessions for the next day (e.g., school clothes, books, lunches, etc.).

17. Have your child put away toys, clothes, etc., before getting out new things to play with or wear.

18. Require your child's room to be neat and organized so there will always be a place to put toys, games, clothes, etc.

19. When your child has a friend over, have them pick up toys and games 15 minutes before the friend leaves so he/she can help your child.

20. If your child fails to pick up clothes, games, toys, etc., before going to bed, pick up the items and take them away from your child for a period of time.

21. Make certain to be consistent when expecting your child to pick up toys (e.g., do not leave the house with toys in the yard one time and expect the toys to be picked up the next time).

22. Do not expect your child to pick up toys and games that friends failed to put away. Encourage your child's friends to pick up toys and games.

23. Communicate with the parents of your child's friends to make certain that your child helps pick up toys when spending time at a friend's house.

24. Tell baby-sitters or others who are involved with your child that your child is responsible for picking up and putting away his/her own materials.

25. Show your child the proper way to take care of things (e.g., shining shoes, hosing off his/her bike, taking care of dolls, etc.). This will teach your child a sense of responsibility with belongings.

26. Do not buy additional toys, games, etc., for your child if he/she is not able to take care of what he/she has.

27. Have your child pay for things he/she wants (e.g., a baseball mitt, a new doll, a new pair of jeans, etc.). If the child has spent some of his/her own money on an item, he/she may be more willing to take care of it.

28. Provide your child with shelving, containers, organizers, etc., for personal possessions. Label the storage areas and require your child to keep possessions organized.

29. Limit your child's use of those things he/she is not responsible for putting away, returning, etc.

30. Make certain your child understands that he/she must replace things which are lost, broken, or destroyed.

31. Make certain that the responsibilities given to your child are appropriate for his/her level of development and ability.

32. Assist your child in performing responsibilities. Gradually require your child to independently assume more responsibilities as he/she demonstrates success.

33. Discuss your child's responsibilities at the beginning of each day so he/she knows what is expected.

8 Does not remain on task to do homework

1. Establish homework rules (e.g., start homework when you get home from school, finish homework before you watch TV or play with others, ask for help when necessary, etc.).

2. Reward your child for following the rules. Possible rewards include verbal praise (e.g., "Thank you for finishing your homework before playing outside."), a kiss on the cheek, a hug, having a friend over to play, staying up late, watching a favorite TV show, and playing a game with a parent. (See Appendix for a Reward Menu.)

3. If there are other children or adolescents in the home, reward them for following the homework rules.

4. Make sure your child has a quiet and well lighted place in which to do homework.

5. Reduce distractions (e.g., turn off the radio and/or TV, have people talk quietly, etc.) in order to help your child complete homework.

6. Remind your child when it is time to do homework.

7. Encourage your child to ask for help when necessary.

8. Ask your child's teacher to send home explanations of how to help your child with homework if necessary.

9. Sit in the same room with your child when he/she is working on homework. You could read, do needlework, etc., while your child works.

10. Write a contract with your child.

For example: I, William, will complete my homework for four days in a row. When I accomplish this, I can stay up an hour later on Friday night.

The contract should be written within the ability level of your child and should focus on only one behavior at a time. (See Appendix for an example of a Behavior Contract.)

11. Make certain that your child sees the relationship between behavior and the consequences which follow (e.g., forgetting to complete homework will result in a low grade).

12. Allow your child to do something enjoyable (e.g., playing a game, watching TV, talking with a friend on the phone, etc.) after completing homework for the evening.

13. Allow natural consequences to occur due to your child's failure to complete homework (e.g., will not get to watch TV, will have to do the homework during playtime, etc.).

14. If you feel that your child is being assigned too much homework, talk with the teacher about your concerns.

15. Allow your child to have a friend come over so they can do their homework together.

16. Have your child put a star or check mark beside each completed assignment and allow your child to turn in stars or check marks for rewards.

17. Make positive comments about school and the importance of completing homework.

18. Have your child begin homework as soon as he/she gets home from school in order to prevent your child from putting it off all evening.

19. Find a tutor (e.g., a volunteer in the community, one of your child's classmates, etc.) to help your child complete homework.

20. Arrange to pick up your child's homework each day if your child has difficulty "remembering" to bring it home.

21. Help your child study for tests, quizzes, etc.

22. If your child appears to need a break, allow some playtime between homework assignments.

23. Set up a homework system with your child's teacher (e.g., two days a week drill with flash cards, three days a week work on book work sent home, etc.). This will add some variety to your child's homework.

24. Let your child set up an "office" where homework can be completed.

25. Develop an assignment sheet with your child's teacher so you are aware of the work that should be completed each night. Send back the assignment sheet the next day so your child's teacher is aware that you saw the sheet. (See Appendix for Assignment Sheet.)

26. Play educational games with your child to make homework more interesting (e.g., a spelling bee, math races, let your child teach the material to you, etc.).

27. Check over your child's homework when he/she is finished so you can be certain that everything is completed.

28. Assist your child in performing homework responsibilities. Gradually require your child to independently assume more responsibility as he/she demonstrates success.

29. Make certain you are familiar with the school district's homework policy (e.g., 15 minutes a day for 1st-3rd grade, 30 minutes a day for 4th-6th grade, etc.). If your child is receiving more homework than the district requires, talk with your child's teacher.

30. Along with a directive, provide an incentive statement (e.g., "When you finish your homework, you may watch TV" etc.)

31. Make certain your child understands that homework not completed and turned in on time must still be completed and turned in at a later time.

32. Review your child's homework responsibilities after school so your child knows what he/she is expected to do that evening.

33. Have another child (e.g., brother, sister, friend) help your child with homework each evening.

34. Have your child and a classmate who has the same assignment do their homework together (e.g., right after school at one home or the other).

35. Set aside quiet time each night when the family turns off TVs and radios to read, do homework, write letters, etc.

36. Hire a tutor to work with your child to help him/her complete homework.

37. Make sure your child has all the necessary materials to perform homework (e.g., pencils, paper, erasers, etc.).

A Reminder: Homework should be a form of "practice" for what your child has already been taught in school. You should not have to teach your child how to work each problem or activity. Talk with your child's teacher if this is a problem.

Note: If your child cannot be successful completing homework at home, speak to the teacher(s) about providing time at school for homework completion.

9 Does not listen to or follow verbal directions

1. Establish rules for listening to and following directions (e.g., listen when someone is giving directions, ask questions about directions if you do not understand, etc.). These rules should be consistent and followed by everyone in the home. Talk about the rules often.

2. Reward your child for listening to and following directions. Possible rewards include verbal praise (e.g., "You did a great job picking up your clothes!" "I like the way you follow directions!" etc.), a kiss on the cheek, a hug, having a friend over to play, staying up late, watching a favorite TV show, and playing a game with a parent. (See Appendix for Reward Menu.)

3. If there are other children or adolescents in the home, reward them for listening to and following directions.

4. Carefully consider your child's age and experience when expecting him/her to listen to and follow directions.

5. Demonstrate the appropriate way to listen to and follow directions (e.g., you give your child directions to feed the dog and then you feed the dog with him/her).

6. When your child does not listen to and follow a direction, explain exactly what he/she did wrong, what should have been done and why.

For example: You tell your child to clean up his/her room before 5:00. At 5:00, go to your child and say that he/she has not cleaned up the room and that he/she needs to follow the direction to clean the room now.

7. Write a contract with your child.

For example: I, William, for three days in a row, will follow directions without having to be told more than once. When I accomplish this, I can watch 30 extra minutes of TV.

The contract should be written within the ability level of your child and should focus on only one behavior at a time. (See Appendix for an example of a Behavior Contract.)

8. Make certain that your child sees the relationship between behavior and the consequences which follow (e.g., failing to listen to and follow the direction to bring in a bike at night may result in the bike being stolen).

9. Allow natural consequences to occur due to your child's failing to listen to and follow directions (e.g., a pet goes hungry if not fed, possessions are lost if not put away, etc.).

10. Along with a directive, provide an incentive statement (e.g., "When you eat your peas, you may have dessert." "You may watch TV after you get ready for bed." etc.).

11. When your child has difficulty listening to and following directions in front of others (e.g., at the grocery store, in the mall, playing a game with family members, etc.), remove your child from the situation until he/she can demonstrate self-control and follow directions.

12. In order to help your child be able to listen to and follow directions, reduce distractions (e.g., turn off the TV, give directions in a room away from friends, etc.).

13. Do not give your child directions to follow with more than two or three steps. Directions that involve several steps can be confusing and cause your child to have difficulty following them. An example of a two-step direction is: "Please turn off your light and go to bed."

14. In order to determine if your child heard a direction, have your child repeat it.

15. Deliver directions in a supportive rather than a threatening manner (e.g., "Please take out the trash." rather than "You had better take out the trash or else!").

16. Give your child a special responsibility (e.g., answering the door, serving food, cleaning, etc.) in order to teach your child to follow directions.

17. Do not criticize. When correcting your child, be honest yet supportive. Never cause your child to feel bad about himself/herself.

18. Be consistent when expecting your child to listen to and follow directions. Do not allow your child to fail to follow directions one time and expect appropriate behavior the next time.

19. Use a timer to help your child know how much time he/she has to follow through with directions.

20. Make a written list of directions you want your child to follow (e.g., feed the dog, take out the trash, etc.).

21. Talk to your child before going into a public place and remind your child of the importance of listening to and following directions.

22. Establish a regular routine for your child to follow on a daily basis in order to help him/her "remember" to take care of responsibilities. (See Appendix for Weekday or Saturday Schedule.)

23. Make sure your child is paying attention to you when you tell him/her to do something. Have your child look directly at you to know he/she is listening and have your child repeat the direction to check for understanding.

24. Do not give directions to your child from another room. Go to your child, get his/her undivided attention, and tell your child what to do.

25. Do not punish your child for accidently forgetting, for accidents that interfere with following directions, etc.

26. Make certain to give directions in a very simple manner and be specific as to what you want your child to do.

27. Establish a certain time each day for your child to take care of responsibilities (e.g., feeding the dog, completing homework, etc., right after school).

28. Have your child do those things that need to be done when it is discussed instead of later (e.g., put swimsuits in the car now so that when you go to the pool later this afternoon, they will not be forgotten, etc.).

29. Make certain that the responsibilities given to your child are appropriate for his/her level of development and ability.

30. Assist your child in performing responsibilities. Gradually require your child to independently assume responsibility as he/she demonstrates success.

31. In order to help your child be able to follow directions, reduce distractions (e.g., turn off the TV, give directions in a room away from friends, etc.).

32. Make sure you have your child's undivided attention when you are talking to him/her. Stand close to your child, maintain eye contact, and have your child repeat what you say.

33. Be sure your child has heard what you said by having him/her acknowledge you (e.g., by saying, "Okay!" "Will do!" etc.).

34. Make certain your child knows that you expect him/her to listen to you (e.g., by saying, "William, it is important that you listen carefully to what I have to say. You need to feed the dog now!").

35. Allow natural consequences to occur due to your child's failure to follow verbal directions given in public places (e.g., having to "sit out" at the pool, losing pool privileges, etc.).

36. Have your child's hearing checked if you have not done so in the past year.

37. Do not reinforce your child's inappropriate behavior by laughing when he/she is silly, rude, etc.

38. Always expect your child to behave at home and in public by following directions.

39. Ask the employees of the public places that your child visits for a copy of the rules. Review the rules daily with your child.

10 "Forgets" to do things

1. Establish rules for taking care of responsibilities (e.g., perform chores, finish homework before bedtime, take care of personal possessions, etc.). These rules should be consistent and followed by everyone in the home, including the parents. Talk about the rules often.

2. Reward your child for "remembering" to do things. Possible rewards include verbal praise (e.g., "You did a great job cleaning up your room." "Thank you for taking out the trash." etc.), a kiss on the cheek, a hug, having a friend over to play, staying up late, watching a favorite TV show, and playing a game with a parent. (See Appendix for Reward Menu.)

3. If there are other children or adolescents in the home, reward them for "remembering" to do things.

4. Carefully consider your child's age and experience when assigning responsibilities to be performed in and around the home.

5. Demonstrate for your child the appropriate way to perform a chore and assist in performing the chore several times before letting your child perform the chore independently.

6. Establish a regular routine for your child to follow on a daily basis in order to help him/her "remember" to take care of responsibilities.

For example:
    6:30 a.m. - get up, make bed, get dressed
    7:00 a.m. - eat breakfast
    7:30 a.m. - leave for school
    3:30 p.m. - return from school
    4:00 p.m. - feed pets
    5:00 p.m. - set the table for dinner
    5:30 p.m. - eat dinner
    7:00 p.m. - do homework
    8:00 p.m. - go to bed

This schedule could be posted in central locations around the home (e.g., on the refrigerator, in your child's room, in the basement, etc.). Seeing the schedule often will increase the likelihood of your child remembering what to do and when to do it. (See Appendix for Weekday or Saturday Schedule.)

7. When your child "forgets" to do something, explain exactly what he/she did wrong, what should have been done and why.

For example: It is 5:20 p.m. and your child is watching TV. Walk up to your child and say directly to him, "William, it is 5:20. You are watching TV and you should be setting the table. You need to set the table now because we are going to eat in 10 minutes."

8. Maintain a chart for your child which indicates responsibilities. Along with your child, place a star beside each responsibility performed for the day. A check mark should be placed next to those responsibilities not performed successfully. Allow your child to trade stars for rewards listed on a "Reward Menu." The rewards should be things that the child has asked to earn and a specific number of stars should be earned in order to obtain each reward. (See Appendix for a Reward Menu.)

9. Write a contract with your child.

For example: I, William, for one week, will remember to take out the trash after dinner. When I accomplish this, I can stay up until 11:00 p.m. on Friday night.

The contract should be written within the ability level of your child and should focus on only one behavior at a time. (See Appendix for an example of a Behavior Contract.)

10. Require your child to perform chores, responsibilities, homework, etc., even though he/she "forgot" to do so at the established time.

11. Make certain that your child sees the relationship between behavior and the consequences which follow (e.g., forgetting to pick up possessions results in their damage or loss, failing to do homework results in a failing grade, etc.).

12. Allow natural consequences to occur due to your child's "forgetting" to take care of responsibilities (e.g., personal possessions being lost, failing a homework assignment, etc.).

13. Provide an incentive to encourage your child to do his/her chores (e.g., "When you clean your room, you can have a friend over.").

14. Schedule your child's chores and responsibilities around highly enjoyable activities (e.g., your child can watch TV after feeding the dog and taking out the trash).

15. In order to help your child be able to remember, reduce distractions (e.g., turn off the TV, give directions in a room away from friends, etc.).

16. Make a written list of directions you want your child to follow (e.g., feed the dog, take out the trash, etc.).

17. Be consistent when expecting your child to finish chores. Do not allow your child to fail to follow directions one time and expect appropriate behavior the next time.

18. Give your child a special responsibility (e.g., answering the door, serving food, cleaning, etc.).

19. Use a timer to help your child know how much time he/she has to follow through with directions.

20. Make sure your child is paying attention to you when you tell him/her to do something. Have your child look directly at you to know he/she is listening and have your child repeat the direction to check for understanding.

21. Do not give directions to your child from another room. Go to your child, get his/her undivided attention, and tell your child what to do.

22. Do not punish your child for accidently forgetting, for accidents that interfere with doing things, etc.

23. Make certain to be specific when telling your child what you want him/her to do.

24. Establish a certain time each day for your child to take care of responsibilities (e.g., feeding the dog, completing homework, etc., right after school).

25. Sit down with your child and discuss a list of chores he/she would like to do.

26. Have your child do those things that need to be done when it is discussed instead of later (e.g., put swimsuits in the car now so that when you go to the pool later this afternoon, they will not be forgotten, etc.).

27. Make certain that the responsibilities given to your child are appropriate for his/her level of development and ability.

28. Assist your child in performing responsibilities. Gradually require your child to independently assume responsibilities as he/she demonstrates success.

11 Changes from one activity to another without finishing the first

1. Establish rules for changing activities (e.g., finish one activity before moving on to another, put things away where they belong, return borrowed items in the same or better condition, complete chores on time, etc.). These rules should be consistent and followed by everyone in the home. Talk about the rules often.

2. Reward your child for following the rules. Possible rewards include verbal praise (e.g., "Thank you for putting your dirty clothes in the hamper!" "I'm so proud of you for finishing your homework before watching TV." etc.), a kiss on the check, a hug, having a friend over to play, staying up late, watching a favorite TV show, and playing a game with a parent. (See Appendix for a Reward Menu.)

3. If there are other children or adolescents in the home, reward them for changing from one activity to another after finishing the first.

4. Carefully consider your child's age and experience before assigning responsibilities to him/her.

5. Show your child how to finish one activity before moving on to another (e.g., return things to their proper places, return borrowed items in the same or better condition, complete chores, etc.) before expecting your child to perform the responsibilities on his/her own.

6. When your child is not responsible, explain exactly what he/she is doing wrong, what he/she is supposed to be doing and why.

7. Write a contract with your child.

For example: I, William, for five nights, will finish my homework before watching TV. When I accomplish this, I can stay up until 11:00 p.m. on Friday night.

The contract should be written within the ability level of your child and should focus on only one behavior at a time. (See Appendix for an example of a Behavior Contract.).

8. Make certain that your child sees the relationship between behavior and the consequences which follow (e.g., failing to finish homework during "homework time" results in having to do homework during "TV time").

9. Allow natural consequences to occur due to your child's failing to finish a task (e.g., failing to finish homework will result in having to get up early to do homework the next morning).

10. Establish a certain time each day for your child to take care of responsibilities (e.g., feeding the dog, completing homework, etc., right after school).

11. Act as a model for your child for being responsible at all times.

12. Tell your child when it is time to complete homework, chores, etc.

13. Post a list of your child's responsibilities (e.g., 1. Take out the trash, 2. Feed the dog, 3. Set the table, etc.). Have your child put a check next to each chore he/she completes. Reward your child for completing chores.

14. Discuss your child's responsibilities at the beginning of each day so he/she knows what is expected.

15. Help your child get out the materials necessary for him/her to complete responsibilities (e.g., paper for homework, cleaning supplies for cleaning his/her room, etc.).

16. Help your child get started with chores and explain to your child where things belong when he/she is finished using them.

17. Make a list of your child's commonly used items and/or materials and have your child make sure that each item and/or material is put in its designated place each day.

18. Make certain there is a designated place for all items in and around the home.

19. Require your child to put his/her coat, gloves, hat, etc., in a designated place upon entering the home.

20. Teach your child to put things back where they belong by putting things back where they belong after you use them.

21. Make certain that responsibilities given to your child are appropriate for his/her level of development and ability.

22. Provide your child with shelving, containers, organizers, etc., for personal possessions. Label the storage areas and require your child to keep possessions together.

23. Assist your child in performing responsibilities. Gradually require your child to independently assume more responsibility as he/she demonstrates success.

24. Make certain your child understands that things which are lost, broken, or destroyed must be replaced by him/her.

25. Do not buy additional toys, games, etc., for your child if he/she is not able to take care of possessions.

26. Limit your child's use of those things he/she is not responsible for putting away, returning, etc.

27. Tell your child what he/she needs to do to complete an activity (e.g., put all materials away before beginning a new activity, have an adult check your homework before putting it away, etc.).

28. Allow your child to do something enjoyable after finishing one activity and putting everything away (e.g., watching TV, playing a game with a parent, playing with a friend, etc.).

29. Along with a directive, provide an incentive statement (e.g., ''You may watch TV after you finish your homework and put away all materials.'').

30. Make certain your child puts away all toys, clothes, etc., before he/she is allowed to get out more toys or clothes.

31. Tell baby-sitters or others who are involved with your child that your child is responsible for picking up and putting away his/her own materials.

32. Show your child the proper way to take care of things (e.g., shining shoes, hosing off his/her bike, taking care of dolls, etc.). This will teach your child a sense of responsibility with belongings.

33. If your child fails to pick up clothes, games, toys, etc., after an activity, pick up the toys and take them away from your child for a period of time.

34. Make certain to be consistent when expecting your child to change from one activity to another (e.g., do not leave the house with toys in the yard one time and expect the toys to be picked up the next time).

35. Reduce distracting activities which interfere with your child's ability to change from one activity to another (e.g., turn off the TV when it is time to set the table, do not allow friends to come over when it is time to do homework, etc.).

12 Has a short attention span

1. Reward your child for completing responsibilities in a reasonable amount of time. Possible rewards include verbal praise (e.g., ''I'm so proud of you for getting your homework done on time tonight!''), a kiss on the cheek, a hug, having a friend over to play, staying up late, watching a favorite TV show, and playing a game with a parent. (See Appendix for Reward Menu.)

2. If there are other children or adolescents in the home, reward them for completing responsibilities in a reasonable amount of time.

3. Carefully consider your child's age when expecting him/her to be able to attend to an activity for a specific amount of time.

4. Discuss your concerns regarding your child's attention span with your family doctor, a school official, etc., in order to see if your child's attention span may be interfering with progress at school.

5. Remind your child to do chores and complete responsibilities.

6. Help your child complete chores and responsibilities.

7. Write a contract with your child.

For example: I, William, for one week, will work on my homework for 30 minutes each day. When I accomplish this, I can have a friend spend the night.

The contract should be written within the ability level of your child and should focus on only one behavior at a time. (See Appendix for an example of a Behavior Contract.)

8. Reduce distractions (e.g., turn off the TV and radio, do not allow friends to come over, etc.) in order to help your child attend to chores and responsibilities.

9. Give your child simple, one-step directions to follow.

10. Break down your child's chores and responsibilities into smaller tasks.

11. Keep your child's chores and responsibilities short and simple. Do not give him/her things to do that take more than 10-15 minutes to complete.

12. Make sure that your child understands his/her chores and responsibilities by having your child tell you what he/she is supposed to do in each case.

13. Provide your child with a quiet place to complete chores and responsibilities whenever possible.

14. Supervise your child through the completion of chores and responsibilities in order to help him/her stay on task and complete the chores and responsibilities.

15. Evaluate your child's responsibilities in order to determine if they are too complicated for him/her to complete successfully.

16. Allow your child to use a timer to remind him/her to complete chores and responsibilities.

17. Make sure that your child has all necessary materials to successfully complete chores and responsibilities.

18. Teach your child how to manage time so that he/she does not wait until the last minute to complete chores and responsibilities.

19. Maintain a chart for your child that indicates responsibilities. Along with your child, put a star beside each responsibility performed for the day. A check mark should be placed next to those responsibilities not performed successfully. Allow your child to trade stars for rewards listed on a ''Reward Menu.'' The rewards should be things that the child has asked to earn, and a specific number of stars should be earned in order to obtain each reward. (See Appendix for Reward Menu.)

20. Provide an incentive statement for your child to help him/her do chores (e.g., ''When you clean your room, you may have a friend over.'' etc.).

21. Establish a regular routine for your child to follow on a daily basis in order to help him/her "remember" to take care of responsibilities.

For example:

6:30 a.m. - get up, make bed, get dressed
7:00 a.m. - eat breakfast
7:30 a.m. - leave for school
3:30 p.m. - return from school
4:00 p.m. - feed pets
5:00 p.m. - set the table for dinner
5:30 p.m. - eat dinner
7:00 p.m. - do homework
8:00 p.m. - go to bed

This schedule could be posted in central locations around the home (e.g., on the refrigerator, in your child's room, in the basement, etc.). Seeing the schedule often will increase the likelihood of your child remembering what to do and when to do it. (See Appendix for Weekday or Saturday Schedule.)

22. Make a written list of directions you want your child to follow (e.g., feed the dog, take out the trash, etc.).

23. Be consistent when expecting your child to finish chores. Do not allow your child to fail to complete chores one time and expect appropriate behavior the next time.

24. Make sure your child is paying attention to you when you tell him/her to do something. Have your child look directly at you to know he/she is listening and have your child repeat the directions to check for understanding.

25. Establish a certain time each day for your child to take care of responsibilities (e.g., feeding the dog, completing homework, etc., right after school).

26. Have your child do those things that need to be done when it is discussed instead of later (e.g., put swimsuits in the car now so that when you go to the pool later this afternoon, they will not be forgotten, etc.).

27. Make certain that the responsibilities given to your child are appropriate for his/her level of development and ability.

28. Assist your child in performing responsibilities. Gradually require your child to independently assume responsibility as he/she demonstrates success.

29. Sit down with your child, one-on-one, for a few minutes at a time to practice schoolwork, read stories, etc. Gradually increase the amount of one-on-one time spent together as your child demonstrates the ability to attend for longer periods of time.

30. Talk to your child's teacher to have your child put into small groups for instruction, have a peer tutor, have assignments shortened, etc.

31. Make certain to give directions in a very simple manner and be specific as to what you want your child to do.

32. Be consistent when expecting your child to follow directions. Do not allow your child to fail to follow directions one time and expect him/her to follow directions the next time.

33. Have everyone in the family work together at the same time in order to help your child get responsibilities done on time.

34. Have your child earn money, privileges, etc., for performing chores.

35. Sit with your child when he/she is working on homework. You could read, do needlework, etc., while your child works.

36. Do not give your child too many things to do at one time.

37. If your child appears to need a break, allow some playtime between homework assignments, chores, etc.

38. Play educational games with your child so it is more interesting to do homework (e.g., a spelling bee, math races, let your child teach the material to you, etc.).

39. Require your child to engage in activities for only brief periods of time. Gradually increase the length of time required for your child to attend to activities.

40. Be certain you are not expecting your child to attend to things that appeal to adults but are of no interest to children (adult conversations, visiting with older relatives, sightseeing, etc.).

41. When your child is expected to engage in social situations, interact frequently with him/her in order to maintain his/her attention (ask your child questions, ask for his/her opinions, stand close to him/her, etc.).

42. Give your child many short responsibilities (e.g., chores, errands) to increase his/her active involvement and give your child a feeling of success or accomplishment.

43. Modify or eliminate those situations which cause your child to experience stress or frustration (e.g., make games easier, use teams instead of single players competing against one another, etc.).

44. If your child believes he/she cannot be successful in activities, your child will have little or no interest in such activities (e.g., homework, school projects, games, etc.).

45. Require your child to clean up, put away, etc., those things he/she is playing with/using before moving on to something else.

46. Make certain to provide your child with a quiet, uncluttered place to do homework, school projects, etc.

47. Establish a regular schedule of daily events so that your child knows what he/she should be doing at any one time and what he/she will be doing next (e.g., watching cartoons, eating lunch, going swimming, etc.). (See Appendix for Weekday or Saturday Schedule.)

48. Assist your child in daily homework, school projects, etc. Gradually reduce the amount of assistance you provide your child as he/she demonstrates success in remaining on task, finishing assignments, etc.

49. Be a model for your child for having an appropriate attention span by reading, conversing, working on a project, etc.

50. Encourage your child to ask for your assistance instead of moving on to something else, giving up, etc.

A Reminder: **Your child's short attention span is not something he/she demonstrates on purpose. Be supportive by not expecting too much from him/her at one time.**

13 Starts but does not complete homework

1. Establish homework rules (e.g., start homework when you get home from school, finish homework before you watch TV or play with others, ask for help when necessary, etc.).

2. Reward your child for following the rules. Possible rewards include verbal praise (e.g., "Thank you for finishing your homework before playing outside."), a kiss on the cheek, a hug, having a friend over to play, staying up late, watching a favorite TV show, and playing a game with a parent. (See Appendix for Reward Menu.)

3. If there are other children or adolescents in the home, reward them for following the homework rules.

4. Make sure your child has a quiet and well lighted place in which to do homework.

5. Reduce distractions (e.g., turn off the radio and/or TV, have people talk quietly, etc.) in order to help your child complete homework.

6. Remind your child when it is time to do homework.

7. Encourage your child to ask for help when necessary.

8. Ask your child's teacher to send home explanations of how to help your child with homework if necessary.

9. Sit with your child when he/she is working on homework. You could read, do needlework, etc., while your child works.

10. Write a contract with your child.

For example: I, William, will complete my homework for four days in a row. When I accomplish this, I can stay up an hour later on Friday night.

The contract should be written within the ability level of your child and should focus on only one behavior at a time. (See Appendix for an example of a Behavior Contract.)

11. Make certain that your child sees the relationship between behavior and the consequences which follow (e.g., forgetting to complete homework will result in a low grade).

12. Allow your child to do something enjoyable (e.g., playing a game, watching TV, talking with a friend on the phone, etc.) after completing homework for the evening.

13. Allow natural consequences to occur due to your child's failure to complete homework during "homework time" (e.g., having to do homework during "TV time," having to get up early to do homework, etc.).

14. If you feel that your child is being assigned too much homework, talk with the teacher about your concerns.

15. Allow your child to have a friend come over so they can do their homework together.

16. Have your child put a star or check mark beside each completed assignment and allow your child to turn in stars or check marks for rewards.

17. Make positive comments about school and the importance of completing homework.

18. Have your child begin homework as soon as he/she gets home from school in order to prevent your child from putting it off all evening.

19. Find a tutor (e.g., a volunteer in the community, one of your child's classmates, etc.) to help your child complete homework.

20. Arrange to pick up your child's homework each day if he/she has difficulty "remembering" to bring it home.

21. Help your child study for tests, quizzes, etc.

22. If your child appears to need a break, allow some playtime between homework assignments.

23. Set up a homework system with your child's teacher (e.g., two days a week drill with flash cards, three days a week work on book work sent home, etc.). This will add some variety to your child's homework.

24. Let your child set up an "office" where homework can be completed.

25. Develop an assignment sheet with your child's teacher so you are aware of the work that should be completed each night. Sign and send back the assignment sheet the next day so your child's teacher is aware that you saw the sheet.

26. Play educational games with your child so it is more interesting to do homework (e.g., a spelling bee, math races, let your child teach the material to you, etc.).

27. Check over your child's homework when he/she is finished so you can be certain that everything is complete.

28. Assist your child in performing homework responsibilities. Gradually require your child to independently assume more responsibility as he/she demonstrates success.

29. Make certain you are familiar with the school district's homework policy (e.g., 15 minutes a day for 1st-3rd grade, 30 minutes a day for 4th-6th grade, etc.). If your child is receiving more homework than the district requires, talk with your child's teacher.

30. Along with a directive, provide an incentive statement (e.g., "When you finish your homework, you may watch TV." etc.)

31. Make certain your child understands that homework not completed and turned in on time must still be completed and turned in.

32. Review your child's homework responsibilities after school so your child knows what he/she is expected to do that evening.

33. Have another child (e.g., brother, sister, friend) help your child with homework each evening.

34. Have your child and a classmate who has the same assignment do their homework together (e.g., right after school at one home or the other).

35. Set aside quiet time each night when the family turns off TV's and radios to read, do homework, write letters, etc.

36. Hire a tutor to work with your child to help him/her complete homework.

37. Make sure your child has all the necessary materials to perform homework (e.g., pencils, paper, erasers, etc.).

A Reminder: Homework should be a form of "practice" for what your child has already been taught in school. You should not have to teach your child how to work each problem or activity. Talk with your child's teacher if this is a problem.

Note: If your child cannot be successful completing homework at home, speak to the teacher(s) about providing time at school for homework completion.

14 Will not independently perform chores

1. Establish rules (e.g., put things away where they belong, return borrowed items in the same or better condition, complete chores on time, etc.). These rules should be consistent and followed by everyone in the home. Talk about the rules often.

2. Reward your child for following the rules. Possible rewards include verbal praise (e.g., "Thank you for putting your dirty clothes in the hamper!" "I'm so proud of you for finishing your homework before watching TV." etc.), a kiss on the cheek, a hug, having a friend over to play, staying up late, watching a favorite TV show, and playing a game with a parent. (See Appendix for Reward Menu.)

3. If there are other children or adolescents in the home, reward them for taking care of their responsibilities.

4. Carefully consider your child's age and experience before assigning responsibilities to him/her.

5. Show your child how to complete chores before expecting your child to perform the responsibilities on his/her own.

6. When your child is not responsible, explain exactly what he/she is doing wrong, what he/she is supposed to be doing and why.

For example: It is 5:30 p.m. and your child has not set the table for dinner. Go to your child and say that he/she has not set the table and that he/she needs to be setting the table because dinner will be at 6:00 p.m.

7. Act as a model for your child at all times by making certain he/she sees you doing chores.

8. Write a contract with your child.

For example: I, William, will set the table by 5:00 p.m. every weeknight for four nights in a row. When I accomplish this, I can stay up until 11:00 p.m. on Friday night.

The contract should be written within the ability level of your child and should focus on only one behavior at a time. (See Appendix for an example of a Behavior Contract.)

9. Make certain that your child sees the relationship between behavior and the consequences which follow (e.g., failing to put away something in its proper place results in its being lost or broken).

10. Allow natural consequences to occur due to your child's failure to be responsible (e.g., his/her forgetting to do chores during "chore time" will result in doing chores during "TV time" or playtime).

11. Establish a certain time each day for your child to take care of responsibilities (e.g., feeding the dog, completing homework, etc., right after school).

12. Tell your child when it is time to complete homework, chores, etc.

13. Post a list of your child's responsibilities (e.g., 1. Take out the trash, 2. Feed the dog, 3. Set the table, etc.). Have your child put a check mark next to each chore he/she completes. Reward your child for completing chores. (See Appendix for List of Chores.)

14. Discuss your child's responsibilities at the beginning of each day so he/she knows what is expected.

15. Help your child get out the materials necessary to complete responsibilities (e.g., paper for homework, cleaning supplies for cleaning his/her room, etc.).

16. Help your child get started with chores and explain to your child where things belong when he/she is finished using them.

17. Set aside a time each day for the family to put away all materials that have been used throughout the day (e.g., bikes, toys, lawn equipment, dishes, etc.).

18. Let your child know that materials not put away at the end of the day may be taken away for a period of time due to lack of responsibility.

19. Make a list of your child's frequently used items and/or materials and have your child make sure that each item and/or material is put in its designated place each day.

20. Make certain there is a designated place for all items in and around the home.

21. Require your child to put his/her coat, gloves, hat, etc., in a designated place upon entering the home.

22. Teach your child to put things back where they belong by putting things back where they belong after you use them.

23. Make certain that responsibilities given to your child are appropriate for his/her level of development and ability.

24. Provide your child with shelving, containers, organizers, etc., for personal possessions. Label the storage areas and require your child to keep possessions in their designated places.

25. Assist your child in performing responsibilities. Gradually require your child to independently assume more responsibility as he/she demonstrates success.

26. Make certain your child understands that things which are lost, broken, or destroyed must be replaced by him/her.

27. Do not buy additional toys, games, etc., for your child if he/she is not able to take care of possessions.

28. Limit your child's use of those things he/she is not responsible for putting away, returning, etc.

29. Do not give your child directions to follow with more than two or three steps. Directions that involve several steps can be confusing and cause your child to have difficulty following them. An example of a two-step direction is: "Please turn off your light and go to bed."

30. Use a timer to help your child know how much time he/she has to follow through with responsibilities.

31. Deliver directions in a supportive rather than a threatening manner (e.g., "Please take out the trash." rather than "You had better take out the trash or else!").

32. Be consistent when expecting your child to take care of responsibilities. Do not allow your child to fail to follow through with responsibilities one time and expect appropriate behavior the next time.

33. Make a written list of directions you want your child to follow (e.g., feed the dog, take out the trash, etc.).

34. Make sure your child is paying attention to you when you tell him/her to do something. Have your child look directly at you to know he/she is listening and have your child repeat the direction to check for understanding.

35. Do not give directions to your child from another room. Go to your child, get his/her undivided attention, and tell your child what to do.

36. Do not punish your child for accidently forgetting, for accidents that interfere with following directions, etc.

37. Limit the number of chores for which your child is responsible and gradually increase the number of chores as your child demonstrates the ability to get them done on time.

38. Show your child how to perform a new responsibility (e.g., show how to set the table several times before expecting your child to do it on his/her own).

39. Explain to your child that responsibilities not done on time will have to be done at other times (e.g., playtime, TV time, weekends, etc.).

40. Reduce distracting activities which interfere with your child's responsibilities (e.g., turn off the TV when it is time to set the table, do not allow friends to come over when it is time to do homework, etc.).

41. Have your child do those things that need to be done when it is discussed instead of later (e.g., put swimsuits in the car now so that when you go to the pool later this afternoon, they will not be forgotten, etc.).

42. Limit your child's use of belongings until he/she can care for them properly.

43. Allow your child to do something enjoyable after caring for belongings (e.g., watch TV, play a game with a parent, play with a friend, etc.).

44. Require your child's room to be neat and organized so there will always be a place to put away toys, games, clothes, etc.

45. Communicate with the parents of friends your child is visiting to make certain that your child helps to pick up toys when spending time at a friend's house.

46. Do not expect your child to pick up toys and games that friends have left out; encourage friends to help pick up the toys.

47. Tell baby-sitters or others who are involved with your child that your child is responsible for picking up and putting away his/her own materials.

48. Show your child the proper way to take care of things (e.g., shining shoes, hosing off his/her bike, taking care of dolls, etc.). This will teach your child a sense of responsibility with belongings.

49. Have your child pay for things he/she wants (e.g., a baseball mitt, a new doll, a new pair of jeans, etc.). If your child has spent some of his/her own money on an item, he/she may be willing to care for it.

15 Does not remain on task to study for tests or quizzes

1. Establish rules for studying (e.g., start studying when you get home from school, finish studying before you watch TV or play with others, ask for help when necessary, etc.).

2. Reward your child for following the rules. Possible rewards include verbal praise (e.g., "Thank you for studying before playing outside."), a kiss on the cheek, a hug, having a friend over to play, staying up late, watching a favorite TV show, and playing a game with a parent. (See Appendix for Reward Menu.)

3. If there are other children or adolescents in the home, reward them for following the rules for studying.

4. Make sure your child has a quiet and well lighted place in which to study.

5. Reduce distractions (e.g., turn off the radio and/or TV, have people talk quietly, etc.) in order to help your child study.

6. Remind your child when it is time to study.

7. Encourage your child to ask for help when necessary.

8. Ask your child's teacher to send home explanations of how to help your child with his/her studying.

9. Sit with your child when he/she is studying. You can read, do needlework, etc., while your child studys.

10. Write a contract with your child.

For example: I, William, will study for four days in a row. When I accomplish this, I can stay up an hour later on Friday night.

The contract should be written within the ability level of your child and should focus on only one behavior at a time. (See Appendix for an example of a Behavior Contract.)

11. Make certain that your child sees the relationship between behavior and the consequences which follow (e.g., failing to study will result in a low grade, loss of privileges, etc.).

12. Allow your child to do something enjoyable (e.g., play a game, watch TV, talk with a friend on the phone, etc.) after he/she studies.

13. Allow natural consequences to occur due to your child's failure to study (e.g., loss of extra-curricular activities, loss of TV privileges, etc.).

14. If you feel that your child is being assigned too much homework, talk with the teacher about your concerns.

15. Allow your child to have a friend come over so they can study together.

16. Have your child put a star or check mark beside each completed assignment and allow your child to turn in stars or check marks for rewards.

17. Make positive comments about school and the importance of studying.

18. Have your child begin studying as soon as he/she gets home from school in order to prevent your child from putting it off all evening.

19. Find a tutor (e.g., a volunteer in the community, one of your child's classmates, etc.) to help your child study.

20. Arrange to pick up your child's homework each day if your child has difficulty "remembering" to bring it home.

21. Help your child study for tests, quizzes, etc.

22. If your child appears to need a break, allow some playtime between study assignments.

23. Have another child (e.g., brother, sister, friend) help your child study each evening.

24. Set up a homework system with your child's teacher (e.g., two days a week drill with flash cards, three days a week work on book work sent home, etc.). This will add some variety to your child's studying.

25. Let your child set up an "office" where he/she can study.

26. Develop an assignment sheet with your child's teacher so you are aware of the work that should be completed each night. Sign and send back the assignment sheet the next day so your child's teacher is aware that you saw the sheet.

27. Play educational games with your child so it is more interesting for him/her to study (e.g., a spelling bee, math races, let your child teach the material to you, etc.).

28. Check over your child's homework when he/she is finished so you can be certain that everything is complete.

29. Assist your child in studying. Gradually require your child to independently assume more responsibility as he/she demonstrates success.

30. Along with a directive, provide an incentive statement (e.g., "When you finish studying, you may watch TV." etc.)

31. Make certain your child understands that homework not completed and turned in on time must still be completed and turned in.

32. Review your child's homework responsibilities after school so your child knows what he/she is expected to do that evening.

33. Have your child and a classmate who has the same assignment study together (e.g., right after school at one home or the other).

34. Set aside quiet time each night when the family turns off TV's and radios to read, study, write letters, etc.

35. Hire a tutor to work with your child to help him/her study.

36. Make sure your child has all the necessary materials to study (e.g., pencils, paper, erasers, etc.).

37. Carefully consider your child's age when expecting him/her to be able to study for a specific amount of time.

38. Discuss your concerns regarding your child's attention span with your family doctor, a school official, etc., in order to see if your child's attention span may be interfering with progress at school.

39. Sit down with your child, one-on-one, for a few minutes at a time to practice schoolwork, read stories, etc. Gradually increase the amount of one-on-one time spent together as your child demonstrates the ability to attend for longer periods of time.

A Reminder: If your child cannot be successful in studying at home, speak to the teacher(s) about providing time at school for studying.

16 Does not organize responsibilities

1. Establish rules for organization (e.g., put things away where they belong, return borrowed items in the same or better condition, etc). These rules should be consistent and followed by everyone in the home. Talk about the rules often.

2. Reward your child for following the rules. Possible rewards include verbal praise (e.g., "Thank you for putting your dirty clothes in the hamper!" "I'm so proud of you for finishing your homework before watching TV." etc.), a kiss on the cheek, a hug, having a friend over to play, staying up late, watching a favorite TV show, and playing a game with a parent. (See Appendix for Reward Menu.)

3. If there are other children or adolescents in the home, reward them for organizing responsibilities.

4. Carefully consider your child's age and experience before assigning responsibilities to him/her.

5. Show your child how to return things to their proper places, return borrowed items in the same or better condition, complete chores, etc., before expecting your child to perform the responsibilities on his/her own.

6. When your child is not responsible, explain exactly what he/she is doing wrong, what he/she is supposed to be doing and why.

For example: It is 9:00 p.m. and your child has not started homework. Go to your child and say that he/she has not done homework and that he/she needs to be doing homework because bedtime is at 9:30 p.m.

7. Write a contract with your child.

For example: I, William, will finish my homework by 8:00 p.m. every weeknight for five nights in a row. When I accomplish this, I can stay up until 11:00 p.m. on Friday night.

The contract should be written within the ability level of your child and should focus on only one behavior at a time. (See Appendix for an example of a Behavior Contract.)

8. Allow natural consequences to occur due to your child's failing to be responsible (e.g., his/her forgetting to do homework will result in low grades).

9. Establish a certain time each day for your child to take care of responsibilities (e.g., feeding the dog, completing homework, etc., right after school).

10. Act as a model for your child for being responsible at all times.

11. Tell your child when it is time to complete homework, chores, etc.

12. Post a list of your child's responsibilities (e.g., 1. Take out the trash, 2. Feed the dog, 3. Set the table, etc.). Have your child put a check mark next to each chore he/she completes. Reward your child for completing chores. (See Appendix for List of Chores.)

13. Discuss your child's responsibilities at the beginning of each day so he/she knows what is expected.

14. Help your child get out the materials necessary to complete responsibilities (e.g., paper for homework, cleaning supplies for cleaning his/her room, etc.).

15. Help your child get started with chores and explain to your child where things belong when he/she is finished using them.

16. Set aside a time each day for the family to put away all materials that have been used throughout the day (e.g., bikes, toys, lawn equipment, dishes, etc.).

17. Let your child know that materials not put away at the end of the day may be taken away for a period of time due to lack of responsibility.

18. Make a list of your child's frequently used items and/or materials and have your child make sure that each item and/or material is put in its designated place each day.

19. Make certain there is a designated place for all items in and around the home.

20. Require your child to put his/her coat, gloves, hat, etc., in a designated place upon entering the home.

21. Teach your child to return things to their places by putting things back where they belong after using them.

22. Make certain that responsibilities given to your child are appropriate for his/her level of development and ability.

23. Provide your child with shelving, containers, organizers, etc., for personal possessions. Label the storage areas and require your child to keep possessions together.

24. Assist your child in performing responsibilities. Gradually require your child to independently assume more responsibility as he/she demonstrates success.

25. Make certain your child understands that things which are lost, broken, destroyed, etc., must be replaced by him/her.

26. Do not buy additional toys, games, etc., for your child if he/she is not able to take care of the things he/she already has.

27. Limit your child's use of those things he/she is not responsible for putting away, returning, etc.

28. Help your child to get ready for things on time.

29. Make sure you are ready for things on time. Organize your time and show your child how to follow a routine in order to be ready for things on time.

30. Make certain that your child sees the relationship between behavior and the consequences which follow (e.g., failing to be ready for school when the bus arrives will result in missing the bus).

31. Have your child begin getting ready 10 minutes before everyone else so he/she will be ready on time.

32. In order to help your child get ready for things on time, reduce distractions (e.g., turn off the radio or TV, do not allow friends to visit, etc.).

33. Make sure your child gets up in plenty of time to be ready when the bus arrives, knows what time you are leaving to go shopping, etc.

34. Establish a routine for getting ready for school (e.g., get up, make bed, eat breakfast, brush teeth, wash face and get dressed).

35. Have breakfast, lunch and dinner at the same time each day in order to help your child organize his/her day.

36. Frequently remind your child of the time he/she needs to be home, ready to go shopping, etc.

37. Use a timer to help your child know how much time he/she has to get ready for an activity (e.g., going shopping, meeting the school bus, eating meals, etc.).

38. Have your child keep a checklist of things he/she has to do in order to get ready for school on time (e.g., eat, brush teeth, dress, etc.) and put a star or check mark by each behavior after he/she completes it. Allow your child to trade in stars or check marks for rewards.

39. Help your child prepare for the next day by selecting and laying out his/her clothes, gathering school materials in one place, and reviewing any special activities or events which will occur the next day.

40. Use motivators for your child (e.g., "If you get ready for school on time, you can help decide what to have for breakfast." "If you can pick up your toys before dinner, you can choose your seat at the table." "If you are ready to go shopping on time, you may buy something special." "If you are ready for dinner on time, you may have ice cream for dessert." etc.).

41. Do not allow your child to become involved in high interest activities just before it is time to get ready for another activity (e.g., going shopping, eating dinner, meeting the school bus, etc.).

17 Does not prepare for school assignments

1. Establish rules for school assignments (e.g., start school assignments when you get home from school, finish school assignments before you watch TV or play with others, ask for help when necessary, etc.).

2. Reward your child for following the rules. Possible rewards include verbal praise (e.g., "Thank you for finishing your school assignments before playing outside."), a kiss on the cheek, a hug, having a friend over to play, staying up late, watching a favorite TV show, and playing a game with a parent. (See Appendix for Reward Menu.)

3. If there are other children or adolescents in the home, reward them for following the rules for school assignments.

4. Make sure your child has a quiet and well lighted place in which to do his/her school assignments.

5. Reduce distractions (e.g., turn off the radio and/or TV, have people talk quietly, etc.) in order to help your child complete his/her school assignments.

6. Remind your child when it is time to do his/her school assignments.

7. Encourage your child to ask for help when necessary.

8. Ask your child's teacher to send home explanations of how to help your child with his/her school assignments if necessary.

9. Sit with your child when he/she is working on his/her school assignments. You could read, do needlework, etc., while your child works.

10. If you feel that your child is being given too many school assignments, talk with the teacher about your concerns.

11. Allow your child to have a friend come over so they can do their school assignments together.

12. Write a contract with your child.

For example: I, William, will complete my school assignments for four days in a row. When I accomplish this, I can stay up an hour later on Friday night.

The contract should be written within the ability level of your child and should focus on only one behavior at a time. (See Appendix for an example of a Behavior Contract.)

13. Make certain that your child sees the relationship between behavior and the consequences which follow (e.g., forgetting to complete his/her school assignments will result in a low grade).

14. Allow your child to do something enjoyable (e.g., playing a game, watching TV, talking with a friend on the phone, etc.) after completing school assignments for the evening.

15. Allow natural consequences to occur due to your child's failure to complete his/her school assignments (e.g., receiving low grades, being excluded from extracurricular activities, etc.).

16. Have your child put a star or check mark beside each completed assignment and allow your child to turn in stars or check marks for rewards.

17. Make positive comments about school and the importance of completing assignments.

18. Have your child begin his/her assignments as soon as he/she gets home from school in order to prevent your child from putting it off all evening.

19. Find a tutor (e.g., a volunteer in the community, one of your child's classmates, etc.) to help your child complete his/her school assignments.

20. Arrange to pick up a list of your child's school assignments each day if your child has difficulty "remembering" to bring it home.

21. Help your child study for tests, quizzes, etc.

22. If your child appears to need a break, allow some playtime between school assignments.

23. Set up an assignment system with your child's teacher (e.g., two days a week drill with flash cards, three days a week work on book work sent home, etc.). This will add some variety to your child's school assignments.

24. Let your child set up an "office" where he/she can finish school assignments.

25. Develop an assignment sheet with your child's teacher so you are aware of the work that should be completed each night. Sign and send back the assignment sheet the next day so your child's teacher is aware that you saw the sheet.

26. Play educational games with your child so it is more interesting for him/her to do school assignments (e.g., a spelling bee, math races, let your child teach the material to you, etc.).

27. Check over your child's assignments when he/she is finished so you can be certain that everything is complete.

28. Assist your child in performing his/her school assignments. Gradually require your child to independently assume more responsibility as he/she demonstrates success.

29. Make certain you are familiar with the school district's homework policy (e.g., 15 minutes a day for 1st-3rd grade, 30 minutes a day for 4th-6th grade, etc.). If your child is receiving more assignments than the district requires, talk with your child's teacher.

30. Along with a directive, provide an incentive statement (e.g., "When you finish your school assignments, you may watch TV." etc.)

31. Make certain your child understands that school assignments not completed and turned in on time must still be completed and turned in.

32. Review your child's assignment responsibilities after school so your child knows what he/she is expected to do that evening.

33. Have another child (e.g., brother, sister, friend) help your child with school assignments each evening.

34. Have your child and a classmate who has the same assignment do their homework together (e.g., right after school at one home or the other).

35. Set aside quiet time each night when the family turns off TV's and radios to read, do school assignments, write letters, etc.

36. Hire a tutor to work with your child to help him/her complete school assignments.

37. Make sure your child has all the necessary materials to perform school assignments (e.g., pencils, paper, erasers, etc.).

A Reminder: If your child cannot be successful completing assignments at home, speak to the teacher(s) about providing time at school for assignment completion.

18 Rushes through chores or tasks carelessly

1. Establish rules for completing tasks (e.g., take your time, ask for help when necessary, plan ahead in order to complete tasks on time, etc.). These rules should be consistent and followed by everyone in the home. Talk about the rules often.

2. Reward your child for not hurrying just to get things done. Possible rewards include verbal praise (e.g., ''I am so proud of you for taking your time when you set the table! It looks very nice.''), a kiss on the cheek, a hug, having a friend over to play, staying up late, watching a favorite TV show, and playing a game with a parent. (See Appendix for Reward Menu.)

3. If there are other children or adolescents in the home, reward them for not hurrying just to get things done.

4. Carefully consider your child's age and experience before expecting your child to complete tasks on his/her own.

5. Help your child to complete tasks so he/she will not have to hurry.

6. Encourage your child to ask for help when necessary.

7. Be a good role model for your child by not hurrying just to get done. Organize your time and get things done without having to hurry.

8. When your child is hurrying just to get things done, explain exactly what he/she is doing wrong, what he/she is supposed to be doing and why.

For example: Your child is hurrying through homework assignments. Tell him/her that he/she is hurrying and that he/she needs to slow down and carefully read the directions so he/she will perform the assignments correctly.

9. Require your child to perform a task again if it has been done incorrectly due to his/her hurrying just to get things done.

10. Write a contract with your child.

For example: I, William, will carefully read the directions for my homework assignments so I will do the problems correctly. When I accomplish this, I can watch the TV show of my choice.

The contract should be written within the ability level of your child and should focus on only one behavior at a time. (See Appendix for an example of a Behavior Contract.)

11. Make certain that your child sees the relationship between behavior and the consequences which follow (e.g., failing to read the directions will result in homework assignments being done incorrectly).

12. Allow natural consequences to occur due to your child's hurrying just to get things done (e.g., doing things incorrectly, breaking things, forgetting to do something, etc.).

13. Reduce distractions (e.g., turn off the radio or TV, do not allow friends to visit, etc.) in order to stop your child from hurrying just to get things done.

14. Remind your child when it is time to set the table, feed the dog, perform homework assignments, etc.

15. Provide your child with plenty of time to perform chores so he/she will not need to hurry just to get things done.

16. Set a timer and have your child work on a task until the timer goes off. In this situation, hurrying just to get done will not be to your child's advantage.

17. Limit the number of responsibilities your child has in order that he/she does not have to hurry to get things done.

18. Help your child schedule his/her time in order that he/she will not need to hurry just to get things done.

19. Let your child play, watch TV, read, etc., when he/she comes home from school so he/she has a break between school and homework in the evening. He/she may be less likely to rush through work if he/she has a break between school and homework.

20. Schedule time each day for your child's work to be done so he/she can expect to work for 45 minutes without distractions/interruptions.

21. Maintain consistency in your expectations for your child to complete a task in a quality fashion.

22. Help your child begin a task and then have him/her check with you before putting materials away so that you can make certain the work was not rushed.

23. Establish a routine for your child to follow in completing chores (e.g., wash out the dog dish, refill food and water, clean up the area around the dog dish, etc.). This will help your child remember what is expected.

24. Sit or stand in a place where you can see your child while he/she is performing his/her tasks. Make your child aware that you can see his/her behavior.

25. Make a list of your child's responsibilities and the amount of time you expect him/her to spend on each chore (e.g., dusting room for 15 minutes, cleaning basement for 30 minutes, homework for 30 minutes, etc.).

26. Make certain to check your child's performance on homework, chores, etc., for quality. Working quickly is acceptable if your child performs responsibilities well.

27. Increase supervision of your child while he/she is performing homework, chores, etc. (e.g., by you, another parent, older brother or sister, etc.).

28. Make certain that the responsibilities given to your child are appropriate for his/her level of development and ability.

29. Assist your child in performing responsibilities. Gradually require your child to independently assume more responsibility as he/she demonstrates more success.

30. Make certain you are not requiring too much of your child at one time and causing him/her to hurry to get things done.

31. Make certain your child understands that work not done appropriately will be redone, corrected, etc., during his/her recreation time.

32. Along with a directive, provide an incentive statement (e.g., ''When you finish your homework correctly, you can watch TV.'' ''You can play outside after your chores are done appropriately.'' etc.).

19 Does not read or follow written directions

1. Establish rules for following directions (e.g., read directions, ask questions about directions if you do not understand, follow the directions, etc.). These rules should be consistent and followed by everyone in the home. Talk about the rules often.

2. Reward your child for following directions. Possible rewards include verbal praise (e.g., "You did a great job of following directions!" "I like the way you follow directions!" etc.), a kiss on the cheek, a hug, having a friend over to play, staying up late, watching a favorite TV show, and playing a game with a parent. (See Appendix for Reward Menu.)

3. If there are other children or adolescents in the home, reward them for following written directions.

4. Carefully consider your child's age and experience when expecting him/her to follow written directions.

5. Demonstrate the appropriate way to follow written directions (e.g., follow directions when putting a model together, making a cake, etc.).

6. When your child does not follow a direction, explain exactly what he/she did wrong, what should have been done and why.

For example: Your child is building a model airplane, and he/she puts the model together the wrong way. Help him/her with the directions and show him/her how to put it together the appropriate way.

7. Write a contract with your child.

For example: I, William, for three days in a row, will follow homework directions on my own. When I accomplish this, I can watch 30 extra minutes of TV.

The contract should be written within the ability level of your child and should focus on only one behavior at a time. (See Appendix for an example of a Behavior Contract.)

8. When your child has difficulty following written directions, help him/her read the directions and review what to do.

9. Make certain that your child sees the relationship between behavior and the consequences which follow (e.g., failing to follow math homework directions will result in poor grades, the homework being done incorrectly, etc.).

10. Allow natural consequences to occur due to your child's failing to follow directions (e.g., his/her schoolwork not done on time, homework done incorrectly, etc.).

11. Along with a directive, provide an incentive statement (e.g., "When you follow your math homework directions and complete the assignment, you can watch TV." etc.).

12. In order to help your child be able to follow written directions, reduce distractions (e.g., turn off the TV, give directions in a room away from friends, etc.).

13. Do not give your child directions to follow with more than two or three steps. Directions that involve several steps can be confusing and cause your child to have difficulty following them. An example of a two-step direction is: "Please empty the dishwasher and take out the trash."

14. In order to determine if your child understands a direction, have your child repeat it.

15. Do not criticize. When correcting your child, be honest yet supportive. Never cause your child to feel bad about himself/herself.

16. Be consistent when expecting your child to follow written directions. Do not allow your child to fail to follow directions one time and expect appropriate behavior the next time.

17. Make a short written list of directions you want your child to follow (e.g., feed the dog, take out the trash, etc.).

18. Talk to your child before going into a public place (e.g., the swimming pool, skating rink, etc.) and remind your child of the importance of reading and following directions.

19. Make certain that the responsibilities given to your child are appropriate for his/her level of development and ability.

20. Do not punish your child for forgetting, for accidents that interfere with following directions, etc.

21. Make certain to given written directions that are specific and simple to understand.

22. Make sure your child is paying attention when he/she is reading directions. Have him/her repeat the directions to check for understanding.

23. Assist your child in reading directions. Gradually require your child to independently assume more responsibility as he/she demonstrates success.

20 Is easily frustrated

1. Immediately remove your child from a situation when he/she begins to get frustrated.

2. Do not allow your child to participate in a situation unless he/she can demonstrate self-control.

3. Closely supervise your child in order to monitor his/her behavior at all times.

4. Inform individuals who will be spending time with your child about his/her tendency to become easily frustrated.

5. Talk with your family doctor, a school official, a social worker, etc., about your child's behavior if it is causing him/her to have problems getting along with others.

6. Provide your child with a quiet place to go when he/she becomes frustrated.

7. Encourage your child to talk with you when he/she is frustrated.

8. Teach your child to recognize when he/she is becoming frustrated and ways in which to deal with his/her feelings.

9. Reward your child for controlling his/her behavior. Possible rewards include verbal praise (e.g., ''I'm so proud of you for remaining calm when James called you a name!''), a kiss on the cheek, a hug, having a friend over to play, staying up late, watching a favorite TV show, and playing a game with a parent. (See Appendix for Reward Menu.)

10. If there are other children or adolescents in the home, reward them for controlling their behavior.

11. Treat your child with respect. Talk to your child in a nonthreatening manner.

12. Make certain that your child sees the relationship between behavior and the consequences which follow (e.g., being avoided by others, not being able to participate in special activities, etc.).

13. When your child becomes frustrated, explain exactly what he/she is doing wrong, what he/she is supposed to be doing and why.

For example: You tell your child that it is time to feed the dog and he/she starts complaining and arguing with you. Get his/her attention and say, ''You are getting frustrated because I told you to feed the dog. You need to get control of yourself and feed the dog because it is your job for this month.''

14. Write a contract with your child.

For example: I, William, for one week, will not get frustrated with my little sister. When I accomplish this, I can see a movie on Saturday.

The contract should be written within the ability level of your child and should focus on only one behavior at a time. (See Appendix for an example of a Behavior Contract.)

15. Discuss your child's behavior with him/her in private rather than in front of others.

16. Try to reduce or prevent things from happening which cause your child to become easily frustrated.

17. Provide your child with a place to go when he/she gets frustrated (e.g., a quiet chair, his/her room, a corner, etc.).

18. Teach your child what to do when he/she becomes frustrated (e.g., count to ten, say the alphabet, leave the room, etc.).

19. Do not let your child have his/her way when he/she becomes frustrated. Help him/her work through the situation.

20. Be consistent. Try to deal with your child and his/her behavior in a manner that is as fair as possible.

21. Immediately remove your child from the attention of others when he/she becomes frustrated.

22. Remind your child of the consequences of getting frustrated before going into a store, going to a friend's house, having friends over, etc.

23. After telling your child that he/she cannot do or have something, explain the reason.

24. Make certain that baby-sitters, grandparents, teachers, etc., understand the importance of maintaining consistency in the discipline of your child.

25. Encourage your child to use problem-solving skills: (a) identify the problem, (b) identify goals and objectives, (c) develop strategies, (d) develop a plan for action, and (e) carry out the plan.

26. Teach your child alternative ways to communicate his/her unhappiness (e.g., talking about a problem, asking for help, etc.).

27. Reduce the emphasis on competition. Repeated failures may cause your child to become frustrated.

28. Provide your child with alternative activities, games, etc., in case some activities prove frustrating.

29. Discourage your child from engaging in those activities which cause him/her unhappiness.

30. Encourage your child to associate with peers with whom he/she gets along well in order to prevent him/her from getting frustrated with a situation.

31. Involve your child in activities in which he/she can be successful and that will help him/her feel good about himself/herself. Repeated failures result in frustration and impatience.

32. Do not place an emphasis on perfection. If your child feels he/she must meet up to your expectations and cannot do so, he/she may become frustrated.

33. Talk to your child's teacher to make certain that he/she is not having trouble in school and becoming frustrated.

34. Make certain you set a good example for your child by dealing in a socially acceptable way with situations that may be upsetting to you.

35. Reinforce your child for demonstrating self-control based on the length of time he/she can be successful. Gradually increase the length of time required for reinforcement as he/she demonstrates success.

36. Prevent frustrating or anxiety-producing situations from occurring (e.g., only give your child chores, responsibilities, etc., which are on his/her ability level).

37. Provide your child with positive feedback which indicates he/she is successful, important, respected, etc.

38. Make necessary adjustments in the environment to prevent your child from experiencing stress, frustration, and anger.

39. Teach your child to verbalize his/her feelings before losing control (e.g., "The work is too hard." "Please leave me alone; you're making me angry." etc.).

40. Monitor the behavior of others (e.g., brothers, sisters, friends, etc.) to make certain they are not teasing or otherwise stimulating your child to become frustrated.

41. Teach your child ways to deal with conflict situations (e.g., talking, reasoning, asking an adult to intervene, walking away, etc.).

42. Look for the warning signs (e.g., arguing, loud voices, etc.) that your child is getting frustrated, and intervene to change the activity.

A Reminder: Learning to control our temper is more difficult for some of us than it is for others. Being a model for your child in demonstrating self-control and displaying appropriate reactions to frustration or disappointment will influence your child's behavior.

21 Fails to follow necessary steps

1. Establish a rule (e.g., take your time and follow directions). This rule should be consistent and followed by everyone in the home. Talk about the rule often and reward your child for following the rule.

2. Attempt to be patient and follow necessary steps in doing things. If you are impatient, your child will learn to be impatient also.

3. Reward your child for being patient and following necessary steps. Possible rewards include verbal praise (e.g., ''Thanks for using the lawn mower the right way.''), a kiss on the cheek, a hug, having a friend over to play, staying up late, watching a favorite TV show, and playing a game with a parent. (See Appendix for Reward Menu.)

4. If there are other children or adolescents in the home, reward them for following necessary steps in doing things.

5. Show your child how to be patient by being patient yourself.

6. Give your child suggestions of things to do (e.g., counting to ten, saying the alphabet to himself/herself, walking away from the situation and then returning, etc.) in order to help him/her learn to be more patient.

7. When your child is impatient, explain exactly what he/she is doing wrong, what should have been done and why.
For example: You see your child using an appliance inappropriately. Go to your child and say, ''William, you are using the mixer the wrong way. You need to read the directions and start again.''

8. Make certain that your child sees the relationship between behavior and the consequences which follow (e.g., things getting broken, chores not getting done, etc.).

9. Immediately remove your child from interacting with others when he/she begins to be impatient and doesn't follow directions.

10. Teach your child how to deal with his/her feelings of frustration in an appropriate manner.

11. Carefully consider your child's age and experience before expecting him/her to always be patient.

12. Encourage your child to ask for help when necessary.

13. Do not make your child wait for long periods of time to get your attention.

14. Remove your child from others when he/she begins to be impatient and is not following directions.

15. Identify the things with which your child is impatient (e.g., appliances, chores, homework, etc.). Remind your child to try to use patience before beginning to do the things with which he/she is impatient.

16. Make certain that your child is able to get those things that he/she needs without having to ask others for help. Your child should be able to reach food, dishes, shampoo, clothes, etc., without needing someone's help.

17. Provide your child with a place to go when he/she becomes impatient (e.g., a quiet corner, his/her room, etc.).

18. Remind your child when he/she begins to get impatient by saying, ''You need to count to ten.'' ''Calm down; you're becoming impatient.'' etc.

19. Discourage your child from engaging in those activities which cause him/her to fail to follow directions.

20. Help your child to be able to identify when he/she is getting upset so he/she can do something to calm down (e.g., walk away, talk about his/her feelings in a socially acceptable way, seek help from an adult, etc.).

21. Involve your child in activities in which he/she can be successful and which will help him/her feel good about himself/herself. Repeated failures result in frustration and impatience.

22. Reinforce your child for demonstrating self-control based on the length of time he/she can be successful. Gradually increase the length of time required for reinforcement as he/she demonstrates success.

23. Prevent frustrating or anxiety-producing situations from occurring (e.g., only give your child chores, responsibilities, etc., on his/her ability level).

24. Look for the warning signs (e.g., arguing, loud voices, etc.) that your child is getting upset or angry and intervene to change the activity.

25. Make certain the activities in which your child engages are not too difficult for him/her.

26. Do not allow your child to participate in a situation unless he/she can demonstrate self-control.

27. Make certain that the activities, situations, etc., in which your child is involved are appropriate for your child's age, maturity, developmental level, etc. It may be that your child is not ready for such activities at this particular time.

28. Help your child perform those activities (e.g., putting a model together, making his/her bed, etc.) which cause him/her to be impatient. Provide less assistance as your child experiences success.

22 Refuses to do what he/she is told, goes on doing what he/she was doing, does the opposite of what he/she is told, etc.

1. Establish rules for following directions (e.g., listen to directions, ask questions about directions if you do not understand, etc.). These rules should be consistent and followed by everyone in the home. Talk about the rules often.

2. Reward your child for following directions. Possible rewards include verbal praise (e.g., "You did a great job picking up your clothes!" "I like the way you follow directions!" etc.), a kiss on the cheek, a hug, having a friend over to play, staying up late, watching a favorite TV show, and playing a game with a parent. (See Appendix for Reward Menu.)

3. If there are other children or adolescents in the home, reward them for following directions.

4. Carefully consider your child's age and experience when giving him/her directions to follow.

5. Demonstrate the appropriate way to follow directions (e.g., give your child directions to feed the dog and then you feed the dog with him/her).

6. When your child does not follow a direction, explain exactly what he/she did wrong, what should have been done and why.

For example: You tell your child to clean up his/her room before 5:00. At 5:00, go to your child and say that he/she has not cleaned up the room and that he/she needs to follow the direction to clean the room now.

7. Write a contract with your child.

For example: I, William, for three days in a row, will follow directions without having to be told more than once. When I accomplish this, I can watch 30 extra minutes of TV.

The contract should be written within the ability level of your child and should focus on only one behavior at a time. (See Appendix for an example of a Behavior Contract.)

8. In order to determine if your child heard the direction, have your child repeat it.

9. Make certain that your child sees the relationship between behavior and the consequences which follow (e.g., failing to follow the direction to bring in a bike at night may result in the bike being stolen).

10. Allow natural consequences to occur due to your child's failing to follow directions (e.g., his/her bike being stolen, loss of school books, schoolwork not done on time, etc.).

11. Along with a directive, provide an incentive statement (e.g., "When you eat your peas, you may have dessert." "You may watch TV after you get ready for bed." etc.).

12. When your child has difficulty following directions in front of others (e.g., at the grocery store, in the mall, playing a game with family members, etc.), remove your child from the situation until he/she can demonstrate self-control and follow directions.

13. In order to help your child be able to follow directions, reduce distractions (e.g., turn off the TV, give directions in a room away from friends, etc.).

14. Do not give your child directions to follow with more than two or three steps. Directions that involve several steps can be confusing and cause your child to have difficulty following them. An example of a two-step direction is: "Please turn off your light and go to bed."

15. Deliver directions in a supportive rather than a threatening manner (e.g., "Please take out the trash." rather than "You had better take out the trash or else!").

16. Give your child a special responsibility (e.g., answering the door, serving food, cleaning, etc.) in order to teach him/her to follow directions.

17. Sit down with your child and discuss a list of chores he/she would like to do.

18. Do not criticize. When correcting your child, be honest yet supportive. Never cause your child to feel bad about himself/herself.

19. Be consistent when expecting your child to follow directions. Do not allow your child to fail to follow directions one time and expect appropriate behavior the next time.

20. Use a timer to help your child know how much time he/she has to follow through with directions.

21. Make a written list of directions you want your child to follow (e.g., feed the dog, take out the trash, etc.).

22. Talk to your child before going into a public place and remind your child of the importance of following directions.

23. Establish a regular routine for your child to follow on a daily basis in order to help him/her "remember" to take care of responsibilities. (See Appendix for Weekday or Saturday Schedule.)

24. Make sure your child is paying attention to you when you tell him/her to do something. Have your child look directly at you to know he/she is listening and have your child repeat the direction to check for understanding.

25. Do not give directions to your child from another room. Go to your child, get his/her undivided attention, and tell your child what to do.

26. Make certain to give directions in a very simple manner and be specific as to what you want your child to do.

27. Establish a certain time each day for your child to take care of responsibilities (e.g., feeding the dog, completing homework, etc., right after school).

28. Have your child do those things that need to be done when it is discussed instead of later (e.g., put swimsuits in the car now so that when you go to the pool later this afternoon, they will not be forgotten, etc.).

29. Do not punish your child for accidently forgetting, for accidents that interfere with following directions, etc.

30. Make certain that the responsibilities given to your child are appropriate for his/her level of development and ability.

31. Assist your child in performing responsibilities. Gradually require your child to independently assume responsibility as he/she demonstrates success.

32. Supervise your child as much as necessary both at home and in public places in order to help him/her follow the rules.

33. Encourage your child to play with other children or adolescents who behave appropriately in public places.

34. Do not allow your child to go to public places unless he/she can follow the rules.

35. Immediately remove your child from a public place when he/she begins to break rules, becomes loud, starts crying, etc.

36. Show your child how to follow the rules posted in public places by reading the rules with him/her and then demonstrating how to follow the rules.

37. Make sure you have your child's undivided attention when you are talking to him/her. Stand close to your child, maintain eye contact, and have your child repeat what you say.

38. Be sure your child has heard what you have said by having him/her acknowledge you (e.g., by saying, "Okay!" "Will do!" etc.).

39. Make certain your child knows that you expect him/her to listen to what you say by saying, "William, it is important that you listen carefully to what I have to say. You need to feed the dog now!"

40. Do not ignore your child when he/she wants to tell you something. When you ignore others, that teaches your child that it is acceptable to ignore people.

41. Have your child's hearing checked if you have not done so in the past year.

42. Allow natural consequences to occur as a result of your child's ignoring you (e.g., missing a favorite TV show because he/she ignored you when you said it was time for the show to begin).

43. When your child ignores you, let your child know that he/she is ignoring you and that he/she needs to listen to what you say.

44. Talk to your child before going into a public place and remind your child of the importance of listening to what is said to him/her.

45. Treat your child with respect. Talk to your child in an objective manner at all times.

46. Provide your child with written directions, chores, rules, etc.

23 Will not take "no" for an answer

1. When telling your child "no," explain why he/she cannot have or do what he/she wants.

2. Treat your child and others with respect. He/she will learn to treat others with respect by watching you.

3. Establish rules (e.g., listen calmly to what others have to say, state your opinion in a kind manner, make appropriate comments, accept directions from authority figures, etc.). These rules should be consistent and followed by everyone in the home. Talk about the rules often.

4. Reward your child for following requests and accepting decisions. Possible rewards include verbal praise (e.g., "Thanks for not arguing with me when I told you that you couldn't go to Kevin's house to play!"), a kiss on the cheek, a hug, having a friend over to play, staying up late, watching a favorite TV show, and playing a game with a parent. (See Appendix for Reward Menu.)

5. If there are other children or adolescents in the home, reward them for following requests and accepting decisions made by parents.

6. When your child does not follow requests or accept decisions, explain exactly what he/she is doing wrong, what should have been done and why.

For example: Your child starts arguing with you when you tell him that he cannot go roller skating. Get his attention and say, "William, you need to stop arguing. I told you that you cannot go roller skating today because we cannot afford it."

7. Write a contract with your child.

For example: I, William, for one week, will not argue when denied a request. When I accomplish this, I can go roller skating with a friend.

The contract should be written within the ability level of your child and should focus on only one behavior at a time. (See Appendix for an example of a Behavior Contract.)

8. Model appropriate ways to question someone's decision.

9. Make certain that your child sees the relationship between behavior and the consequences which follow (e.g., being removed from activities, not getting to do what he/she wants, etc.).

10. Do not "give in" to your child when he/she is arguing and demanding. If you do, your child will argue and demand things in order to get his/her own way.

11. Allow natural consequences to occur as a result of your child's inability to take "no" for an answer (e.g., being removed from activities, having to go to his/her room, losing special privileges, etc.).

12. Do not argue with your child. Arguing with your child tells him/her that arguing and not taking "no" for an answer is acceptable.

13. Let your child know that "questioning" should be done in private (at home) and not in public places (e.g., at the mall, skating rink, grocery store, etc.).

14. Be consistent with your child when he/she is unable to follow requests or accept decisions. Decide on an appropriate consequence (e.g., going to his/her room for five minutes) and use the consequence every time your child does not take "no" for an answer.

15. Separate your child from those individuals who encourage him/her to argue and talk back.

16. Immediately remove your child from the attention of others when he/she has difficulty following requests or accepting decisions.

17. Provide your child with an alternative activity when you deny a request (e.g., having a friend spend the night at your house if you do not want your child to spend the night at his/her friend's house).

18. Develop a routine schedule of activities and chores for your child in order that he/she knows what to expect at all times.

19. Avoid confrontations with your child which lead to arguing by giving him/her options (e.g., say, "You can either have a friend over to spend the night or you can spend the evening at Grandma's. Which do you want to do?").

20. Be flexible in helping your child be able to do those things he/she wants to do (e.g., if you do not think it would be appropriate for your child to spend the night at his/her friend's house, allow the friend to spend the night at your house).

21. Carefully consider your child's age and experience before asking him/her to do something that is too difficult and may result in arguing.

22. Along with a directive, provide an incentive statement (e.g., "When you finish the dishes, you may watch TV." "You may play outside after you finish your homework." etc.).

23. When your child will not take "no" for an answer in public (e.g., at the grocery store, in the mall, playing with friends, etc.), remove your child from the situation until he/she can demonstrate self-control and refrain from arguing.

24. Deliver directions in a supportive rather than a threatening manner (e.g., "Please take out the trash." rather than "You had better take out the trash or else!").

25. Make certain your child understands that total fairness is impossible. Sometimes we have to do more than others or do things we do not want to do simply because they have to be done.

26. Encourage your child to ask permission and/or discuss things he/she wants to do well in advance in order to avoid misunderstandings and increase the likelihood of finding solutions to disagreements without arguing.

27. Encourage your child to express his/her feelings and teach him/her how to talk about his/her feelings in a controlled manner.

28. Be consistent; do not "give in" to your child's arguing one time and expect appropriate behavior the next time.

29. Intervene early when your child is arguing with someone else. Do not allow your child to return to the situation unless he/she can behave appropriately.

30. Make certain that the people in the homes your child visits are aware of the behavioral expectations that you have for your child (e.g., picking up, not arguing, being friendly, etc.).

31. Make certain that your child does not get out of doing things or get his/her way simply because he/she is persistent in arguing (e.g., arguing about who will take out the trash will not let him/her get away with not taking out the trash, etc.).

32. Do not surprise your child with requests, chores, etc. Be consistent in expectations so your child knows what his/her responsibilities are and has no reason to argue (e.g., trash is taken out each evening, he/she washes the dishes on Tuesdays and Thursdays, etc.).

33. Make certain your child gets attention from you, from others, in the presence of others, etc., for appropriate behavior and not for arguing. Include your child in conversations, activities, etc., when others are present in order to satisfy your child's need for attention.

34. Children often talk back, have the last word, etc., in order to get the attention of others. Make certain that your child gets your attention when he/she is behaving appropriately.

35. Refrain from correcting your child in front of his/her peers as much as possible. Your child is more likely to talk back if he/she is told to do something, corrected, etc., in front of friends. Speak with your child in private to scold or correct him/her.

36. Make certain that baby-sitters, grandparents, neighbors, etc., understand the importance of maintaining consistency in discipline with your child.

37. Make certain that your child's demands are not met by anyone else (e.g., if you deny your child a dollar, make certain he/she does not go to someone else to get the money).

38. After telling your child that he/she cannot do or have something, explain the reason.

39. Remind your child of the consequences of not taking "no" for an answer before going into a grocery store, the shopping mall, a friend's house, etc.

40. Make certain you do not "give in" to your child's demanding because there are others present. Maintain consistency at all times.

41. Make certain your child understands that he/she may earn (for appropriate behavior) those things he/she wants, but you will not "give in" when he/she does not take "no" for an answer.

42. Remind your child when you go in a store that he/she is not to ask for things, whine, beg, etc.

43. Establish a rule that your child is not to ask for permission to do things with friends standing around, in public places, etc.

44. Require your child to ask permission in private, where you and he/she can discuss the request.

45. Make certain when you do have to say "no" to your child's requests, that you provide your child with options, alternatives, etc. (e.g., "No, you cannot have Matt stay over tonight. He may stay over on Friday night, since Saturday is not a school day.").

A Reminder: Saying "NO" is a lot easier if you explain the reason and offer other possibilities which are acceptable.

24 Will not wait his/her turn in activities

1. Establish a rule (e.g., be patient with others). This rule should be consistent and followed by everyone in the home. Talk about the rule often and reward your child for following the rule.

2. Attempt to be patient and wait your turn. If you are impatient, your child will learn to be impatient also.

3. Reward your child for being patient and waiting his/her turn. Possible rewards include verbal praise (e.g., ''Thanks for waiting patiently for your turn.''), a kiss on the cheek, a hug, having a friend over to play, staying up late, watching a favorite TV show, and playing a game with a parent. (See Appendix for Reward Menu.)

4. If there are other children or adolescents in the home, reward them for being patient and taking turns.

5. Give your child suggestions of things to do (e.g., counting to ten, saying the alphabet to himself/herself, walking away from the situation and then returning, etc.) in order to help him/her learn to wait his/her turn.

6. When your child does not wait his/her turn, explain exactly what he/she is doing wrong, what should have been done and why.

For example: You overhear your child yelling at a friend to hurry. Go to your child and say, ''William, you are yelling at Matt. You need to wait patiently until he is ready to play, or he may not want to play with you.''

7. Write a contract with your child.

For example: I, William, for two days in a row, will wait patiently for my turn to use the telephone. When I accomplish this, I can go to the movies on Saturday.

The contract should be written within the ability level of your child and should focus on only one behavior at a time. (See Appendix for an example of a Behavior Contract.)

8. Teach your child how to deal with his/her feelings of frustration in an appropriate manner.

9. Make certain that your child sees the relationship between behavior and the consequences which follow (e.g., hurting others' feeling, others avoiding him/her, etc.).

10. Immediately remove your child from interacting with others when he/she begins to be impatient and not wait his/her turn.

11. Provide supervision when your child interacts with others.

12. Carefully consider your child's age and experience before expecting your child to always be patient.

13. Encourage your child to ask for help when necessary.

14. Do not make your child wait for long periods of time to get your attention.

15. Make sure that your child has something to do if he/she has to wait on others (e.g., reading, playing a game, listening to music, etc.).

16. Remove your child from the presence of others when he/she begins to be impatient.

17. Do not allow your child to play with children with whom he/she has little patience.

18. Have your child spend short periods of time with younger brothers/sisters and friends in order to help him/her be more patient with them. Gradually increase the amount of time your child spends with younger brothers/sisters and friends as he/she demonstrates increased patience.

19. Identify the games and activities with which your child is impatient (e.g., playing with younger brothers/sisters or friends, playing games, etc.). Remind your child to try to use patience before he/she begins doing the thing with which he/she is impatient.

20. Provide your child with a place to go when he/she becomes impatient (e.g, a quiet corner, his/her room, etc.).

21. Remind your child when he/she begins to get impatient by saying, "You need to count to ten." "Calm down, you're becoming impatient." etc.

22. Discourage your child from engaging in those activities which cause him/her unhappiness.

23. Help your child to be able to identify when he/she is getting upset so he/she can do something to calm down (e.g., walk away, talk about his/her feelings in a socially acceptable way, seek help from an adult, etc.).

24. Involve your child in activities in which he/she can be successful and which will help him/her feel good about himself/herself. Repeated failures result in frustration and impatience.

25. Do not place an emphasis on perfection. If your child feels he/she must meet up to your expectations and cannot, it may cause him/her to become impatient with himself/herself.

26. Reinforce your child for demonstrating self-control based on the length of time he/she can be successful. Gradually increase the length of time required for reinforcement as he/she demonstrates success.

27. Teach your child to verbalize his/her feelings before losing control (e.g., "I'm getting tired of doing this." "I'm getting bored standing here." etc.).

28. Monitor the behavior of others (e.g., brothers/sisters, friends, etc.) to make certain they are not teasing or otherwise stimulating your child to become upset or angry.

29. Look for the warning signs (e.g., arguing, loud voices, etc.) that your child is getting upset or angry and intervene to change the activity.

30. Before competitive activities, discuss with your child how he/she should react if he/she becomes impatient.

31. Make certain the activities in which your child engages are not too difficult for him/her.

32. Do not allow your child to participate in a situation unless he/she can demonstrate self-control.

33. Make certain that the activities, situations, etc., in which your child is involved are appropriate for your child's age, maturity, developmental level, etc. It may be that your child is not ready for such activities at this particular time.

34. Reduce the emphasis on competition. Highly competitive activities may cause your child to be impatient to win, "beat" someone, etc.

35. Prevent your child from becoming overly frustrated by activities or situations. Intervene to keep your child from becoming too upset. Repeated frustration/impatience only contributes to more frequent impatience occurring at shorter intervals.

A Reminder: Impatience to participate, get things done, etc., while annoying, is a characteristic of youth. Patience is learned with personal success and by satisfaction with our accomplishments.

25 Grabs things away from others

1. Establish rules (e.g., be friendly, ask permission to borrow things, share, etc.). These rules should be consistent and followed by everyone in the home. Talk about the rules often.

2. Reward your child for not taking things from others in a forceful manner. Possible rewards include verbal praise (e.g., "Thank you for asking your brother's permission to use his bike."), a kiss on the cheek, a hug, having a friend over to play, staying up late, watching a favorite TV show, and playing a game with a parent. (See Appendix for Reward Menu.)

3. If there are other children or adolescents in the home, reward them for not taking things from others in a forceful manner.

4. Show your child how to ask permission to use something and how to react if he/she is told "no."

5. When your child forcefully takes things from others, explain exactly what he/she did wrong, what should have been done and why.

For example: You see your child forcefully taking a toy away from a peer. Go to your child and say, "William, you grabbed the toy from Kim. You need to ask permission to use things before taking them. If you don't, others will not want to play with you."

6. Write a contract with your child.

For example: I, William, will not take things from others in a forceful manner, for four days in a row. When I accomplish this, I can spend one dollar at the store.

The contract should be written within the ability level of your child and should focus on only one behavior at a time. (See Appendix for an example of a Behavior Contract.)

7. Make certain that your child sees the relationship between behavior and the consequences which follow (e.g., others avoiding him/her, being removed from an activity, hurting someone, breaking something, etc.).

8. Immediately remove your child from interacting with others when he/she begins to take things in a forceful manner.

9. Supervise your child at all times in order to prevent him/her from taking things from others in a forceful manner.

10. Make certain that your child returns, as soon as possible, those things which he/she has taken from others in a forceful manner.

11. Do not allow others to take things from your child in a forceful manner.

12. Teach your child to handle his/her anger, frustration, disappointment, etc., by walking away from the situation, talking with an adult, etc.

13. Do not take things from others in a forceful manner. Your child will learn to forcefully take things from others if you do so.

14. Teach your child to ask for things in a positive manner. Teach him/her key words and phrases (e.g., "May I please use your bike?" "May I borrow your skateboard?" "Do you mind if I play with your doll?" etc.).

15. Set an example for your child by asking for things in a positive manner. Use key words and phrases (e.g., "May I please use your pencil?" "May I use your brush?" etc.).

16. Do not allow your child to play with those children with whom he/she has trouble getting along.

17. Intervene early when your child begins to take things forcefully in order to prevent him/her from fighting.

18. Give your child suggestions of things to do (e.g., count to 10, say the alphabet to himself/herself, walk away from the situation and then return, etc.) in order to avoid taking things from others in a forceful manner.

19. Carefully consider your child's age and experience in playing with others before expecting your child to play cooperatively.

20. Show your child how to play cooperatively, share, talk in an acceptable manner, and refrain from fighting with others.

21. Make sure that you get along with others. Your child learns how to interact with others by watching how you interact.

22. Do not allow your child to play stimulating activities which cause him/her to have trouble getting along with friends.

23. Do not make your child play with a certain child or group of children. Allow him/her to pick his/her own friends.

24. Encourage your child to play with children or adolescents who get along well with others.

25. Be consistent. Try to deal with your child and his/her behavior in a manner that is as consistent as possible by reacting in the same manner each time, using the same consequences, etc.

26. Provide your child with a quiet place to go when he/she becomes upset or angry with a friend or friends.

27. Help your child choose activities, toys, games to play, etc., when friends are over that do not cause him/her to become angry, frustrated, etc.

28. Arrange for your child to be involved in many activities with other children to help him/her learn the skills necessary to interact appropriately with them.

29. Make sure your child understands that the privilege of having a friend over or going to a friend's house will be taken away if he/she is not nice to friends.

30. Get to know your child's friends and their parents and maintain open communication with them.

31. Make certain that your child does not get away with taking things from others by having him/her return what he/she takes forcefully.

32. Make certain your child understands that things he/she breaks, destroys, etc., when taking things forcefully, will be replaced by him/her.

33. Remind your child before going to a friend's house, having a friend over, etc., about sharing and not taking things forcefully from others.

34. Do not expect your child to share everything with others. He/she should have some belongings that he/she does not have to share with others.

35. Teach your child the concept of borrowing by "loaning" him/her those things he/she has been taking from others and then requiring the return of those things. Repeat this process so your child is comfortable asking for things, returning them, etc.

36. Identify those things your child has been taking from others and provide those items as reinforcers for appropriate behavior.

37. Make certain your child understands that he/she can earn those things he/she wants. Anything can be earned to avoid stealing or forcefully taking things from others.

38. Teach your child to "take turns" sharing possessions (e.g., each child may use the remote control car for 15 minutes, one child bats while the other throws the ball, players change places after three hits, etc.).

39. Make certain your child understands that toys, games, etc., which he/she forcefully takes from others will be taken from him/her for a period of time.

40. Provide your child and his/her brothers/sisters, friends, etc., with more than one of those things he/she forcefully takes.

41. Increase supervision of your child and those activities in which he/she is likely to forcefully take things from others.

42. Make certain other children do not take things forcefully from your child; that may result in your child attempting to forcefully take things from others.

43. Make certain when your child has a friend over that there are plenty of things with which the friend can play.

44. Make certain when your child visits a friend that he/she takes along things of his/her own to prevent the need to forcefully take things from others.

26 Interrupts others

1. Establish rules for conversing with others (e.g., wait your turn to talk, stand quietly by the person with whom you want to talk until you are noticed, excuse yourself when you interrupt others, etc.). These rules should be consistent and followed by everyone in the home. Talk about the rules often.

2. Reward your child for not interrupting others. Possible rewards include verbal praise (e.g., "Thank you for waiting until I finished talking."), a kiss on the cheek, a hug, having a friend over to play, staying up late, watching a favorite TV show, and playing a game with a parent. (See Appendix for a Reward Menu.)

3. If there are other children or adolescents in the home, reward them for not interrupting.

4. Carefully consider your child's age before expecting him/her not to interrupt others when they are talking, working, reading, etc.

5. Show your child the appropriate way to get someone's attention without interrupting.

6. Make sure that you do not interrupt others. If you interrupt others, your child will learn to do so also.

7. When your child interrupts others, explain exactly what he/she is doing wrong, what he/she is supposed to be doing and why.

For example: You are talking on the phone and your child interrupts you. Stop talking and say to your child, "You are interrupting me. You need to stand here quietly until I ask you what you want because I am talking with someone else right now."

8. Make sure your child knows when it is acceptable to interrupt others (e.g., in an emergency).

9. Acknowledge your child's presence and need to talk with you (e.g., by saying, "Just a minute"; putting your arm around him/her; smiling and nodding your head; etc.).

10. Do not require your child to wait more than a minute to talk with you.

11. Write a contract with your child.

For example: I, William, will not interrupt others for five times in a row. When I accomplish this I can have a friend over for dinner.

The contract should be written within the ability level of your child and should focus on only one behavior at a time. (See Appendix for an example of a Behavior Contract.)

12. Do not allow your child to interrupt you by letting him/her talk to you at the time he/she interrupts. Tell him/her that he/she will need to wait until you are finished talking. Allowing your child to talk after interrupting you just reinforces the behavior and may increase the number of times he/she interrupts others.

13. Set aside a time each day when your child has your undivided attention and can tell you things that he/she needs or wants to tell you.

14. Make certain that your child sees the relationship between behavior and the consequences which follow (e.g., others ignoring him/her, hurting others' feelings, etc.).

15. Explain to your child why it is important not to interrupt others. Help him/her understand that it is impolite, that he/she might hurt someone's feelings, etc.

16. Do not interrupt your child when he/she is doing something, talking to someone, etc.

17. Do not continue talking while your child continues to interrupt. Stop what you are doing after giving your child the opportunity to behave appropriately, and deal with your child concerning his/her unacceptable behavior.

18. Before beginning a conversation, task, etc., that will be time-consuming ask your child if he/she needs to talk with you or ask any questions.

19. Have regular activities planned for your child (e.g., drawing, watching TV, etc.) when you know you cannot be interrupted for a period of time.

20. Be consistent when expecting your child to behave appropriately while you are busy. Do not allow your child to interrupt one time and expect appropriate behavior the next time.

21. If your child needs to interrupt for an emergency, make certain he/she does it in a way which helps you to understand the urgency (e.g., ''I'm sorry for interrupting.'' ''May I stop you for a minute?'' etc.).

22. Develop a message board for your child so he/she can list the things about which he/she wants to talk after you are finished with what you are doing.

23. When your child does interrupt, be certain to calmly explain that you are talking now and he/she may talk to you in a few moments.

24. Give your child frequent opportunities to join in your conversations with others by allowing him/her time to talk, asking him/her to re-state an experience, etc.

27 Is impulsive

1. Establish a rule (e.g., stop and think before acting). This rule should be consistent and followed by everyone in the home. Talk about the rule often.

2. Reward your child for thinking before acting. Possible rewards include verbal praise (e.g., "I'm proud of you for thinking about your behavior before you acted!"), a kiss on the cheek, a hug, having a friend over to play, staying up late, watching a favorite TV show, and playing a game with a parent. (See Appendix for Reward Menu.)

3. If there are other children or adolescents in the home, reward them for thinking before acting.

4. Carefully consider your child's age before expecting your child to always think before acting.

5. Show your child how to stop and think before acting.

6. Make sure that you stop and think before acting in order to teach your child to do the same.

7. When your child acts without thinking, explain exactly what he/she is doing wrong, what should have been done and why.

For example: You ask your child to clean his/her room and your child immediately starts arguing with you. Get his/her attention and say, "William, you are arguing with me. You need to stop and think about your behavior and the consequences that will occur."

8. Write a contract with your child.

For example: I, William, will stop and think before I get angry with others. Each time that I do this, I can earn a nickel.

The contract should be written within the ability level of your child and should focus on only one behavior at a time. (See Appendix for an example of a Behavior Contract.)

9. Supervise your child in order to make sure he/she thinks before acting.

10. Make certain that your child sees the relationship between behavior and the consequences which follow (e.g., hurting others' feelings, not being allowed to participate in special activities, being avoided by others, etc.).

11. Allow natural consequences to occur as a result of your child's failure to think before acting.

12. Immediately remove your child from the situation until he/she can demonstrate acceptable behavior and self-control.

13. Remind your child to "stop and think" when he/she begins to do something without thinking first.

14. Immediately stop your child from behaving inappropriately and discuss the consequences of the behavior with him/her.

15. Provide constant, positive reinforcement for appropriate behavior. Ignore as many inappropriate behaviors as possible.

16. Prevent your child from becoming overstimulated by an activity (e.g., monitor or supervise your child's behavior to limit overexcitement in physical activities, games, parties, etc.).

17. Provide your child with a clearly identified list of consequences for inappropriate behavior.

18. Supervise your child closely in situations in which he/she is likely to act impulsively (e.g., maintain close physical proximity, maintain eye contact, etc.).

19. Talk with your family doctor, a school official, a social worker, a mental health worker, etc., about your child's failure to consider the consequences of his/her behavior.

20. Teach your child ways to settle down (e.g., counting to 10, saying the alphabet, walking away, etc.) when he/she needs to slow down and think about what he/she is doing.

21. Remove your child from a group or activity until he/she can demonstrate self-control.

22. Make it possible for your child to earn those things he/she wants or needs so that he/she will not have to engage in inappropriate behavior to get them (e.g., lying or stealing to get something important to him/her).

23. Do not make it too difficult for your child to earn those things he/she wants. If it is too difficult to earn something, the negative consequences of getting it in an inappropriate way (e.g., stealing) may seem like a worthwhile risk.

24. Each time a consequence is delivered, whether it is positive or negative, have your child explain to you why he/she thinks it is happening (e.g., ''Because I was a helpful shopper, I can have a treat at the checkout line.'').

25. Make certain your child understands that consequences naturally follow behavior, whether it is his/hers, yours, or someone else's. It is his/her own behavior that makes the consequences occur in his/her life.

26. Discuss consequences with your child before he/she begins an activity (e.g., acting impatiently in a game will result in the game ending and people not playing again).

27. Reduce the opportunity for your child to act impulsively by limiting decision making. Gradually increase opportunities for decision making as he/she demonstrates success.

28. Make necessary adjustments in the environment to prevent your child from experiencing stress, impatience, frustration, etc.

29. Teach your child to verbalize his/her feelings before losing control (e.g., ''I'm getting tired of doing this.'' ''I'm getting bored standing here.'' etc.).

30. Provide your child with a place to go when he/she becomes overly excited (e.g., a quiet corner, his/her room, etc.).

31. Remind your child when he/she begins to lose control (e.g., by saying, ''You need to count to ten.'' ''Calm down.'' etc.).

32. Monitor the behavior of others (e.g., brothers, sisters, friends, etc.) to make certain they are not teasing or otherwise stimulating your child to lose control.

33. Teach your child ways to deal with conflict situations (e.g., talking, reasoning, asking an adult to intervene, walking away, etc.).

34. Look for the warning signs (e.g., arguing, loud voices, etc.) that your child is getting upset or angry, and intervene to change the activity.

35. Prevent your child from becoming so stimulated that he/she reacts with impulsive behavior (i.e., intervene when your child is becoming overexcited to prevent him/her from losing self-control).

36. Teach your child to ''think'' before he/she acts (e.g., ask himself/herself, ''What is happening?'' ''What am I doing?'' ''What should I do?'' ''What will be best for me?'').

37. Reduce the emphasis on competition. Highly competitive activities may stimulate impulsive behavior.

38. Teach your child decision-making steps: (a) think about how other persons may be influenced, (b) think about consequences, (c) carefully consider the unique situation, (d) think of different courses of action which are possible, and (e) think about what is ultimately best for him/her.

39. Point out natural consequences of impulsive behavior in order to help your child learn that persons who act in a more deliberate fashion are more successful than those who act impulsively (e.g., if you begin before understanding directions or what is needed, you may finish first; but you may do things wrong, things may be broken or destroyed, etc.).

40. ''Prepare'' your child in advance for those things which you know will occur (e.g., changes in routine, guests, visitors, special events, highly stimulating outings, etc.).

41. Reduce those activities which stimulate your child's impulsive behavior (e.g., ''roughhousing,'' loud music, having friends over, etc.).

42. Go over the rules before your child engages in activities in order to reduce the likelihood of impulsive behavior (e.g., ''When we get out of the car we will hold hands walking across the parking lot.'').

43. Maintain, as much as possible, a routine for your child to follow in order to increase stable behavior.

A Reminder: Do not confuse impulsive behavior with enthusiasm; impulsive behavior should be controlled while enthusiasm should be encouraged.

28 Is unable to follow a routine

1. Carefully determine if your child is capable of performing the responsibilities expected on his/her own. Do not give your child too many chores to do at once, make sure he/she gets up early enough to get to school on time, provide more than enough time to perform a responsibility, and do not expect perfection.

2. Establish rules for performing everyday expectations (e.g., get up on time for school, do your chores right after you get home from school, finish your homework before you watch TV, etc.). These rules should be consistent and followed by everyone in the home. Talk about the rules often.

3. Establish a routine for your child to follow for getting ready for school, doing chores, completing homework, etc. This will help your child remember what is expected.

4. Reward your child for getting things done on time. Possible rewards include verbal praise (e.g., "You're on time for school. Good for you!" "Thank you for remembering to finish your homework before you turned on the TV." etc.), a kiss on the cheek, a hug, having a friend over to play, staying up late, watching a favorite TV show, and playing a game with a parent. (See Appendix for Reward Menu.)

5. If there are other children or adolescents in the home, reward them for getting things done on time and following a routine.

6. Model for your child the appropriate ways to get things done on time. Show your child how to follow a routine by following one yourself and getting things done on time.

7. When your child does not get something done on time, explain exactly what he/she did wrong, what should have been done and why.

For example: Your child is supposed to catch the school bus at 7:45 a.m. and is still getting dressed when the bus arrives. Go to your child and tell him that he/she has missed the bus because of not being ready on time. Explain that it is unacceptable to miss the bus because you don't have time to take him/her to school.

8. Write a contract with your child.

For example: I, William, will be ready and waiting for the school bus at 7:40 a.m. for three days in a row. When I accomplish this, I can watch 30 extra minutes of TV.

The contract should be written within the ability level of your child and should focus on only one behavior at a time. (See Appendix for an example of a Behavior Contract.)

9. Make certain that your child sees the relationship between behavior and the consequences which follow (e.g., failing to feed the dog will cause the dog to go hungry).

10. Allow natural consequences to occur due to your child putting off doing things (e.g., a bike being stolen because he/she did not put it in the garage overnight).

11. Along with a directive, provide an incentive statement (e.g., "After you get ready for bed, you may watch TV.").

12. Provide your child with written reminders (e.g., a list posted in the bathroom indicating what his/her chores are and when they need to be done). (See Appendix for Sample List.)

13. Tell your child when it is time to set the table, feed the dog, etc.

14. Allow your child to help decide what his/her routine responsibilities will be.

15. Limit the number of chores for which your child is responsible and gradually increase the number of chores as your child demonstrates the ability to get them done on time.

16. Have your child perform the same responsibilities each day, week, etc.

17. Show your child how to perform a new responsibility (e.g., setting the table) several times before expecting your child to do it on his/her own.

18. Make sure your child has all the necessary materials needed in order to get chores done on time.

19. Explain to your child that responsibilities not done on time will have to be done at other times (e.g., playtime, TV time, weekends, etc.).

20. Have everyone in the family work together at the same time in order to help your child get responsibilities done on time.

21. Reduce distracting activities which interfere with your child performing responsibilities (e.g., turning off the TV when it is time to set the table, not allowing friends to come over when it is time to do homework, etc.).

22. Have your child put a star or check mark beside each responsibility performed on time, and allow your child to trade in the stars or check marks for rewards.

23. Set aside time each day for everyone in your home to complete their responsibilities (e.g., after dinner, everyone does their assigned chores).

24. Do not accept your child's excuse of "forgetting" responsibilities. Have your child make up the chores forgotten during free time, TV time, etc.

25. Provide an atmosphere where everyone works together to get things done around the house.

26. Set aside time each week for your child to straighten his/her room and clothes, put toys away, etc.

27. Have your child do those things that need to be done when it is discussed instead of at a later time (e.g., put swimsuits in the car now so that when you go to the pool later this afternoon, they will not be forgotten, etc.).

28. Sit down and explain changes in routine to your child a few days before they happen, if possible.

29. Try to give your child as much structure and "sameness" in his/her life as possible.

30. Allow your child to participate in deciding when changes in his/her routine will occur.

31. Have a calendar of family activities and indicate on the calendar when guests will visit, doctors' appointments will occur, baby-sitters will come, etc.

32. Plan things for your child to do when changes in his/her routine occur (e.g., caring for a younger brother or sister, going to see a movie, having a friend spend the night, etc.).

33. Be personally available when your child is dealing with changes in his/her routine (e.g., take him/her to the first day of swim lessons, have the new baby-sitter come over to play games with your child while you are home, etc.).

34. Allow your child to take part in changing his/her routine (e.g., let him/her decide which day he/she would like to visit Grandma, let him/her decide which baby-sitter he/she would like to have, etc.).

35. Carefully consider your child's age and maturity level before expecting him/her to accept changes in routine.

36. Have your child help plan special events (e.g., family gatherings, parties, etc.) in your home by choosing refreshments, planning a schedule of events, etc.

37. Provide your child with a revised schedule of daily events which identifies the activities for the day and the times when they will occur. (See Appendix for Weekday or Saturday Schedule.)

38. Provide your child with notes on the refrigerator, in his/her room, etc., to remind him/her of changes in the routine.

39. Provide your child with a verbal reminder of changes in his/her routine.

40. Limit the number of changes in your child's established routine. Gradually increase the number of changes in routine as your child demonstrates success.

41. Make certain that anyone who assumes responsibility in your home (e.g., grandparents, baby-sitter, etc.) is provided with rules, schedules, mealtimes and bedtimes, appropriate activities, consequences, etc., in order that their supervision will be as consistent with yours as possible.

29 Begins things before receiving directions

1. Immediately remove your child from a situation when he/she begins doing things before receiving directions or instructions.

2. Do not allow your child to participate in a situation unless he/she can demonstrate self-control and listen to directions or instructions before beginning.

3. Closely supervise your child in order to monitor his/her behavior at all times.

4. Inform individuals who will be spending time with your child about his/her tendency to begin things before receiving directions or instructions.

5. Talk with your family doctor, a school official, a social worker, etc., about your child's behavior if it is causing him/her to have problems getting along with others, getting things done, etc.

6. Provide your child with a quiet place to go when he/she begins a task, chore, etc.

7. Teach your child to recognize when he/she is becoming overanxious and beginning things before having directions or instructions.

8. Reward your child for controlling his/her behavior. Possible rewards include verbal praise (e.g., "I'm so proud of you for waiting for directions before beginning the game."), a kiss on the cheek, a hug, having a friend over to play, staying up late, watching a favorite TV show, and playing a game with a parent. (See Appendix for Reward Menu.)

9. If there are other children or adolescents in the home, reward them for controlling their behavior and waiting for directions or instructions.

10. Treat your child with respect. Talk to your child in a nonthreatening manner.

11. Do not allow your child to participate in a situation unless he/she can demonstrate self-control.

12. When your child becomes overanxious, explain exactly what he/she is doing wrong, what he/she is supposed to be doing and why.

For example: You are playing a new game with your child and he/she starts to play before receiving directions. Stop the game, get his/her attention, and say, "William, you need to wait for directions. Others will not want to play with you if you cannot follow the rules."

13. Write a contract with your child.

For example: I, William, will not begin an activity until I know the directions. When I accomplish this, I can go to the movies on Saturday.

The contract should be written within the ability level of your child and should focus on only one behavior at a time. (See Appendix for an example of a Behavior Contract.)

14. Make certain that your child sees the relationship between behavior and the consequences which follow (e.g., being avoided by others, not being able to participate in special activities, others making fun of him/her, chores and responsibilities not performed correctly, etc.).

15. Discuss your child's behavior with him/her in private rather than in front of others.

16. Try to reduce or prevent your child from beginning something before being given directions or instructions (e.g., sit next to him/her, give out materials when it is time to begin the task, etc.).

17. Teach your child how to handle feelings of frustration (e.g., ask for help, count to 10, etc.).

18. Before a competitive activity, remind your child of the importance of following directions and instructions, personal improvement, doing his/her best, contributing to team success, etc.

19. If your child needs improvement in particular skill areas in order to be competitive, help him/her improve in those areas with more practice, additional coaching, etc.

20. Encourage your child to talk with you when he/she is overly anxious or excited.

21. Provide your child with a place to go when he/she gets overexcited (e.g., a quiet chair, his/her room, a corner, etc.).

22. Make certain that the activities, situations, etc., in which your child is involved are appropriate for your child's age, maturity, developmental level, etc. It may be that your child is not ready for such activities at this particular time.

23. Immediately remove your child from the attention of others when he/she becomes overly anxious or excited.

24. Do not place an emphasis on perfection. If your child feels he/she must meet up to your expectations and cannot, it may cause him/her to become frustrated.

25. Make certain you set an example by dealing in a socially acceptable way with situations which require you to sit through directions or instructions.

26. When your child becomes overly excited, tell him/her to calm down, count to ten, etc.

27. Reinforce your child for demonstrating self-control based on the length of time he/she can be successful. Gradually increase the length of time required for reinforcement as he/she demonstrates success.

28. Prevent frustrating or anxiety-producing situations from occurring (e.g., give your child chores, responsibilities, etc., only on his/her ability level).

29. Make necessary adjustments in the environment to prevent your child from becoming overly excited or anxious (e.g., give out materials after delivering directions or instructions).

30. Monitor the behavior of others (e.g., brothers, sisters, friends, etc.) to make certain they are not stimulating your child to become overly anxious or excited.

31. Look for the warning signs (e.g., getting up, walking around, etc.) that your child is overly anxious or excited.

32. Make certain that the activities in which your child engages are not too difficult for him/her.

33. Reduce the emphasis on competition. Highly competitive activities may cause your child to feel anxious or excited.

34. Encourage your child to avoid those activities which cause him/her to become overly excited. He/she can always participate in the activities at a later time.

35. Before competitive activities, discuss with your child the importance of waiting for directions or instructions.

36. Encourage your child to play a game in such a manner that he/she can return and play it again tomorrow (e.g., do not behave foolishly or upset your opponent so that he/she will not want to compete against you again, begin the game after receiving directions or instructions).

A Reminder: Anyone would be frustrated by continued disappointment or failure. Make certain your child is not engaged in activities with which he/she cannot have some success.

30 Intrudes on others

1. Establish rules for conversing with others (e.g., wait your turn to talk, stand quietly by the person with whom you want to talk until they notice you, excuse yourself when you interrupt others, etc.). These rules should be consistent and followed by everyone in the home. Talk about the rules often.

2. Reward your child for not intruding on others. Possible rewards include verbal praise (e.g., "Thank you for waiting until I finished talking."), a kiss on the cheek, a hug, having a friend over to play, staying up late, watching a favorite TV show, and playing a game with a parent. (See Appendix for a Reward Menu.)

3. If there are other children or adolescents in the home, reward them for not intruding on others.

4. Carefully consider your child's age before expecting him/her not to intrude on others when they are talking, working, reading, etc.

5. Show your child the appropriate way to get someone's attention without intruding.

6. Make sure that you do not intrude on others. If you intrude on others, your child will learn to do so also.

7. When your child intrudes on others, explain exactly what he/she is doing wrong, what he/she is supposed to be doing and why.

For example: You are talking on the phone and your child interrupts you. Stop talking and say to your child, "You are interrupting me. You need to stand here quietly until I ask you what you want because I am talking with someone else right now."

8. Do not require your child to wait more than a minute to talk with you.

9. Make sure your child knows when it is acceptable to intrude on others (e.g., in an emergency).

10. Do not intrude on your child when he/she is doing something, talking to someone, etc.

11. Acknowledge your child's presence and need to talk with you (e.g., by saying, "Just a minute"; putting your arm around him/her; smiling and nodding your head; etc.).

12. Write a contract with your child.

For example: I, William, will not interrupt others for five times in a row. When I accomplish this I can have a friend over for dinner.

The contract should be written within the ability level of your child and should focus on only one behavior at a time. (See Appendix for an example of a Behavior Contract.)

13. Do not allow your child to talk to you at the time he/she interrupts you. Tell him/her that he/she will need to wait until you are finished talking. Allowing your child to talk after he/she has interrupted you just reinforces the behavior and may increase the number of times he/she interrupts others.

14. Set aside a time each day when your child has your undivided attention and can tell you things he/she needs or wants to tell you.

15. Make certain that your child sees the relationship between behavior and the consequences which follow (e.g., others ignoring him/her, hurting others' feelings, etc.).

16. Explain to your child why it is important not to intrude on others. Help him/her understand that it is impolite, that he/she might hurt someone's feelings, etc.

17. Do not continue talking while your child continues to intrude. Stop what you are doing after giving your child the opportunity to behave appropriately, and deal with your child concerning his/her unacceptable behavior.

18. Before beginning a conversation, task, etc., that will be time-consuming, ask your child if he/she needs to talk with you or ask any questions.

19. Have regular activities planned for your child (e.g., drawing, watching TV, etc.) when you know you cannot be interrupted.

20. Be consistent when expecting your child to behave appropriately while you are busy. Do not allow your child to interrupt one time and expect appropriate behavior the next time.

21. If your child needs to interrupt for an emergency, make certain he/she does it in a way which helps you to understand he/she needs you urgently (e.g., ''I'm sorry for interrupting.'' ''May I stop you for a minute?'' etc.).

22. Develop a message board for your child so he/she can list the things about which he/she wants to talk after you are finished with what you are doing.

23. When your child does intrude on you or others, be certain to calmly explain that you are talking now and he/she may talk to you in a few moments.

24. Give your child frequent opportunities to join in your conversations with others by allowing him/her time to talk, asking him/her to restate an experience, etc.

31 Is easily angered, annoyed, or upset

1. Immediately remove your child from a situation when he/she begins to be upset, annoyed or angry.

2. Do not allow your child to participate in a situation unless he/she can demonstrate self-control.

3. Closely supervise your child in order to monitor his/her behavior at all times.

4. Inform individuals who will be spending time with your child about his/her ability to become easily upset, annoyed or angry.

5. Talk with your family doctor, a school official, a social worker, etc., about your child's behavior if it is causing him/her to have problems getting along with others.

6. Provide your child with a quiet place to go when he/she becomes upset, annoyed or angry.

7. Encourage your child to talk with you when he/she is upset, annoyed or angry.

8. Teach your child to recognize when he/she is becoming upset, annoyed or angry and ways in which to deal with his/her feelings.

9. Reward your child for controlling his/her behavior. Possible rewards include verbal praise (e.g., "I'm so proud of you for remaining calm when James called you a name!"), a kiss on the cheek, a hug, having a friend over to play, staying up late, watching a favorite TV show, and playing a game with a parent. (See Appendix for Reward Menu.)

10. If there are other children or adolescents in the home, reward them for controlling their behavior.

11. Treat your child with respect. Talk to your child in a nonthreatening manner.

12. Try to reduce or prevent things from happening which cause your child to become easily upset, annoyed or angry.

13. When your child becomes upset, annoyed or angry, explain exactly what he/she is doing wrong, what he/she is supposed to be doing and why.

For example: You tell your child that it is time to feed the dog and he/she starts complaining and arguing with you. Get his/her attention and say, "You are getting angry because I told you to feed the dog. You need to get control of yourself and feed the dog because it is your job for this month."

14. Write a contract with your child.

For example: I, William, for one week, will not get angry when asked if I have done my homework. When I accomplish this, I can see a movie on Saturday.

The contract should be written within the ability level of your child and should focus on only one behavior at a time. (See Appendix for an example of a Behavior Contract.)

15. Make certain that your child sees the relationship between behavior and the consequences which follow (e.g., being avoided by others, not being able to participate in special activities, etc.).

16. Discuss your child's behavior with him/her in private rather than in front of others.

17. Provide your child with a place to go when he/she gets upset, annoyed or angry (e.g., a quiet chair, his/her room, a corner, etc.).

18. Teach your child what to do when he/she becomes upset, annoyed or angry (e.g., count to 10, say the alphabet, leave the room, etc.).

19. Ignore your child's burst of anger when he/she is upset. Do not let him/her have his/her way when he/she gets angry.

20. Be consistent. Try to deal with your child and his/her behavior in a manner that is as fair as possible.

21. Immediately remove your child from the attention of others when he/she gets upset, annoyed or angry.

22. Remind your child of the consequences of getting upset, annoyed or angry before going into a store, going to a friend's house, having friends over, etc.

23. Make certain that your child does not go to another adult to get his/her way after you have said "no."

24. After telling your child that he/she cannot do or have something, explain to him/her the reason.

25. Offer another suggestion to your child after you have said "no" to something (e.g., if your child wants to spend the night at someone else's house and he/she cannot do that, suggest that he/she have the friend come to your house; if your child wants a new toy but cannot get one, suggest getting it for his/her birthday or earning it for good behavior; etc.).

26. Make certain that baby-sitters, grandparents, teachers, etc., understand the importance of maintaining consistency in the discipline of your child.

27. Make certain your child understands that he/she may earn (for appropriate behavior) those things about which he/she gets upset or angry, but you will not "give" him/her those things about which he/she gets upset or angry.

28. Encourage your child to use problem-solving skills: (a) identify the problem, (b) identify goals and objectives, (c) develop strategies, (d) develop a plan for action, and (e) carry out the plan.

29. Teach your child alternative ways to communicate his/her unhappiness (e.g., talking about a problem, asking for help, etc.).

30. Reduce the emphasis on competition. Repeated failures may cause your child to become upset, annoyed and angry.

31. Provide your child with alternative activities, games, etc., in case some activities prove upsetting.

32. Discourage your child from engaging in those activities which cause him/her unhappiness.

33. Encourage your child to associate with peers with whom he/she gets along well in order to prevent him/her from getting upset, annoyed or angry.

34. Involve your child in activities in which he/she can be successful and that will help him/her feel good about himself/herself. Repeated failures result in frustration and impatience.

35. Do not place an emphasis on perfection. If your child feels he/she must meet up to your expectations and cannot do so, he/she may become upset, annoyed or angry.

36. Talk to your child's teacher to make certain that he/she is not having trouble in school and becoming upset, annoyed or angry.

37. Make certain you set a good example for your child by dealing in a socially acceptable way with situations that may be upsetting.

38. Reinforce your child for demonstrating self-control based on the length of time he/she can be successful. Gradually increase the length of time required for reinforcement as he/she demonstrates success.

39. Prevent frustrating or anxiety-producing situations from occurring (e.g., only give your child chores, responsibilities, etc., which are on his/her ability level).

40. Provide your child with positive feedback which indicates he/she is successful, important, respected, etc.

41. Make necessary adjustments in the environment to prevent your child from experiencing stress, frustration, and anger.

42. Teach your child to verbalize his/her feelings before losing control (e.g., "The work is too hard." "Please leave me alone; you're making me angry." etc.).

43. Monitor the behavior of others (e.g., brothers, sisters, friends, etc.) to make certain they are not teasing or otherwise stimulating your child to become upset or angry.

44. Teach your child ways to deal with conflict situations (e.g., talking, reasoning, asking an adult to intervene, walking away, etc.).

45. Look for the warning signs (e.g., arguing, loud voices, etc.) that your child is getting upset or annoyed, and intervene to change the activity.

A Reminder: Learning to control our temper is more difficult for some of us than it is for others. Being a model for your child in demonstrating self-control and displaying appropriate reactions to frustration or disappointment will influence your child's behavior.

32 Bothers others

1. Establish rules for conversing with others (e.g., wait for your turn to talk, stand quietly by the person with whom you want to talk until they notice you, excuse yourself when you interrupt others, etc.). These rules should be consistent and followed by everyone in the home. Talk about the rules often.

2. Reward your child for not bothering others. Possible rewards include verbal praise (e.g., "Thank you for waiting until I finished talking."), a kiss on the cheek, a hug, having a friend over to play, staying up late, watching a favorite TV show, and playing a game with a parent. (See Appendix for Reward Menu.)

3. If there are other children or adolescents in the home, reward them for not bothering others who are working, playing, etc.

4. Carefully consider your child's age before expecting him/her not to interrupt others who are talking, working, reading, playing, etc.

5. Show your child the appropriate way to get someone's attention without interrupting.

6. Make sure that you do not interrupt others. If you interrupt others, your child will learn to interrupt others also.

7. When your child bothers others, explain exactly what he/she is doing wrong, what he/she is supposed to be doing and why.

For example: You are talking on the phone and your child interrupts you. Stop talking and say to your child, "You are interrupting me. You need to stand here quietly until I ask you what you want because I am talking with someone else right now."

8. Do not require your child to wait more than a minute to talk with you.

9. Make sure your child knows when it is acceptable to interrupt others (e.g., in an emergency).

10. Do not interrupt your child when he/she is doing something, talking to someone, etc.

11. Acknowledge your child's presence and his/her need to talk with you (e.g., by saying, "Just a minute"; putting your arm around him/her; smiling and nodding your head; etc.).

12. Write a contract with your child.

For example: I, William, will not bother others for five times in a row. When I accomplish this I can have a friend over for dinner.

The contract should be written within the ability level of your child and should focus on only one behavior at a time. (See Appendix for an example of a Behavior Contract.)

13. When your child interrupts you, do not let him/her talk to you at that time. Tell him/her that he/she will need to wait until you are finished. Allowing your child to talk after he/she has interrupted you reinforces the behavior and may increase the number of times he/she interrupts others.

14. Set aside a time each day when your child has your undivided attention and can tell you the things that he/she needs or wants to tell you.

15. Make certain that your child sees the relationship between behavior and the consequences which follow (e.g., others ignoring him/her, hurting others' feelings, etc.).

16. Explain to your child why it is important not to bother others. Help him/her understand that it is impolite, that he/she might hurt someone's feelings, etc.

17. Do not continue talking while your child continues to interrupt. Stop what you are doing after giving your child the opportunity to behave appropriately, and deal with your child concerning his/her unacceptable behavior.

18. Before beginning a conversation, task, etc., that will be time-consuming, ask your child if he/she needs to talk with you or ask any questions.

19. Have regular activities planned for your child (e.g., drawing, watching TV, etc.) when you know you cannot be bothered for a period of time.

20. Be consistent when expecting your child to behave appropriately while you are busy. Do not discipline for his/her interruption one time and tolerate interruption the next time.

21. If your child needs to interrupt for an emergency, make certain he/she does so in a way which helps you to understand the urgency (e.g., ''I'm sorry for interrupting.'' ''May I stop you for a minute?'' etc.).

22. Develop a message board for your child so he/she can list the things about which he/she wants to talk after you are finished with what you are doing.

23. When your child bothers you, calmly explain that you are busy now and he/she may talk to you in a few moments.

24. Give your child frequent opportunities to join in your conversations with others (e.g., allow him/her time to talk, ask him/her to restate an experience, etc.).

1. Teach your child to stop and think about the consequences of his/her behavior before behaving in a certain manner.

2. Make sure that you consider the consequences of your behavior before behaving in a certain manner.

3. Immediately stop your child from behaving inappropriately and discuss the consequences of the behavior with him/her.

4. Reward your child for considering the consequences of his/her behavior. Possible rewards include verbal praise (e.g., ''I'm proud of you for not hitting your sister when she called you a name!''), a kiss on the cheek, a hug, having a friend over to play, staying up late, watching a favorite TV show, and playing a game with a parent. (See Appendix for Reward Menu.)

5. If there are other children or adolescents in the home, reward them for considering the consequences of their behavior.

6. Allow natural consequences to occur due to your child's failure to consider the consequences of his/her behavior (e.g., hitting others will result in being hit in return, stealing will result in being fined, etc.).

7. Make certain that your child sees the relationship between behavior and the consequences which follow (e.g., failing to bring in a bike at night may result in the bike being stolen).

8. When your child fails to consider the consequences of his/her behavior, explain exactly what he/she did wrong, what he/she should have done and why.

For example: You get a call from your child's teacher reporting that your child stole a stopwatch from her desk during recess. Go to your child and say, ''Billy, I just talked with your teacher about your stealing a stopwatch from her desk today. You took something that belonged to someone, and stealing is wrong. You should not steal from others. If you do, they will not trust you.''

9. Write a contract with your child.

For example: I, William, for one day, will stop and consider the consequences of my behavior before I act. When I accomplish this, I can play a game with Mother.

The contract should be written within the ability level of your child and should focus on only one behavior at a time. (See Appendix for an example of a Behavior Contract.)

10. Talk with your family doctor, a school official, a social worker, a mental health worker, etc., about your child's failure to consider the consequences of his/her behavior.

11. Teach your child ways to settle down (e.g., count to ten, say the alphabet, walk away, etc.) when he/she needs to slow down and think about what he/she is doing.

12. Remove your child from a group or activity until he/she can demonstrate self-control.

13. Make certain that consequences are consistently delivered for the behavior that is demonstrated (e.g., appropriate behavior results in positive consequences, and inappropriate behavior results in negative consequences).

14. Provide constant, positive reinforcement for appropriate behavior. Ignore as many inappropriate behaviors as possible.

15. Prevent your child from becoming overstimulated by an activity (e.g., monitor or supervise your child's behavior to limit overexcitement in physical activities, games, parties, etc.).

16. Provide your child with a clearly identified list of consequences for inappropriate behavior.

17. Teach your child to be a problem-solver when he/she encounters a personal or school problem:
  Step 1: Identify the problem
  Step 2: Identify goals and objectives
  Step 3: Develop strategies
  Step 4: Develop a plan for action
  Step 5: Carry out the plan

18. Carefully consider your child's age before expecting your child to always think before acting.

19. Show your child how to stop and think before acting.

20. Remind your child to "stop and think" when he/she begins to do something without thinking first.

21. Supervise your child closely in situations where he/she is likely to act impulsively (e.g., maintain close physical proximity, maintain eye contact, etc.).

22. Deliver natural consequences to help your child learn that his/her behavior determines the consequences which follow (e.g., work not done during work time has to be made up during recreational time, what he/she wastes or destroys has to be replaced by him/her, etc.).

23. Be certain to take every opportunity to explain to your child that it is his/her behavior that determines the consequences, whether they are positive or negative (e.g., your child may choose a movie to see or rent because he/she did all his/her chores for the week, your child has to make his/her bed and clean his/her room on a Saturday afternoon because he/she did not do it on Saturday morning, etc.).

24. Each time a consequence is delivered, whether it is positive or negative, have your child explain to you why he/she thinks it is happening (e.g., "Because I was a helpful shopper, I can have a treat at the checkout line.").

25. Make it possible for your child to earn those things he/she wants or needs in order that he/she will not have to engage in inappropriate behavior to get them (e.g., lying or stealing to get something important to him/her).

26. Do not make it too difficult for your child to earn those things he/she wants. If it is too difficult to earn something, the negative consequences of getting it in an inappropriate way (e.g., stealing) may seem like a worthwhile risk.

27. Make certain your child understands that consequences naturally follow behavior. You do not make the consequence happen; it is his/her behavior that makes the consequence occur.

28. Discuss consequences with your child before he/she begins an activity (e.g., cheating in a game will result in the game ending and people not playing again).

29. Reduce the opportunity to act impulsively by limiting decision making. Gradually increase opportunities for decision making as the student demonstrates success.

A Reminder: Perhaps the most important lesson we will learn in our lifetime is that it is our behavior that determines the consequences which follow.

34 Has accidents as a result of impulsive behavior

1. Carefully consider your child's age and experience before giving responsibilities (e.g., dusting furniture, washing dishes, setting the table, etc.).

2. Directly supervise your child when he/she is engaged in activities which require care (e.g., pouring milk, setting the table, washing the dishes, passing food at the table, etc.).

3. Establish rules (e.g., walk in the house, use both hands when carrying breakables, etc.). These rules should be consistent and followed by everyone in the home. Talk about the rules often.

4. Reward your child for being careful. Possible rewards include verbal praise (e.g., "Thank you for walking in the house." "I like it when you pass food with both hands." etc.), a kiss on the cheek, a hug, having a friend over to play, staying up late, watching a favorite TV show, and playing a game with a parent. (See Appendix for Reward Menu.)

5. If there are other children or adolescents in the home, reward them for being careful with breakables.

6. Show your child the correct way to care for breakables. Help him/her set the table, dust furniture, wash the dishes, etc., in order to model the correct way to care for breakables.

7. Do not rush your child when he/she is working with breakables (e.g., allow him/her plenty of time to set the table, pass food, wash the dishes, clean, etc.).

8. When your child is impulsive or careless, explain exactly what he/she is doing wrong, what should have been done and why.

For example: Your child is carrying a hot dish from the stove to the table with one hand. Go to your child and point out that he/she is using only one hand when carrying the breakable item. Explain that he/she needs to use both hands when carrying the breakable item because it is hot and he/she is less likely to drop it if using both hands.

9. Write a contract with your child.

For example: I, William, for three days in a row, will walk and not run while in the house. When I accomplish this, I can have a friend over to spend the night.

The contract should be written within the ability level of your child and should focus on only one behavior at a time. (See Appendix for an example of a Behavior Contract.)

10. Make certain that your child sees the relationship between behavior and the consequences which follow (e.g., throwing a ball in the house may result in something being broken).

11. Allow natural consequences to occur due to your child's impulsiveness and carelessness (e.g., a car window being broken due to the careless handling of a baseball).

12. Make certain your child has plenty of room when he/she is required to sit near breakables (e.g., at the dinner table, in a crowded room, at the shopping center, etc.).

13. Reduce distractions when your child is around breakables (e.g., turn off the TV during dinner, have him/her play outside with friends, etc.).

14. Require your child to replace items when he/she breaks them because of carelessness.

15. Make certain that items which your child often uses (e.g., toys, bats, balls, etc.) are stored in a place away from breakables in order to prevent accidents.

16. Encourage your child to ask for help when he/she wants something to eat, a play toy, etc., so he/she will not need to climb on counters, get into cupboards, etc.

17. Show your child how to hold breakables, hot items, etc., so that he/she can learn to handle such items successfully.

18. Use plastic containers as often as possible for those things which your child handles.

19. Allow your child to perform difficult tasks (e.g., pouring water, cleaning the table, etc.) while you are present to supervise.

20. Make certain your child puts glasses of water, hot dishes, and breakables back from the edges of counters, tables, etc.

21. Make certain your child moves things away from his/her arms and elbows when working, eating, cutting, etc.

22. Do not allow any kind of ball-playing in the house (e.g., throwing, bouncing, etc.).

23. Teach your child how to pass things at the dinner table (e.g., the left hand passes to the right hand, pass to the person on the right, etc.).

24. Require your child to ask for assistance when trying to pour from large containers, move heavy things, handle hot containers, etc.

25. Limit your child's use of those things which he/she is not responsible for putting away, returning, etc.

26. Give your child suggestions of things to do (e.g., counting to ten, saying the alphabet to himself/herself, walking away from the situation and then returning, etc.) in order to help him/her learn to be more patient and less impulsive.

27. Immediately remove your child from interacting with others when he/she begins to act impulsively.

28. Encourage your child to ask for help when necessary.

29. Involve your child in activities in which he/she can be successful and which will help him/her feel good about himself/herself. Repeated failures result in frustration and impulsive behavior.

30. Do not place an emphasis on perfection. If your child feels he/she must meet up to your expectations and cannot do so, he/she may become impulsive.

31. Talk to your child's teacher to make certain that the child is not having trouble in school and becoming impulsive with schoolwork.

32. Reinforce your child for demonstrating self-control based on the length of time he/she can be successful. Gradually increase the length of time required for reinforcement as he/she demonstrates success.

33. Prevent frustrating or anxiety-producing situations from occurring (e.g., only give your child chores, responsibilities, etc., on his/her ability level).

34. Do not allow your child to participate in a situation unless he/she can demonstrate self-control.

35. Make certain that the activities, situations, etc., in which your child is involved are appropriate for your child's age, maturity, developmental level, etc. It may be that your child is not ready for such activities at this particular time.

36. Help your child perform those activities (e.g., putting a model together, making his/her bed, etc.) which cause him/her to be impatient. Provide less assistance as your child experiences success.

35 Fidgets, squirms, etc.

1. Establish rules (e.g., sit quietly while at the table, quiet down before you enter a building, etc.). These rules should be consistent and followed by everyone in the home. Talk about the rules often.

2. Reward your child for sitting quietly. Possible rewards include verbal praise (e.g., "Thank you for remembering to walk in the house!"), a kiss on the cheek, a hug, having a friend over to play, staying up late, watching a favorite TV show, and playing a game with a parent. (See Appendix for Reward Menu.)

3. If there are other children or adolescents in the home, reward them for sitting quietly, keeping hands and feet to themselves, etc.

4. Supervise your child in order to prevent him/her from getting too excited and moving about.

5. Carefully consider your child's age before expecting him/her to sit quietly without fidgeting and squirming.

6. Provide your child with quiet, calming activities (e.g., listening to music, sitting, lying on his/her bed, listening to a story, etc.) in order to help him/her quiet down after getting excited.

7. Immediately remove your child from an activity when he/she becomes too excited and cannot sit still.

8. Have your child engage in another activity until he/she can settle down and gain control of his/her behavior.

9. When your child cannot sit quietly, explain exactly what he/she is doing wrong, what he/she is supposed to be doing and why.

For example: Your child is playing with friends at the pool and begins splashing, pushing, and encouraging his/her friends to behave inappropriately. Go to your child and say, "William, you are not following the pool rules. You need to stop splashing, pushing, and encouraging your friends to break the pool rules. If you cannot follow the pool rules, we will have to go home."

10. Write a contract with your child.

For example: I, William, will follow the pool rules today. When I accomplish this, I can invite a friend to go to the pool with me tomorrow.

The contract should be written within the ability level of your child and should focus on only one behavior at a time. (See Appendix for an example of a Behavior Contract.)

11. Make certain that your child sees the relationship between behavior and the consequences which follow (e.g., not being allowed to go somewhere, such as the pool or the movies; being avoided by friends; missing out on special activities; etc.).

12. Give your child a special signal when he/she is fidgeting, squirming, etc. (e.g., a secret word, a hand signal, etc.).

13. Give your child plenty of time to settle down after a stimulating activity (e.g., have your child stop the activity 20 minutes before coming into the house, turn off the TV one hour before bedtime, stop swimming 15 minutes before it is time to go home, etc.).

14. Let your child know when activities will begin and end in enough time to allow him/her to settle down and sit quietly.

15. Be consistent when expecting your child to settle down and sit quietly. Do not allow your child to run in the house one day and expect appropriate behavior the next day.

16. Do not allow your child to participate in activities that cause him/her to become so excited that he/she cannot settle down.

17. Clearly state the manner in which you expect your child to act before going out in public or to a place where your child has never been before.

18. Do not take your child places where he/she will have difficulty sitting still and demonstrating acceptable behavior.

19. Do not allow your child to go to public places unless he/she can follow the rules.

20. Read your child a relaxing story, let him/her listen to a tape, tell him/her a story, etc., when it is time to settle down before a quiet activity (e.g., mealtime, bedtime, quiet family time, etc.).

21. Increase supervision of your child when he/she is involved in activities that tend to overexcite him/her.

22. Remove your child from the situation when he/she becomes overly excited.

23. Encourage your child to play games, sports, etc., with friends who do not encourage him/her to get overly excited.

24. Do not allow your child to participate in games, sports, etc., that make him/her overly excited.

25. Teach your child some ways to settle down when he/she gets overly excited (e.g., count to ten, say the alphabet, sit in a chair, leave the situation, etc.).

26. Be consistent when expecting your child to leave the situation when he/she becomes overly excited (e.g., send your child to his/her room for 10 minutes, make him/her sit in a chair for 15 minutes, etc.).

27. Make certain that baby-sitters, grandparents, visitors in your home, teachers, etc., are aware of your child's tendency to get excited and not sit still, fidget, squirm, etc.

28. Prevent your child from becoming overstimulated by an activity. Supervise your child's behavior in order to limit overexcitement in physical activities, games, parties, etc.

29. Use reminders to prepare your child well in advance (e.g., one hour, 30 minutes, etc.) for such activities as dinner, bathing, etc.

30. Allow a transition period between activities (e.g., playtime and mealtime, watching TV and bedtime, etc.) in order that your child can make adjustments in his/her behaviors. You cannot expect your child to go to bed if the TV is still on and everyone is watching it.

31. Establish definite time limits and provide your child with this information before an activity (e.g., one hour to watch TV, 30 minutes to play before dinner, 30 minutes until bath time, etc.).

32. Make certain that all stimulating activities end well before quiet times (e.g., the TV is turned off one hour before bedtime, music is turned off thirty minutes before bedtime, your child must come in thirty minutes before dinner, etc.).

33. Maintain consistency in your child's daily routine.

34. Prevent your child from becoming so stimulated by an event or activity that he/she cannot control his/her behavior.

35. Keep your child's chores and responsibilities short and simple. Do not give him/her things to do that take more than 10-15 minutes to complete.

36. Break down your child's homework and responsibilities into smaller tasks.

37. Provide your child with a quiet place to complete responsibilities.

38. Supervise your child through the completion of responsibilities in order to help him/her stay on task and complete responsibilities.

39. Sit down with your child, one-on-one, for a few minutes at a time to practice schoolwork, read stories, etc. Gradually increase the amount of one-on-one time spent together as your child demonstrates the ability to sit for longer periods of time.

40. Talk to your child's teacher to have your child put into small groups for instruction, have a peer tutor assigned to your child, have assignments shortened, etc., so your child is less likely to fidget and squirm.

41. Do not give your child too many things to do at one time.

42. If your child appears to need a break, allow some playtime between homework assignments, chores, etc.

43. Play educational games with your child to make it more interesting to do homework (e.g., a spelling bee, math races, let your child teach the material to you, etc.).

44. Be certain you are not expecting your child to attend to things that appeal to adults but are of no interest to children (adult conversations, visiting with older relatives, sightseeing, etc.).

45. Require your child to engage in activities for only brief periods of time. Gradually increase the length of time required for your child to attend to activities.

46. When your child is expected to engage in social situations, interact frequently with him/her in order to maintain his/her attention (e.g., ask him/her questions, ask for his/her opinions, stand close to him/her, etc.).

47. Give your child many responsibilities which are short in length (e.g., chores, errands, etc.) to increase his/her active involvement and give him/her a feeling of success or accomplishment.

48. Modify or eliminate those situations which cause your child to experience stress or frustration (e.g., make games easier, use teams instead of single players competing against one another, etc.).

1. Reward your child for completing chores and responsibilities in a reasonable amount of time. Possible rewards include verbal praise (e.g., "I'm so proud of you for getting your homework done on time tonight!"), a kiss on the cheek, a hug, having a friend over to play, staying up late, watching a favorite TV show, and playing a game with a parent. (See Appendix for Reward Menu.)

2. If there are other children or adolescents in the home, reward them for standing or sitting quietly.

3. Carefully consider your child's age when expecting him/her to be able to attend to an activity and not act restless.

4. Discuss your concerns regarding your child's attention span with your family doctor, a school official, etc., in order to see if his/her attention span may be interfering with his/her progress at school.

5. Help your child complete responsibilities.

6. Write a contract with your child.

For example: I, William, for one week, will work for 30 minutes each day on my homework without acting restless. When I accomplish this, I can have a friend spend the night.

The contract should be written within the ability level of your child and should focus on only one behavior at a time. (See Appendix for an example of a Behavior Contract.)

7. Reduce distractions (e.g., turn off the TV and radio, do not allow friends to come over, etc.) in order to help your child attend to chores and responsibilities, homework, etc.

8. Give your child simple, one-step directions to follow.

9. Keep your child's chores and responsibilities short and simple. Do not give him/her things to do that take more than 10-15 minutes to complete.

10. Break down your child's responsibilities into smaller tasks.

11. Make sure that your child understands responsibilities by having him/her tell you what he/she is supposed to do in each case.

12. Provide your child with a quiet place to complete responsibilities.

13. Supervise your child through the completion of responsibilities in order to help him/her stay on task and complete the responsibilities.

14. Evaluate your child's responsibilities in order to determine if they are too complicated for him/her to complete successfully and are causing him/her to act restless.

15. Allow your child to use a timer to remind him/her to complete responsibilities.

16. Make sure that your child has all necessary materials to successfully complete responsibilities.

17. Make a written list of directions you want your child to follow (e.g., feed the dog, take out the trash, etc.).

18. Be consistent when expecting your child to finish chores without becoming restless. Do not allow your child to fail to complete chores one time and expect appropriate behavior the next time.

19. Make sure your child is paying attention to you when you tell him/her to do something. Have your child look directly at you to know he/she is listening and have your child repeat the directions to check for understanding.

20. Establish a certain time each day for your child to take care of responsibilities (e.g., feeding the dog, completing homework, etc., right after school).

21. Make certain that the responsibilities given to your child are appropriate for his/her level of development and ability.

22. Have your child do those things that need to be done when they are discussed instead of later (e.g., put swimsuits in the car now so that when you go to the pool later this afternoon, they will not be forgotten; etc.).

23. Assist your child in performing responsibilities. Gradually require your child to independently assume responsibility as he/she demonstrates success.

24. Sit down with your child, one-on-one, for a few minutes at a time to practice schoolwork, read stories, etc. Gradually increase the amount of one-on-one time spent together as your child demonstrates the ability to attend for longer periods of time.

25. Talk to your child's teacher to have your child put into small groups for instruction, have a peer tutor assigned to your child, have assignments shortened, etc.

26. Make certain to give directions in a very simple manner and be specific as to what you want your child to do.

27. Sit with your child when he/she is working on homework. You can read, do needlework, etc., while your child works.

28. Do not give your child too many things to do at one time.

29. If your child appears to need a break, allow some playtime between homework assignments, chores, etc.

30. Play educational games with your child to make it more interesting to do homework (e.g., a spelling bee, math races, let your child teach the material to you, etc.).

31. Be certain you are not expecting your child to attend to things that appeal to adults but are of no interest to children (adult conversations, visiting with older relatives, sightseeing, etc.).

32. Require your child to engage in activities for only brief periods of time. Gradually increase the length of time required for your child to attend to activities.

33. When your child is expected to engage in social situations, interact frequently with him/her in order to maintain his/her attention (ask him/her questions, ask for his/her opinions, stand close to him/her, etc.).

34. Give your child many short responsibilities (e.g., chores, errands, etc.) to increase his/her active involvement and give him/her a feeling of success or accomplishment.

35. Modify or eliminate those situations which cause your child to experience stress or frustration (e.g., make games easier, use teams instead of single players competing against one another, etc.).

36. Establish a regular schedule of daily events in order that your child knows what he/she should be doing at any one time and what he/she will be doing next (e.g., watching cartoons, eating lunch, going swimming, etc.). (See Appendix for Weekday or Saturday Schedule.)

37. Make certain to provide your child with a quiet, uncluttered place to do homework, school projects, etc.

38. Assist your child in daily homework, school projects, etc. Gradually reduce the amount of assistance you provide your child as he/she demonstrates success in remaining on task, finishing assignments, etc.

39. Encourage your child to ask for your assistance instead of moving on to something else, giving up, etc.

40. Have your child engage in another activity until he/she can settle down and gain control of his/her behavior.

41. Let your child know when activities will begin and end in enough time to allow him/her to settle down.

42. Do not allow your child to participate in activities that cause him/her to become too restless.

43. Remove your child from the situation when he/she becomes restless.

44. Do not take your child places where he/she will have difficulty settling down and demonstrating acceptable behavior.

45. Clearly state the manner in which you expect your child to act before going out in public or to a place where your child has never been before.

46. Read your child a relaxing story, let him/her listen to a tape, tell him/her a story, etc., when it is time to settle down before a quiet activity (e.g., mealtime, bedtime, quiet family time, etc.).

47. Increase supervision of your child when he/she is involved in activities that tend to overexcite him/her and cause him/her to become restless.

A Reminder: Your child's short attention span is not something he/she demonstrates on purpose. Be supportive by not expecting too much from him/her at one time.

37 Does not follow the rules of games

1. Establish rules for playing competitive games (e.g., play by the rules, wait your turn, share materials, do not fight, etc.). These rules should be consistent and followed by everyone in the home. Talk about the rules often.

2. Do not allow your child to cheat. Immediately correct him/her when he/she begins to cheat.

3. Make sure that you play by the rules, wait your turn, share materials, and do not argue with others when playing competitive games. Set a good example for your child.

4. Reward your child for playing fairly in competitive games. Possible rewards include verbal praise (e.g., ''I am glad that you are playing fairly.'' ''I like to play cards with you when you play by the rules.'' etc.), a kiss on the cheek, a hug, having a friend over to play, staying up late, watching a favorite TV show, and playing a game with a parent. (See Appendix for Reward Menu.)

5. If there are other children or adolescents in the home, reward them for playing fairly.

6. Make sure that others follow rules when they play competitive activities with your child.

7. Carefully consider your child's age and experience before expecting him/her to play fairly.

8. Make sure your child knows the rules of the game and how to play before letting him/her play with others.

9. Supervise your child at all times when he/she is playing competitive games with others.

10. When your child has trouble following rules, explain exactly what he/she is doing wrong, what he/she is supposed to be doing and why.

For example: You see your child cheating at cards. Stop playing and say, ''William, you are cheating. You need to play fairly if you want to continue playing.''

11. Immediately remove your child from the competitive activity when he/she begins to have trouble following the rules.

12. When playing competitive activities, put the emphasis on personal improvement, getting along, sharing, and having fun.

13. Write a contract with your child.

For example: I, William, will play fairly at cards. When I accomplish this, I can play a game with Mother.

The contract should be written within the ability level of your child and should focus on only one behavior at a time. (See Appendix for an example of a Behavior Contract.)

14. Teach your child to ask for help, stop playing, etc., when he/she feels like not following the rules.

15. Discourage your child from participating in activities where other people cheat to win.

16. Make certain that your child sees the relationship between behavior and the consequences which follow (e.g., others not wanting to play with him/her, making others angry, not being allowed to play, etc.).

17. Help your child improve his/her skills in activities in which he/she has not followed rules in order to reduce his/her need to not play fairly.

18. Do not put an emphasis on winning. If your child feels that winning is the most important thing, he/she may resort to not following rules in order to win.

19. Limit your child's participation in competitive activities.

20. Teach your child appropriate ways in which to deal with his/her anger, frustrations, etc., so he/she does not feel like he/she needs to cheat.

21. Be a model for participating for enjoyment rather than always needing to ''win'' or ''beat'' someone else.

22. Before beginning a game or competitive activity, make sure your child knows the rules, is familiar with the game, and will be compatible with the other individuals who will be playing.

23. Make sure that activities are not so difficult as to make cheating necessary to win, to be a member of the team, to participate, etc.

24. Encourage your child to engage in less competitive activities (e.g., reading, clubs, scouting, student council, etc.).

25. Encourage your child to participate in activities, sports, etc., for self-improvement rather than "winning" or "beating" someone else (e.g., trying to improve his/her own batting average or defensive skills rather than being disappointed if his/her team does not win).

26. Encourage your child to participate in more individualized sports (e.g., aerobics, swimming, track and field, golf, etc.).

27. Help your child to have self-confidence and satisfaction in his/her own self-worth and successes by pointing out his/her strengths, emphasizing his/her positive aspects, etc.

28. Reduce the emphasis on competition among brothers and sisters in your family. Competitiveness learned in the home will be demonstrated at school and elsewhere.

29. Deal with your child's behavior consistently each time he/she has a problem with not following rules (e.g., when your child cheats, remove him/her from the situation and do not allow him/her to return; etc.).

30. Deal with your child's inability to follow rules privately rather than in public.

31. Do not take action unless you know for certain that your child is not playing fair.

32. Talk to your child before going to school, a friend's house, a sporting event, etc., about the importance of following rules, taking turns, etc.

33. Play games with your child and help him/her do well so there is no need to cheat.

34. If your child does not win awards (trophies, plaques, certificates) in competition, provide an award at home for good sportsmanship, improvement, finishing a season, etc.

35. Make certain that teachers, baby-sitters, etc., know that your child has a tendency to not follow the rules when playing games.

36. Increase supervision when your child is involved in competitive situations to help prevent him/her from not following rules.

37. Encourage your child to interact with less competitive friends (e.g, older friends, younger friends, children of the opposite sex, etc.).

38. Encourage your child and others to engage in activities where winning is not a high priority (e.g., kick the can, tag, hide-and-seek, etc.).

39. Talk to older brothers, sisters, friends, etc., to encourage them to help your child be successful in activities rather than always trying to "beat" him/her.

40. Find competitive activities for your family where your child is likely to be the most successful member of the family (e.g., *Candy Land*, *Memory*, jacks, jump rope, etc.).

41. Encourage your child to take up a hobby; assist in developing the hobby into a success.

42. Make certain your child understands that not following rules in competitive activities may result in others not wanting to interact, play, compete, etc., with him/her again.

Note: Some enjoyable noncompetitive activities are: building, cooking, camping, reading, hiking, scouting, fishing, aerobics, skating, boating, playing at the swimming pool, watching movies, visiting the library, magic tricks, coloring, painting, shopping, slumber parties, bike riding, playing at the neighborhood park, running errands, writing, etc.

38 Does not remain seated

1. Reward your child for staying seated. Possible rewards include verbal praise (e.g., "I'm so proud of you for getting your homework done on time tonight!"), a kiss on the cheek, a hug, having a friend over to play, staying up late, watching a favorite TV show, and playing a game with a parent. (See Appendix for Reward Menu.)

2. If there are other children or adolescents in the home, reward them for staying seated.

3. Carefully consider your child's age when expecting him/her to be able to stay seated.

4. Discuss your concerns regarding your child's attention span and inability to remain seated with your family doctor, a school official, etc., in order to see if his/her attention span may be interfering with his/her progress at school.

5. Remind your child to remain in his/her seat when needed.

6. Write a contract with your child.

For example: I, William, for one week, will stay in my seat and work on my homework for 30 minutes each day. When I accomplish this, I can have a friend spend the night.

The contract should be written within the ability level of your child and should focus on only one behavior at a time. (See Appendix for an example of a Behavior Contract.)

7. Reduce distractions (e.g., turn off the TV and radio, do not allow friends to come over, etc.) in order to help your child attend to chores and responsibilities.

8. Limit the amount of time you expect your child to perform chores and responsibilities that require being seated. Do not give him/her things to do that take more than 10-15 minutes to complete.

9. Break down into smaller tasks your child's chores and responsibilities that require being seated.

10. Provide your child with a quiet place to complete chores and responsibilities that require being seated.

11. Supervise your child through the completion of chores and responsibilities in order to help him/her stay on task and complete the chores and responsibilities.

12. Provide an incentive statement for your child to help him/her do chores (e.g., "When you stay in your seat for 10 minutes, you may watch TV." etc.).

13. Be consistent when expecting your child to stay seated. Do not allow your child to get up and walk around one time and expect appropriate behavior the next time.

14. Make certain that the responsibilities given to your child are appropriate for his/her level of development and ability.

15. Assist your child in performing responsibilities. Gradually require your child to independently assume responsibility as he/she demonstrates success.

16. Sit down with your child, one-on-one, for a few minutes at a time to practice schoolwork, read stories, etc. Gradually increase the amount of one-on-one time spent together as your child demonstrates the ability to attend for longer periods of time.

17. Talk to your child's teacher to have your child put into small groups for instruction, have a peer tutor assigned to your child, have assignments shortened, etc.

18. Be consistent when expecting your child to follow directions. Do not allow your child to fail to follow directions one time and expect him/her to follow directions the next time.

19. Sit with your child when he/she is working on homework. You can read, do needlework, etc., while your child works.

20. Do not give your child too many things to do at one time.

21. If your child appears to need a break, allow some playtime between homework assignments, chores, etc.

22. Play educational games with your child so it is more interesting to do homework (e.g., a spelling bee, math races, let your child teach the material to you, etc.).

23. Be certain you are not expecting your child to attend to things that appeal to adults but are of no interest to children (adult conversations, visiting with older relatives, sightseeing, etc.).

24. Require your child to engage in activities for only brief periods of time. Gradually increase the length of time required for your child to attend to activities.

25. Make certain to provide your child with a quiet, uncluttered place to do homework, school projects, etc.

26. Assist your child in daily homework, school projects, etc. Gradually reduce the amount of assistance you provide your child as he/she demonstrates success in remaining on task, finishing assignments, etc.

27. Be a model for your child for having an appropriate attention span while reading, conversing, working on a project, etc.

28. Prevent your child from becoming overstimulated by an activity. Supervise your child's behavior in order to limit overexcitement in physical activities, games, parties, etc.

29. Prevent your child from becoming so stimulated by an event or activity that he/she cannot control his/her behavior.

30. If your child is easily overexcited, make certain that others (e.g., brothers/sisters, friends, relatives) assist you in preventing overstimulation rather than teasing or otherwise stimulating your child when he/she is expected to remain seated.

31. Do not let your child engage in overexciting activities for long periods of time.

A Reminder: Your child's short attention span is not something he/she demonstrates on purpose. Be supportive by not expecting too much from him/her at one time.

Note: Intervene early to keep your child from getting overly excited.

39 Does not adjust behavior to different situations

1. Sit down and explain changes in routine to your child a few days before they happen, if possible.

2. Try to give your child as much structure and "sameness" in his/her life as possible.

3. Have a calendar of family activities and indicate on the calendar when guests will visit, doctors' appointments will occur, baby-sitters will come, etc.

4. Plan things for your child to do when changes in his/her routine occur (e.g., caring for a younger brother or sister, going to see a movie, having a friend spend the night, etc.).

5. If there are other children or adolescents in the home, reward them for adjusting behavior to different situations.

6. Write a contract with your child.

For example: I, William, will come inside and watch TV quietly before dinner. When I accomplish this, I can have a friend spend the night.

The contract should be written within the ability level of your child and should focus on only one behavior at a time. (See Appendix for an example of a Behavior Contract.)

7. When your child has difficulty adjusting to a change in his/her routine, explain exactly what he/she is doing wrong, what he/she is supposed to be doing and why.

For example: You tell your child that dinner will be 15 minutes late and he begins to cry and stomp around. Go to your child and say, "William, you are crying. You need to stop crying and wash up so you'll be ready for dinner in 15 minutes."

8. Remind your child, as often as possible, of changes that will occur in his/her routine and that he/she needs to settle down quietly when the activity is over.

9. Try to limit the number of changes in your child's routine whenever possible.

10. Present changes in routine in the most attractive manner possible (e.g, "Rather than going to school this morning, we are going out to eat breakfast and then to see the dentist." etc.).

11. Be personally available when your child is dealing with changes in his/her routine (e.g., take him/her to the first day of swim lessons, have the new baby-sitter come over to play games with your child while you are home, etc.).

12. Allow your child to take part in changing his/her routine (e.g., let him/her decide which day he/she would like to visit Grandma, let him/her decide which baby-sitter he/she would like to have, etc.).

13. Carefully consider your child's age and maturity level before expecting him/her to accept changes in routine without becoming excited.

14. Help your child plan changes in routine (e.g., a slumber party, visiting relatives, etc.).

15. Attempt to limit the number of changes that need to occur in your child's routine.

16. Provide your child with a verbal reminder of changes in his/her routine.

17. Provide your child with frequent opportunities to become accustomed to changes in the routine (e.g., having guests in your home, having a baby-sitter, etc.).

18. Limit the number of changes in your child's established routine. Gradually increase the number of changes in routine as your child demonstrates success.

19. Make certain that anyone who assumes responsibility in your home (e.g., grandparents, baby-sitter, etc.) is provided with rules, schedules, mealtimes and bedtimes, appropriate activities, consequences, etc., in order that their supervision will be as consistent with yours as possible.

20. Establish rules (e.g., do not run or yell in the house, quiet down before you enter a building, etc.). These rules should be consistent and followed by everyone in the home. Talk about the rules often.

21. Supervise your child in order to prevent him/her from getting too excited to settle down.

22. Provide your child with quiet, calming activities (e.g., listening to music, sitting, lying on his/her bed, listening to a story, etc.) in order to help him/her to quiet down after getting excited.

23. Immediately remove your child from an activity when he/she becomes too excited and cannot calm down.

24. When your child cannot calm down, explain exactly what he/she is doing wrong, what he/she is supposed to be doing and why.

For example: Your child is playing with friends at the pool and begins splashing, pushing, and encouraging his/her friends to behave inappropriately. Go to your child and say, "William, you are not following the pool rules. You need to stop splashing, pushing, and encouraging your friends to break the pool rules. If you cannot follow the pool rules, we will have to go home."

25. Make certain that your child sees the relationship between behavior and the consequences which follow (e.g., not being allowed to go somewhere, such as the pool or the movies; being avoided by friends; missing out on special activities; etc.).

26. Give your child a special signal when he/she is not settling down (e.g., a secret word, a hand signal, etc.).

27. Have your child engage in another activity until he/she can settle down and gain control of his/her behavior.

28. Give your child plenty of time to settle down after a stimulating activity (e.g., have your child stop the activity 20 minutes before coming into the house, turn off the TV one hour before bedtime, stop swimming 15 minutes before it is time to go home, etc.).

29. Let your child know when activities will begin and end in enough time to allow him/her to settle down.

30. Be consistent when expecting your child to settle down after getting excited. Do not allow your child to run in the house one day and expect appropriate behavior the next day.

31. Give your child a schedule of daily activities so he/she will be aware of when he/she needs to settle down if he/she becomes excited.

32. Do not allow your child to participate in activities that cause him/her to become so excited that he/she cannot settle down.

33. Clearly state the manner in which you expect your child to act before going out in public or to a place where your child has never been before.

34. Do not take your child places where he/she will have difficulty settling down and demonstrating acceptable behavior.

35. Read your child a relaxing story, let him/her listen to a tape, tell him/her a story, etc., when it is time to settle down before a quiet activity (e.g., mealtime, bedtime, quiet family time, etc.).

36. Do not allow your child to go to public places unless he/she can follow the rules.

37. Increase supervision of your child when he/she is involved in activities that tend to overexcite him/her.

38. Remove your child from the situation when he/she becomes overly excited.

39. Encourage your child to play games, sports, etc., with friends who do not encourage him/her to get overly excited.

40. Do not allow your child to participate in games, sports, etc., that make him/her overly excited.

41. Prevent your child from becoming so stimulated by an event or activity that he/she cannot control his/her behavior.

42. Teach your child some ways to settle down when he/she gets overly excited (e.g., count to ten, say the alphabet, sit in a chair, leave the situation, etc.).

43. Make certain that baby-sitters, grandparents, visitors in your home, teachers, etc., are aware of your child's tendency to get excited and not settle down.

44. Prevent your child from becoming overstimulated by an activity. Supervise your child's behavior in order to limit overexcitement in physical activities, games, parties, etc.

45. Use reminders to prepare your child well in advance (e.g., one hour, 30 minutes, etc.) for such activities as dinner, bathing, etc.

46. Allow a transition period between activities (e.g., playtime and mealtime, watching TV and bedtime, etc.) in order that your child can make adjustments in his/her behaviors. You cannot expect your child to go to bed if the TV is still on and everyone is watching it.

47. Establish definite time limits and provide your child with this information before an activity (e.g., one hour to watch TV, 30 minutes to play before dinner, 30 minutes until bath time, etc.).

48. Make certain that all stimulating activities end well before quiet times (e.g., the TV is turned off one hour before bedtime, music is turned off 30 minutes before bedtime, your child must come in 30 minutes before dinner, etc.).

49. If your child is easily overexcited, make certain that others (e.g., brothers/sisters, friends, relatives) assist you in preventing overstimulation rather than teasing or otherwise stimulating your child.

50. Reduce the emphasis on competition. Competitive activities may cause your child to become overly excited.

51. Remain calm when your child becomes overexcited. Your behavior will have a calming effect on your child.

52. Do not let your child engage in overexciting activities for long periods of time.

A Reminder: Intervene early to keep your child from getting overly excited.

40   Becomes overexcited

1. Establish rules (e.g., do not run or yell in the house, quiet down before you enter a building, etc.). These rules should be consistent and followed by everyone in the home. Talk about the rules often.

2. Reward your child for settling down after he/she gets excited. Possible rewards include verbal praise (e.g., "Thank you for remembering to walk in the house!"), a kiss on the cheek, a hug, having a friend over to play, staying up late, watching a favorite TV show, and playing a game with a parent. (See Appendix for Reward Menu.)

3. If there are other children or adolescents in the home, reward them for settling down after getting excited.

4. Supervise your child in order to prevent him/her from getting too excited to settle down.

5. Carefully consider your child's age before expecting him/her to quiet down after getting excited.

6. Provide your child with quiet, calming activities (e.g., listening to music, sitting, lying on his/her bed, listening to a story, etc.) in order to help him/her quiet down after getting excited.

7. Immediately remove your child from an activity when he/she becomes too excited and cannot calm down.

8. Be consistent when expecting your child to settle down after getting excited. Do not allow your child to run in the house one day and expect appropriate behavior the next day.

9. When your child cannot calm down, explain exactly what he/she is doing wrong, what he/she is supposed to be doing and why.

For example: Your child is playing with friends at the pool and begins splashing, pushing, and encouraging his/her friends to behave inappropriately. Go to your child and say, "William, you are not following the pool rules. You need to stop splashing, pushing, and encouraging your friends to break the pool rules. If you cannot follow the pool rules, we will have to go home."

10. Write a contract with your child.

For example: I, William, will follow the pool rules today. When I accomplish this, I can invite a friend to go to the pool with me tomorrow.

The contract should be written within the ability level of your child and should focus on only one behavior at a time. (See Appendix for an example of a Behavior Contract.)

11. Make certain that your child sees the relationship between behavior and the consequences which follow (e.g., not being allowed to go somewhere, such as the pool or the movies; being avoided by friends; missing out on special activities; etc.).

12. Give your child a special signal when he/she is becoming excited (e.g., a secret word, a hand signal, etc.).

13. Have your child engage in another activity until he/she can settle down and gain control of his/her behavior.

14. Give your child plenty of time to settle down after a stimulating activity (e.g., have your child stop an activity 20 minutes before coming into the house, turn off the TV one hour before bedtime, stop swimming 15 minutes before it is time to go home, etc.).

15. Let your child know when activities will begin and end in enough time to allow him/her to settle down.

16. Give your child a schedule of daily activities so he/she will be aware of when he/she needs to settle down if he/she becomes excited.

17. Do not allow your child to participate in activities that cause him/her to become so excited that he/she cannot settle down.

18. Clearly state the manner in which you expect your child to act before going out in public or to a place where your child has never been before.

19. Do not take your child places where he/she will have difficulty settling down and demonstrating acceptable behavior.

20. Read your child a relaxing story, let him/her listen to a tape, tell him/her a story, etc., when it is time to settle down before a quiet activity (e.g., mealtime, bedtime, quiet family time, etc.).

21. Do not allow your child to go to public places unless he/she can follow the rules.

22. Increase supervision of your child when he/she is involved in activities that tend to overexcite him/her.

23. Remove your child from the situation when he/she becomes overly excited.

24. Encourage your child to play games, sports, etc., with friends who do not encourage him/her to get overly excited.

25. Teach your child some ways to settle down when he/she gets overly excited (e.g., count to ten, say the alphabet, sit in a chair, leave the situation, etc.).

26. Be consistent when expecting your child to leave the situation when he/she becomes overly excited (e.g., send your child to his/her room for 10 minutes, make him/her sit in a chair for 15 minutes, etc.).

27. Make certain that baby-sitters, grandparents, visitors in your home, teachers, etc., are aware of your child's tendency to get excited and not settle down.

28. Prevent your child from becoming overstimulated by an activity. Supervise your child's behavior in order to limit overexcitement in physical activities, games, parties, etc.

29. Use reminders to prepare your child well in advance (e.g., one hour, thirty minutes, etc.) for such activities as dinner, bath time, etc.

30. Allow a transition period between activities (e.g., playtime and mealtime, watching TV and bedtime, etc.) in order that your child can make adjustments in his/her behaviors. You cannot expect your child to go to bed if the TV is still on and everyone is watching it.

31. Prevent your child from becoming so stimulated by an event or activity that he/she cannot control his/her behavior.

32. Establish definite time limits and provide your child with this information before an activity (e.g., one hour to watch TV, 30 minutes to play before dinner, 30 minutes until bath time, etc.).

33. Make certain that all stimulating activities end well before quiet times (e.g., the TV is turned off one hour before bedtime, music is turned off 30 minutes before bedtime, your child must come in 30 minutes before dinner, etc.).

34. Maintain consistency in your child's daily routine.

35. Do not let your child start an activity he/she will not have time to finish (e.g., do not let him/her leave on his/her bike fifteen minutes before dinnertime).

36. If your child is easily overexcited, make certain that others (e.g., brothers/sisters, friends, relatives, etc.) assist you in preventing overstimulation rather than teasing or otherwise stimulating your child.

37. Provide your child with a list of daily events in order that he/she will know which activity comes next and can prepare for it. (See Appendix for Weekday or Saturday Schedule.)

38. Reduce the emphasis on competition. Competitive activities may cause your child to become overly excited.

39. Remain calm when your child becomes overexcited. Your behavior will have a calming effect on your child.

40. Do not let your child engage in overexciting activities for long periods of time.

A Reminder: Intervene early to keep your child from becoming overly excited.

41 Climbs on things

1. Establish rules around the house (e.g., do not jump on the beds, sit in chairs, no running in the house, etc.). These rules should be consistent and followed by everyone in the house. Talk about the rules often.

2. Reward your child for following directions. Possible rewards include verbal praise (e.g., "You did a great job of sitting quietly." "I like the way you follow directions!" etc.), a kiss on the cheek, a hug, having a friend over to play, staying up late, watching a favorite TV show, and playing a game with a parent. (See Appendix for Reward Menu.)

3. If there are other children or adolescents in the home, reward them for following the rules of the house.

4. Carefully consider your child's age and experience when expecting him/her to follow the house rules.

5. Demonstrate the appropriate way to follow house rules.

6. Write a contract with your child.

For example: I, William, for three days in a row, will follow the house rules without having to be told more than once. When I accomplish this, I can watch 30 extra minutes of TV.

The contract should be written within the ability level of your child and should focus on only one behavior at a time. (See Appendix for an example of a Behavior Contract.)

7. Make certain that your child sees the relationship between behavior and the consequences which may follow (e.g., jumping on the beds may cause the bed to break).

8. Along with a directive, provide an incentive statement (e.g., "When you stop jumping on the beds, you may play with the video games.").

9. When your child has difficulty following directions in front of others (e.g., when friends are over, playing a game with family members, etc.), remove your child from the situation until he/she can demonstrate self-control and follow directions.

10. In order to help your child follow directions, reduce distractions (e.g., turn off the TV, give directions in a room away from friends, etc.).

11. In order to determine if your child heard a direction, have your child repeat it.

12. Deliver directions in a supportive rather than a threatening manner (e.g., "Please stop jumping on the beds." rather than "You had better quit or else!").

13. Do not criticize. When correcting your child, be honest yet supportive. Never cause your child to feel bad about himself/herself.

14. Be consistent when expecting your child to follow directions. Do not allow your child to climb on things one time and expect appropriate behavior the next time.

15. Make sure your child is paying attention to you when you tell him/her to do something. Have your child look directly at you to know he/she is listening and have your child repeat the direction to check for understanding.

16. Do not give directions to your child from another room. Go to your child, get his/her undivided attention, and tell your child what to do.

17. Supervise your child as much as necessary both at home and in public places in order to help him/her follow the rules.

18. Encourage your child to play with other children or adolescents who behave appropriately in people's homes and in public places.

19. Help your child to understand why it is important to follow rules at home (e.g., if you jump off the chair you may fall and hurt yourself).

20. Do not allow your child to invite those friends to your home who stimulate your child's inappropriate behavior.

21. Make certain that your child is individually supervised if he/she consistently fails to follow rules in your home.

22. Make certain your child knows what the reward will be for appropriate behavior (e.g., "For following the rules today, you can choose your favorite dessert for dinner.").

23. Provide your child with quiet activities (e.g., board games, listening tapes, etc.) so he/she will not get overexcited and climb on things.

1. Establish rules (e.g., sit quietly at the dinner table, do not walk in front of the TV when others are watching it, etc.). These rules should be consistent and followed by everyone in the home. Talk about the rules often.

2. Reward your child for settling down after he/she gets excited. Possible rewards include verbal praise (e.g., "Thank you for remembering to walk in the house!"), a kiss on the cheek, a hug, having a friend over to play, staying up late, watching a favorite TV show, and playing a game with a parent. (See Appendix for Reward Menu.)

3. If there are other children or adolescents in the home, reward them for sitting quietly and not moving around unnecessarily.

4. Supervise your child in order to prevent him/her from not sitting quietly and moving around unnecessarily.

5. Provide your child with quiet, calming activities (e.g., listening to music, sitting, lying on his/her bed, listening to a story, etc.) in order to help him/her not move about unnecessarily.

6. Immediately remove your child from an activity when he/she is moving about unnecessarily until he/she can participate appropriately.

7. When your child cannot calm down, explain exactly what he/she is doing wrong, what he/she is supposed to be doing and why.

For example: Your child is playing with friends at the pool and begins rocking. Go to your child and say, "William, you are rocking. You need to stop rocking. If you cannot stop, we will have to go home."

8. Write a contract with your child.

For example: I, William, will sit appropriately at the dinner table. When I accomplish this, I can invite a friend to go to the pool with me.

The contract should be written within the ability level of your child and should focus on only one behavior at a time. (See Appendix for an example of a Behavior Contract.)

9. Make certain that your child sees the relationship between behavior and the consequences which follow (e.g., others not wanting to be around him/her, people making fun of him/her, etc.).

10. Give your child a special signal when he/she is moving about unnecessarily (e.g., a secret word, a hand signal, etc.).

11. Have your child engage in another activity until he/she can settle down and gain control of his/her behavior.

12. Be consistent when expecting your child to sit quietly without moving about unnecessarily. Do not allow your child to move about unnecessarily one day and expect appropriate behavior the next day.

13. Do not allow your child to participate in activities that cause him/her to become so excited that he/she moves about unnecessarily.

14. Clearly state the manner in which you expect your child to act before going out in public or to a place where your child has never been before.

15. Do not take your child places where he/she will have difficulty settling down and demonstrating acceptable behavior.

16. Increase supervision of your child when he/she is involved in activities that tend to cause him/her to move about unnecessarily.

17. Remove your child from the situation when he/she begins to move about unnecessarily.

18. Teach your child some ways to settle down rather than moving about unnecessarily (e.g., count to ten, say the alphabet, sit in a chair, leave the situation, etc.).

19. Be consistent in having your child leave a situation when he/she begins to move about unnecessarily (e.g., send your child to his/her room for 10 minutes, make him/her sit in a chair for 15 minutes, etc.).

20. Make certain that baby-sitters, grandparents, visitors in your home, teachers, etc., are aware of your child's tendency to move about unnecessarily.

21. Prevent your child from becoming overstimulated by an activity. Supervise your child's behavior in order to limit overexcitement in physical activities, games, parties, etc.

22. Use reminders to prepare your child well in advance (e.g., one hour, thirty minutes, etc.) for such activities as dinner, bath time, etc.

23. Prevent your child from becoming so stimulated by an event or activity that he/she cannot control his/her behavior.

24. Reduce the emphasis on competition. Competitive activities may cause your child to become anxious and move about unnecessarily.

25. Remain calm when your child moves about unnecessarily. Your behavior will have a calming effect on your child.

26. Do not let your child engage in overexciting activities for long periods of time.

43 Runs in the house, jumps on furniture

1. Establish rules (e.g., do not run or yell in the house, quiet down before you enter the house, etc.). These rules should be consistent and followed by everyone in the home. Talk about the rules often.

2. Reward your child for behaving appropriately in the house. Possible rewards include verbal praise (e.g., "Thank you for remembering to walk in the house!"), a kiss on the cheek, a hug, having a friend over to play, staying up late, watching a favorite TV show, and playing a game with a parent. (See Appendix for Reward Menu.)

3. If there are other children or adolescents in the home, reward them for following the rules of the home.

4. Supervise your child in order to prevent him/her from getting too excited to settle down.

5. Carefully consider your child's age before expecting him/her to quiet down after getting excited.

6. Provide your child with quiet, calming activities (e.g., listening to music, sitting, lying on his/her bed, listening to a story, etc.) in order to help him/her quiet down after getting excited.

7. Immediately remove your child from an activity when he/she becomes too excited and cannot calm down.

8. When your child cannot calm down, explain exactly what he/she is doing wrong, what he/she is supposed to be doing and why.

For example: Your child is running in the house. Go to your child and say, "William, you are not following the rules. You need to quit running in the house. If you cannot follow the rules, you will have to go to your room."

9. Give your child plenty of time to settle down after a stimulating activity (e.g., have your child stop the activity 20 minutes before coming into the house, turn off the TV one hour before bedtime, etc.).

10. Write a contract with your child.

For example: I, William, will follow the house rules today. When I accomplish this, I can invite a friend to play with me tomorrow.

The contract should be written within the ability level of your child and should focus on only one behavior at a time. (See Appendix for an example of a Behavior Contract.)

11. Make certain that your child sees the relationship between behavior and the consequences which follow (e.g., not being allowed to go somewhere, such as to a friend's house; being avoided by friends; missing out on special activities; etc.).

12. Give your child a special signal when he/she is not settling down (e.g., a secret word, a hand signal, etc.).

13. Have your child engage in another activity until he/she can settle down and gain control of his/her behavior.

14. Let your child know when activities will begin and end in enough time to allow him/her to settle down.

15. Be consistent when expecting your child to settle down after getting excited. Do not allow your child to run in the house one day and expect appropriate behavior the next day.

16. Do not allow your child to participate in activities that cause him/her to become so excited that he/she cannot settle down.

17. Read your child a relaxing story, let him/her listen to a tape, tell him/her a story, etc., when it is time to settle down before a quiet activity (e.g., mealtime, bedtime, quiet family time, etc.).

18. Increase supervision of your child when he/she is involved in activities that tend to overexcite him/her.

19. Remove your child from the situation when he/she becomes overly excited.

20. Encourage your child to play games, sports, etc., with friends who do not encourage him/her to get overly excited.

21. Do not allow your child to participate in games, sports, etc., that make him/her overly excited.

22. Teach your child some ways to settle down when he/she gets overly excited (e.g., count to ten, say the alphabet, sit in a chair, leave the situation, etc.).

23. Be consistent in having your child leave a situation when he/she becomes overly excited (e.g., send your child to his/her room for 10 minutes, make him/her sit in a chair for 15 minutes, etc.).

24. Make certain that baby-sitters, grandparents, visitors in your home, teachers, etc., are aware of your child's tendency to get excited and not settle down.

25. Prevent your child from becoming overstimulated by an activity. Supervise your child's behavior in order to limit overexcitement in physical activities, games, parties, etc.

26. Use reminders to prepare your child well in advance (e.g., one hour, 30 minutes, etc.) for such activities as dinner, bath time, etc.

27. Allow a transition period between activities (e.g., playtime and mealtime, watching TV and bedtime, etc.) in order that your child can make adjustments in his/her behaviors. You cannot expect your child to go to bed if the TV is still on and everyone is watching it.

28. Establish definite time limits and provide your child with this information before an activity (e.g., one hour to watch TV, 30 minutes to play before dinner, 30 minutes until bath time, etc.).

29. Make certain that all stimulating activities end well before quiet times (e.g., the TV is turned off one hour before bedtime, music is turned off 30 minutes before bedtime, your child must come in 30 minutes before dinner, etc.).

30. Prevent your child from becoming so stimulated by an event or activity that he/she cannot control his/her behavior.

31. If your child is easily overexcited, make certain that others (e.g., brothers/sisters, friends, relatives, etc.) assist you in preventing overstimulation rather than teasing or otherwise stimulating your child.

32. Remain calm when your child becomes overexcited. Your behavior will have a calming effect on your child.

33. Do not let your child engage in overexciting activities for long periods of time.

44 Runs in the mall, pushes and makes noises in line, yells in stores, etc.

1. Establish rules for behavior in public places (e.g., be polite, follow rules, ask for assistance if necessary, etc.). These rules should be consistent and followed by everyone in the home. Talk about the rules often.

2. Before going to a public place, review the rules for appropriate behavior and explain to your child why he/she should behave appropriately in public.

3. Reward your child for behaving appropriately in public places. Possible rewards include verbal praise (e.g., "Thank you for following the rules at the mall today!"), a kiss on the cheek, a hug, having a friend over to play, staying up late, watching a favorite TV show, and playing a game with a parent. (See Appendix for a Reward Menu.)

4. If there are other children or adolescents in the home, reward them for behaving in public.

5. Supervise your child as much as necessary in public places in order to help him/her follow the rules.

6. Encourage your child to play with other children or adolescents who behave appropriately in public places.

7. Do not allow your child to go to public places unless he/she can follow the rules.

8. Immediately remove your child from a public place when he/she begins to break rules, becomes loud, starts crying, etc.

9. When your child acts inappropriately in public, explain exactly what he/she did wrong, what he/she should have done and why.

For example: You see your child dunking another child in the pool. Go to your child and say, "William, you are dunking! There is a rule against dunking people in the pool. You need to stop dunking and follow the rules or we will go home."

10. Write a contract with your child.

For example: I, William, will not run on the decks at the pool for two days in a row. When I accomplish this, I can take a friend to the pool.

The contract should be written within the ability level of your child and should focus on only one behavior at a time. (See Appendix for an example of a Behavior Contract.)

11. Make certain that your child sees the relationship between behavior and the consequences which follow (e.g., failing to follow the rules at the skating rink results in your child being "kicked out" for one week).

12. Allow natural consequences to occur due to your child's inability to follow the rules in public places (e.g., he/she will have to "sit out" at the pool, will lose pool privileges, etc.).

13. Do not reinforce your child's inappropriate behavior by laughing when he/she is silly, rude, etc.

14. Make sure that you follow the rules in public places.

15. Do not encourage your child to be silly and to entertain others and then scold him/her when he/she begins to act too silly.

16. Always expect your child to behave at home and in public.

17. Show your child how to follow the rules posted in public places by reading the rules with him/her and then demonstrating how to follow the rules.

18. Have your child tell you the rules of the swimming pool, skating rink, movie theater, shopping mall, etc., before going to the public place. Make sure he/she understands the consequences of not following the rules.

19. Ask the employees of the public places which your child visits for a copy of the rules. Review the rules daily with your child.

20. Make certain that the employees of the public facility which your child is visiting know that you will deliver consequences if your child does not follow rules.

21. Help your child understand why it is important to follow rules at home and in public places (e.g., if you push Timmy off the slide, he may fall and break his arm; if you hold Molly under the water, she may panic; etc.).

22. Make certain that your child is individually supervised if he/she consistently fails to follow rules in public places.

23. Make certain your child knows what the reward will be for appropriate behavior each time he/she goes to the movie, mall, etc. (e.g., "For following the rules at the movie today, we will stop at Dairy Queen for a milk shake on the way home." etc.).

24. Do not allow your child to go to the movie, shopping mall, etc., unaccompanied if there are other children there who stimulate inappropriate behavior, fight, etc.

45 Makes excessive noise

1. Establish rules for behavior at home and in public places (e.g., wait quietly, follow rules, ask for assistance if necessary, etc.). These rules should be consistent and followed by everyone in the home. Talk about the rules often.

2. Before going to a public place, review the rules for appropriate behavior and explain to your child why he/she should behave appropriately in public.

3. Reward your child for behaving appropriately at home and in public places. Possible rewards include verbal praise (e.g., "Thank you for waiting quietly in line."), a kiss on the cheek, a hug, having a friend over to play, staying up late, watching a favorite TV show, and playing a game with a parent. (See Appendix for a Reward Menu.)

4. If there are other children or adolescents in the home, reward them for waiting quietly, not making excessive noise, etc.

5. Supervise your child as much as necessary, both at home and in public places, in order to help him/her wait quietly.

6. Encourage your child to play with other children or adolescents who behave appropriately in public places.

7. Do not allow your child to go to public places unless he/she can behave appropriately.

8. Immediately remove your child from a public place when he/she begins to make excessive noise, becomes loud, starts crying, etc.

9. Show your child how to wait quietly, visit with others, etc.

10. When your child acts inappropriately at home or in public, explain exactly what he/she did wrong, what he/she should have done and why.

For example: Your child is making excessive noise. Go to your child and say, "William, you are making too much noise! You must wait quietly, or we will go home."

11. Write a contract with your child.

For example: I, William, for two days in a row, will wait quietly when I want to talk to someone. When I accomplish this, I can have a friend over.

The contract should be written within the ability level of your child and should focus on only one behavior at a time. (See Appendix for an example of a Behavior Contract.)

12. Make certain that your child sees the relationship between behavior and the consequences which follow (e.g., making excessive noise will cause others to not want to be around him/her).

13. Allow natural consequences to occur due to your child's inability to wait quietly (e.g., he/she will have to sit alone while others wait in line, he/she will lose privileges, etc.).

14. Do not reinforce your child's inappropriate behavior by laughing when he/she is silly, rude, etc.

15. Make sure that you do not make excessive noise.

16. Do not encourage your child to be silly and to entertain others some of the time, and then scold him/her when he/she begins to act too silly at other times.

17. Always expect your child to behave at home and in public.

18. Help your child understand why it is important to wait quietly (e.g., if you are making excessive noise you may not hear what is being said, others will not hear, etc.).

19. Make certain that your child is individually supervised if he/she consistently continues to make excessive noise.

20. Make certain your child knows what the reward will be for appropriate behavior each time he/she goes to a public place (e.g., "For waiting quietly in the doctor's office, we will stop at Dairy Queen for a milk shake on the way home.").

46 Behaves inappropriately in the car

1. Establish rules for riding in the car (e.g., do not throw things out the window; wear a seat belt at all times; keep hands, arms and head inside the car; keep hands, feet, and objects to yourself; etc.). Talk about the rules often.

2. Reward your child for following the "car rules." Possible rewards include verbal praise (e.g., "I like the way you are wearing your seat belt." "Thank you for putting your gum wrapper in the trash bag." etc.), a kiss on the cheek, a hug, having a friend over to play, staying up late, watching a favorite TV show, and playing a game with a parent. (See Appendix for Reward Menu.)

3. If there are other children or adolescents in the car, reward them for following the "car rules."

4. Help your child fasten his/her seat belt and/or sit next to him/her in order to help him/her be successful in following the "car rules."

5. Establish a routine for riding in the car (e.g., open the car door, tell your child where to sit, be sure all doors are locked and seat belts fastened before the car is started, discuss "car rules," etc.).

6. Parents should follow the "car rules" in order to set an example for their child to follow.

7. Assign your child organizational responsibilities when riding in the car (e.g., being in charge of dispensing paper towels, reading road signs, choosing a game to play, etc.).

8. Provide things to entertain your child (e.g., headphones, coloring books, puzzles, games, comic books, reading material, etc.).

9. Maintain consistency in your child's behavior by having him/her sit in the same place each time he/she gets in the car, reviewing the rules, always having him/her wear his/her seat belt, etc.

10. Make certain that your child sees the relationship between behavior and the consequences which follow (e.g., throwing a soft drink can out the window results in not being able to drink in the car, fighting over the front seat results in both children riding in the back seat, hanging out of the car window results in having to keep the windows closed, etc.).

11. Separate those children who have difficulty behaving appropriately in the car by sitting between them or putting one in the front seat and one in the back seat.

12. Inform others (e.g., neighbors, aunts, uncles, etc.) of the appropriate behavior expected of your child in the car in order that they encourage appropriate behavior while riding in their car.

13. Do not criticize. When correcting your child, be honest yet supportive. Never cause your child to feel bad about himself/herself.

14. Intervene early when there is a problem in the car in order to prevent more serious problems.

15. Speak with your child to let your child know what he/she is doing wrong, what he/she should be doing, and what the consequences are for inappropriate behavior.

16. Talk to your child before riding in the car and remind him/her of the car rules and expectations as well as the rewards he/she may earn.

17. Make a list of car rules and review them each time you and your child get in the car.

18. Assign your child important safety responsibilities while riding in the car (e.g., making certain seat belts are fastened, mirrors are adjusted, doors are locked, etc.).

Note: The behaviors and related interventions in Section III have been included to provide parents with additional strategies for helping their child with Attention-deficit Disorders to be more successful.

III. Supplemental Behaviors and Solutions

47 Has to have several reminders

1. Establish rules for following directions (e.g., listen carefully to the directions, ask questions if you do not understand, follow the directions without having to be reminded, etc.). These rules should be consistent and followed by everyone in the home. Talk about the rules often.

2. Reward your child for not requiring reminders to do what he/she is told to do. Possible rewards include verbal praise (e.g., ''Thank you for making your bed without having to be reminded.''), a kiss on the cheek, a hug, having a friend over to play, staying up late, watching a favorite TV show, and playing a game with a parent. (See Appendix for Reward Menu.)

3. If there are other children or adolescents in the home, reward them for doing what they are told to do without requiring reminders.

4. Carefully consider your child's age and experience when giving your child a job to do or telling him/her to do something.

5. Demonstrate for your child what he/she should do when given a chore (e.g., show your child how to take out the trash when told to do so).

6. When your child requires a reminder(s) to do something, explain what he/she did wrong, what should have been done and why.

For example: You told your child to set the table before dinner. It is now five minutes until dinner time and the table is not set. Go to your child, tell him/her that this is a reminder to set the table and that it needs to be done immediately because dinner is ready.

7. Make sure your child is paying attention to you when you tell him/her to do something. Have your child look directly at you to know he/she is listening and have your child repeat the direction to check for understanding.

8. Do not give directions to your child from another room. Go to your child, get his/her undivided attention, and tell him/her what should be done.

9. Write a contract with your child.

For example: I, William, will make my bed without having to be reminded to do so for five days in a row. When I accomplish this, I can watch 30 extra minutes of TV.

The contract should be written within the ability level of your child and should focus on only one behavior at a time. (See Appendix for an example of a Behavior Contract.)

10. Allow natural consequences to occur as a result of your child's failure to do what he/she is told (e.g., forgetting to put a bike in the garage may result in it being stolen, leaving a toy in the street may result in it being run over by a car, etc.).

11. Make certain that your child sees the relationship between his/her behavior and the consequences which follow (e.g., failing to retrieve a toy from the street results in having a broken toy).

12. Along with a directive, provide an incentive statement (e.g., ''You may have a bowl of ice cream after you get ready for bed.'').

13. Do not give your child more than two or three steps to follow in one direction. Directions that involve several steps can be confusing and cause your child to have difficulty following them. An example of a two-step direction is: "Please brush your teeth and go to bed."

14. Deliver directions in a supportive, rather than threatening, manner (e.g., "Please take out the trash." rather than "You had better take out the trash or else!").

15. Provide your child with a list of daily chores, weekly chores, etc., and put it where it will be seen often (e.g., on the closet door, on his/her desk, on the refrigerator, etc.). (See Appendix for List of Chores.)

16. Let your child know that directions will only be given once and that you will not remind him/her to follow the directions.

17. When giving your child a chore to do, tell your child when it needs to be done, how long he/she has to do the chore, and how long you think it will take to do it.

For example: William, please set the table before dinner. You have thirty minutes until then and it will probably take you 10 minutes.

18. Help your child begin a chore, such as cleaning up his/her room, in order to get your child started.

19. Make certain to give directions in a very simple manner and be specific as to what you want your child to do.

20. Make certain that your child has all the materials needed in order to perform the chore.

21. Establish a regular routine for your child to follow in order to help your child learn to perform chores without requiring reminders.

22. Give your child special responsibilities (e.g., answering the door, serving food, cleaning, etc.) in order to teach your child to follow directions.

23. Do not criticize. When correcting your child, be honest yet supportive. Never cause your child to feel bad about himself/herself.

24. Be consistent when expecting your child to follow directions. Do not allow your child to fail to follow directions one time and then expect him/her to follow directions the next time.

25. Use a timer to help your child know how much time he/she has to follow through with directions.

26. Do not punish your child for forgetting, being interrupted, etc.

27. In order to help your child remember directions, reduce distractions (e.g., turn off the TV, give directions in a room away from friends, etc.).

28. Make a written list of directions you want your child to follow.

29. Have your child do those things that need to be done when they are discussed instead of later (e.g., put swimsuits in the car now so that when you go to the pool later this afternoon, they will not be forgotten, etc.).

30. Make certain that the responsibilities given to your child are appropriate for his/her level of development and ability.

31. Assist your child in performing responsibilities. Gradually require your child to independently assume responsibility as he/she demonstrates success.

A Reminder: We all have to be "reminded" sometimes to do things we do not particularly enjoy doing.

48 Ignores what he/she is told

1. Make sure you have your child's undivided attention when you are talking to him/her. Stand close to your child, maintain eye contact, and have your child repeat what you say.

2. Be sure your child hears what you have said by having him/her acknowledge you (e.g., saying, "Okay!" "Will do!" etc.).

3. Make certain your child knows that you expect him/her to listen to you (e.g., by saying, "William, it is very important that you listen carefully to what I have to say. You need to feed the dog now!").

4. Establish rules for listening (e.g., look at the person who is talking; ask questions if necessary; acknowledge understanding by saying, "Okay!" etc.). These rules should be consistent and followed by everyone in the home. Talk about the rules often.

5. Reward your child for not ignoring you. Possible rewards include verbal praise (e.g., "I like it when you do what I ask." "Thank you for looking at me when I talk to you." etc.), a kiss on the cheek, a hug, having a friend over to play, staying up late, watching a favorite TV show, and playing a game with a parent. (See Appendix for Reward Menu.)

6. If there are other children or adolescents in the home, reward them for not ignoring you.

7. Do not ignore your child when he/she wants to tell you something. When you ignore your child, you teach your child that it is acceptable to ignore people.

8. Write a contract with your child.

For example: I, William, for seven days in a row, will look at my parents when they talk to me. When I accomplish this, I can buy a Matchbox car at the store.

The contract should be written within the ability level of your child and should focus on only one behavior at a time. (See Appendix for an example of a Behavior Contract.)

9. Have your child's hearing checked if you have not done so in the past year.

10. Allow natural consequences to occur as a result of your child's ignoring you (e.g., the child misses a favorite TV show because he/she ignores you when you say it is time for the show to begin).

11. Do not give your child more than two or three steps to follow in one direction. Directions that involve several steps can be confusing and cause your child to ignore you. An example of a two-step direction is: "Please turn off the TV and go to bed."

12. When your child ignores you, let your child know that he/she is ignoring you and that he/she needs to listen to what you say.

13. Do not talk to your child across a room or from another room. Your child may not be able to hear you and/or may not know that you are talking directly to him/her.

14. Make certain that your child sees the relationship between his/her behavior and the consequences which follow (e.g., failing to acknowledge that he/she was told to let in the dog may mean that the dog will get lost or run away from home).

15. Along with a directive, provide an incentive statement (e.g., "When you do what I ask, you may have a cookie.").

16. In order to determine if your child has heard what you have said, have your child repeat it.

17. Talk to your child in a supportive, rather than a threatening, manner (e.g., "Please take out the trash." rather than "You had better take out the trash or else!").

18. Talk to your child before going into a public place and remind your child of the importance of listening to what is said.

19. Treat your child with respect. Talk in an objective manner at all times.

20. Provide your child with written directions, chores, rules, etc. (See Appendix for List of Chores.)

21. Evaluate your child's chores and responsibilities in order to determine if they are too complicated for him/her to complete successfully.

22. Make certain your child knows what the consequences will be in your home for ignoring to do what he/she is told (e.g., privileges taken away, loss of freedom, etc.).

23. Tell your child exactly what he/she is to do (e.g., ''You need to put away your bike now.'' etc.).

24. When giving your child directions to follow, reduce distractions (e.g., turn off the TV or radio, send friends home, etc.) so that your child can understand what it is you want him/her to do.

25. Make certain grandparents, baby-sitters, visitors in your home, etc., are aware of consequences for inappropriate behavior and the importance of maintaining consistency.

26. Maintain a regular routine of chores, meals, bedtime, TV, sports, etc., so your child knows what is expected at all times.

27. After asking your child to do something, explain why it is necessary to do what you ask.

28. Before going into a store, the shopping mall, a friend's house, etc., remind your child of the importance of listening to what he/she is told.

29. After you tell your child ''no,'' explain exactly why he/she cannot do what he/she wants to do.

30. Be careful to avoid embarrassing your child by giving him/her orders, demands, etc., in front of others.

31. Speak to your child quietly and privately to provide reminders about behavior, when to come home, etc.

32. Make certain your child is aware of the dangers involved in ignoring to do what he/she is told (e.g., getting lost, frightening others, etc.).

1. Carefully determine if your child is capable of performing the expected responsibilities on his/her own. Do not give your child too many chores to do at once, make sure he/she gets up early enough to get to school on time, provide more than enough time to perform a chore, and do not always expect perfection.

2. Establish rules for performing everyday expectations (e.g., get up on time for school, do your chores right after you get home from school, finish your homework before you watch TV, etc.). These rules should be consistent and followed by everyone in the home. Talk about the rules often and reward your child for following the rules.

3. Establish a routine for your child to follow for getting ready for school, doing chores, completing homework, etc. This will help your child remember what is expected.

4. Reward your child for getting things done on time. Possible rewards include verbal praise (e.g., "You're on time for school. Good for you!" "Thank you for remembering to finish your homework before you turned on the TV." etc.), a kiss on the cheek, a hug, having a friend over to play, staying up late, watching a favorite TV show, and playing a game with a parent. (See Appendix for Reward Menu.)

5. If there are other children or adolescents in the home, reward them for getting things done on time.

6. Model for your child the appropriate way to get things done on time. Show your child how to follow a routine by following one yourself and getting things done on time.

7. When your child does not get something done on time, explain exactly what he/she did wrong, what should have been done and why.

For example: Your child is supposed to catch the school bus at 7:45 a.m. and is still getting dressed when the bus arrives. Tell your child that he/she missed the bus because he/she was not ready on time. Explain that it is unacceptable to miss the bus because you don't have time to take him/her to school.

8. Write a contract with your child.

For example: I, William, will be ready and waiting for the school bus at 7:40 a.m. for three days in a row. When I accomplish this, I can watch 30 extra minutes of TV.

The contract should be written within the ability level of your child and should focus on only one behavior at a time. (See Appendix for an example of a Behavior Contract.)

9. Make certain that your child sees the relationship between his/her behavior and the consequences which follow (e.g., failing to feed the dog will cause the dog to go hungry).

10. Allow natural consequences to occur due to your child putting off doing things (e.g., the child's bike being stolen because it was not put in the garage overnight).

11. Along with a directive, provide an incentive statement (e.g., "After you get ready for bed, you may watch TV.").

12. Provide your child with written reminders (e.g., a list posted in the bathroom indicating what his/her chores are and when they need to be done). (See Appendix for Sample List.)

13. Tell your child when it is time to set the table, feed the dog, etc.

14. Allow your child to help decide what his/her routine chores will be.

15. Limit the number of chores for which your child is responsible and gradually increase the number of chores as your child demonstrates the ability to get them done on time.

16. Have your child perform the same chores each day, week, etc.

17. Reduce distracting activities which interfere with your child performing responsibilities (e.g., turning off the TV when it is time to set the table, not allowing friends to come over when it is time to do homework, etc.).

18. Show your child how to perform a new chore (e.g., setting the table) several times before expecting him/her to do it independently.

19. Make sure your child has all the necessary materials needed in order to get chores done on time.

20. Explain to your child that responsibilities not done on time will have to be done at other times (e.g., playtime, TV time, weekends, etc.).

21. Have everyone in the family work together at the same time in order to help your child get responsibilities done on time.

22. Make certain your child knows what the consequences will be in your home for putting off doing things (e.g., loss of privileges, responsibilities taken away, etc.).

23. Tell your child exactly what to do (e.g., "You need to pick up your clothes right now.").

24. Assist your child in performing responsibilities. Gradually require your child to independently assume responsibility as he/she demonstrates success.

25. Make certain that the responsibilities assigned are appropriate for your child's level of development and ability.

26. In order to help your child get things done on time, get chores done, etc., reduce distractions (e.g., turn off the TV, give directions in a room away from friends, etc.).

27. Have your child do those things that need to be done when they are discussed instead of at a later time (e.g., put swimsuits in the car now so that when you go to the pool later this afternoon, they will not be forgotten; etc.).

28. Make sure your child is paying attention to you when you tell him/her to do something. Have your child look directly at you to know he/she is listening and have your child repeat the direction to check for understanding.

29. Use a timer to help your child know how much time he/she has to follow through with directions.

30. Make certain grandparents, baby-sitters, visitors in your home, etc., understand the importance of maintaining consistency in the discipline of your child.

A Reminder: Your child needs to understand that things not done at the appropriate time will have to be made up during recreational time.

50 Requires eye contact in order to listen successfully

1. Make certain your child's hearing has been checked recently.

2. Reward your child for listening. Possible rewards include verbal praise, (e.g., "Thank you for listening to what I told you to do without requiring me to repeat it several times."), a kiss on the cheek, a hug, having a friend over to play, watching a favorite TV show, and playing a game with a parent. (See Appendix for Reward Menu.)

3. Speak to your child and explain (a) what your child is doing wrong (e.g., failing to listen to directions, explanations, and instructions), and (b) what your child should be doing (e.g., listening to directions, explanations, and instructions).

4. If there are other children or adolescents in the home, reward them for listening.

5. Reward your child for listening based on the length of time your child can be successful. Gradually increase the length of time required for listening as your child demonstrates success.

6. Write a contract with your child.

For example: I, William, will listen to directions the first time they are given, for two days in a row. When I accomplish this, I can watch 30 extra minutes of TV.

The contract should be written within the ability level of your child and should focus on only one behavior at a time. (See Appendix for an example of a Behavior Contract.)

7. Have your child question any directions or instructions which are not understood.

8. Determine what it is in the environment that interferes with your child's ability to listen (e.g., others talking, the TV, music playing, etc.) and remove what interferes when you are talking to your child.

9. Have your child close books, put away writing materials, put away toys, etc., when you are talking to your child, giving directions, etc.

10. Reduce those things in the environment that distract your child when you are talking (e.g., close the door, turn off the TV, ask friends to leave, etc.).

11. Talk to your child on a one-to-one basis. Gradually include more people in the conversation as your child demonstrates success in listening.

12. Maintain eye contact when delivering information to your child.

13. Reward your child for attending to the source of information. Continuous eye contact is not necessary for rewarding.

14. When speaking to your child, speak in a clear and concise manner.

15. Deliver information in both verbal and written form (e.g., write down your child's chores on a piece of paper to hang on the refrigerator and give your child the chore list verbally). (See Appendix for List of Chores.)

16. Determine if the level of information given to your child is presented at a level your child can understand.

17. Make certain information is given loudly enough to be heard by your child.

18. Stand so your child can see you when you are talking, giving directions, etc.

19. Make certain that your child is not engaged in activities that interfere with listening (e.g., looking at a book, playing with toys, talking to others, etc.).

20. Have your child repeat the information just given in order to check for understanding.

21. Teach your child listening skills (e.g., keep hands free of toys, paper, etc., and pay attention to the person who is talking).

22. Let your child know when directions are going to be given.

23. Allow natural consequences to occur as a result of your child's failure to listen (e.g., not putting a swimsuit in the pool bag will result in not swimming at the pool, not putting toys away will result in them being hard to find the next day, etc.)

24. Use multiple modalities (e.g., auditory, visual, tactile, etc.) when giving directions, explanations, and information. Determine which modality is stronger and utilize the results.

25. Make the subject manner meaningful to your child (e.g., explain the purpose of an assignment, relate the subject matter to the child's environment, etc.).

26. Stop at various points during the presentation of information to check your child's comprehension.

27. Tell your child what to listen for when being given directions, receiving information, etc.

51 Fails to demonstrate short-term memory skills

1. Make certain your child's hearing has been checked recently.

2. Reward your child for demonstrating short-term memory skills. Possible rewards include verbal praise (e.g., "Thank you for remembering to take out the trash without a reminder from me."), a kiss on the cheek, a hug, having a friend over to play, staying up late, watching a favorite TV show, playing a game with a parent. (See Appendix for Reward Menu.)

3. Write a contract with your child.

For example: I, William, will remember to take out the trash every morning without having to be reminded, for five days in a row. When I accomplish this, I can watch 30 extra minutes of TV.

The contact should be written within the ability level of your child and should focus on only one behavior at a time. (See Appendix for an example of a Behavior Contract.)

4. Determine if some memory tasks are too difficult for your child (e.g., two- or three-step directions, too much information presented at one time, etc.).

5. Have your child question any directions, explanations, and instructions which are not understood.

6. Have your child act as a messenger. Give your child a verbal message to deliver to a brother, sister, parent, etc. Increase the length of the message as your child demonstrates success.

7. Review the schedule of morning or afternoon activities for your child and have your child repeat the sequence. Increase the length of the sequence as your child demonstrates success.

8. Have your child play concentration games with a limited number of symbols. Gradually increase the number of symbols as your child demonstrates success.

9. Reward your child for remembering to have things ready (e.g., book bag by the door and ready for school, bringing both gloves home, returning library books, etc.).

10. At the end of the day have your child recall three things that he/she did during the day. As success is demonstrated, gradually increase the number of activities your child is required to recall.

11. After a trip to the store, a fun activity, a day at a friend's home, etc., have your child sequence the activities which occurred.

12. After reading a story, have your child identify the main characters, sequence the events, and give the outcome of the story.

13. Have your child deliver the sequence of the day's events (e.g., going to the store, a friend's house, the movies, etc.) to a brother, sister, or parent.

14. Teach your child to use memory clues.

15. Use multiple modalities (e.g., auditory, visual, tactile, etc.) when presenting directions, instructions, explanations to your child.

16. Record a message on a tape recorder. Have your child write the message after listening to it. Increase the length of the message as your child demonstrates success.

17. Have your child practice repetition of information in order to increase short-term memory skills (e.g., repeating names, telephone numbers, dates or events, etc.)

18. Teach your child how to organize information into smaller units (e.g., break number sequence 132563 into units of 13, 25, 63).

19. Show your child an object or a picture for a few seconds. Ask your child to recall what the object or picture looked like, what color it was, how big it was, etc.

20. Talk to your child in a clear manner and at an appropriate pace.

21. Have your child practice making notes for specific information which needs to be remembered.

22. Teach your child to recognize key words and phrases related to information in order to increase your child's short-term memory.

23. Make certain your child is attending to the source of information (e.g., eye contact is being made, hands are free of toys, others are not distracting your child, etc.).

24. Reduce distracting stimuli when talking to your child (e.g., turn off the, TV send friends home, close the door, etc.).

25. Stop at various points in a conversation with your child to check for understanding of what is being discussed.

26. Give your child only one task to perform at a time. Introduce the next task only when your child has successfully competed the first task.

27. Have your child memorize the first sentence or line of a poem, song, etc. Have your child memorize more as success is demonstrated.

28. Teach your child information-gathering skills (e.g., listen carefully, write down important points, ask for clarification, wait until all information is received before beginning, etc.).

29. Have your child repeat/paraphrase directions, explanations, and instructions.

30. Provide your child with written lists of things to do.

31. Establish a regular routine for your child to follow in performing chores, tasks, etc. (e.g., first brush your teeth and wash your face, next get out your pajamas, last climb in to bed).

52 Fails to demonstrate logical thinking

1. Reward your child for demonstrating logical thinking. Possible rewards include verbal praise (e.g., "Thank you for thinking about what you were going to so rather than rushing into something."), a kiss on the cheek, a hug, having a friend over to play, staying up late, watching a favorite TV show, and playing a game with a parent. (See Appendix for Reward Menu.)

2. If there are other children or adolescents in the home, reward them for logical thinking.

3. Have your child question any directions, explanations, and instructions which are not understood.

4. Give your child responsibilities which require logical thinking (e.g., instruct your child to water the plants; and provide a watering can and a glass, telling your child to use the most appropriate container).

5. Each day provide your child with a problem solving situation which requires logical thinking (e.g., "A stranger takes you by the arm in a department store. What do you do?" "You see smoke coming out of the neighbor's house and no one is home. What do you do?" etc.).

6. Make certain your child experiences the consequences of not using logical thinking (e.g., appropriate behavior results in positive consequences while inappropriate behavior results in negative consequences).

7. Provide your child with a list of questions, involving logical thinking, which can be answered orally (e.g., "Why do we post wet paint signs?" "Why do we have stop sign at intersections?" "Why do we wear seat belts?" etc.)

8. When something is broken, lost, etc., have your child identify what could have been done to prevent the situation. When possessions are properly organized, maintained, and serviced, have you child discuss the value of such practices.

9. Read stories to your child involving a moral (e.g., "The Tortoise and the Hare," "The Boy Who Cried Wolf," etc.) and explain the reason for the outcome of the story.

10. Have your child read short stories without endings. Require the student to develop logical endings for the stories.

11. Describe situations/pictures and have your child explain the effects of the variables (e.g., "Snow is falling; the wind is blowing. Is the temperature hot or cold? What should you wear outdoors?").

12. Have your child sequence cartoon strips, after they have been cut apart and rearranged, and explain the logic of the sequence created.

13. Give your child fill-in-the-blank statements requiring an appropriate response from multiple-choice possibilities (e.g., The boy's dog was dirty so the boy decided to give his dog a ___ (dog, biscuit, bath, toy).).

14. Show your child pictures of dangerous situations and have your child explain why they are dangerous (e.g., a child running into the street between parked cars, a child riding a bicycle without using hands, etc.).

15. Use cause-and-effect relationships as they apply to nature and people. Discuss what led up to a specific situation in a story or picture, what could happen next, etc.

16. Make certain that your child can verbalize the reasons for real-life outcomes of behavior (e.g., why the child had to go home early, why the bike was taken away, etc.).

17. Have your child make up rules and explain the need for the rules.

18. Have your child identify appropriate consequences for rules (e.g., consequences for following rules and consequences for not following rules). Have your child explain the choice of consequence he/she identifies.

19. Have your child explain the answers to questions such as, "Why do we have rules?" "Why do we need to be a certain age before we can drive a car?" etc.

20. Have your child answer analogy situations (e.g., a garage is to a car as a house is to a ___).

21. Set aside time each day for a problem-solving game, analogies, decision-making activities, assigned responsibilities, etc.

22. Make certain your child is attending to the source of information (e.g., eye contact is being made, hands are free of materials, your child is looking at his/her work, etc.).

1. Have your child write down important information that should be remembered.

2. Have your child tape record important information that may need to be repeated.

3. If your child has difficulty remembering information in written form, present the information auditorily.

4. Have your child repeat/paraphrase important information that needs to be remembered.

5. Have your child outline, highlight, underline, or summarize information that should be remembered.

6. Use concrete examples and experiences when sharing information with your child.

7. Teach your child to recognize main points, important facts, etc.

8. Make certain your child has adequate opportunities for repetition of information through different experiences in order to enhance your child's memory.

9. Make certain information is presented to your child in the most clear and concise manner possible.

10. Reduce distracting stimuli when your child is attempting to remember important information.

11. Teach your child to rely on resources in the environment to recall information (e.g., notes, pictures, books, etc.).

12. When your child is required to recall information, provide auditory cues to help your child remember the information (e.g., key words, a brief oral description to help cue the child, etc.).

13. When your child is required to recall information, remind your child of the situation in which the information was originally presented (e.g., "Remember yesterday when we talked about going to Grandma's house..." "Remember last week when we talked about the library books you checked out..." etc.).

14. Assess the meaningfulness of situations, information, etc., to your child. Remembering is more likely to occur when the information is meaningful and your child can relate to real experiences.

15. Relate the information being presented to your child's previous experiences.

16. Have your child make notes, lists, etc., of things that need to be remembered. Have your child carry the reminders in a pocket, purse, book bag, etc.

17. Have your child follow a regular routine of daily events to establish consistency in your child's routine.

18. Have your child repeat to himself/herself information just heard in order to help your child remember important facts.

19. Make certain your child is not required to learn more information than he/she is capable of at any one time.

20. Give your child a choice of answers (e.g., more than one possible answer, multiple-choice on a worksheet, etc.). This increases your child's opportunity for recognizing the correct answer.

21. Use daily drill activities to help your child memorize math facts, vocabulary words, etc.

22. Provide reminders throughout your child's home environment in order to help your child be more successful in remembering information (e.g., rules, lists, schedules, etc.).

23. Help your child employ memory aids in order to recall words (e.g., a name might be linked to another word; for example, "Mr. Green is a very colorful person.").

24. Make certain your child has adequate opportunities for repetition of information through different experiences in order to enhance his/her memory.

25. Review, on a daily basis, those skills, concepts, tasks, etc., which have been previously introduced to help your child remember information previously learned.

26. As soon as your child learns a new skill or information, make certain that he/she applies it to other situations (e.g., when your child learns to count by fives, have him/her practice adding nickels; vocabulary words learned should be pointed out in reading selections; etc.).

27. Identify your child's most efficient learning mode and use it consistently to increase the probability of understanding (e.g., If your child fails to understand directions or information given verbally, present them in written form. If your child has difficulty understanding written directions or information, present them verbally.).

54 Requires slow, sequential, broken-down directions or explanations

1. Make certain that your child's hearing has been checked recently.

2. Reward your child for listening to what is said. Possible rewards include verbal praise (e.g., ''Thank you for listening to what I said!''), a kiss on the cheek, a hug, having a friend over to play, staying up late, watching a favorite TV show, and playing a game with a parent. (See Appendix for Reward Menu.)

3. Speak to your child to explain (a) what your child is doing wrong (e.g., failing to listen to word endings, key words, etc.), and (b) what your child should be doing (e.g., listening for word endings, key words, etc.).

4. Reward your child for listening carefully based on the length of time your child can be successful. Gradually increase the length of time required for listening as your child demonstrates success.

5. Evaluate the level of difficulty of the information to which your child is expected to listen (e.g., information communicated on the child's ability level).

6. Have your child question any directions, explanations, and instructions which are not understood.

7. Have your child repeat or paraphrase what is said to him/her in order to determine what was heard.

8. Give your child short directions, explanations, instructions to follow. Gradually increase the length of the directions, explanations, and instructions as your child demonstrates success.

9. Maintain consistency in the delivery of verbal directions.

10. Make certain your child is attending to the source of information (e.g., making eye contact, hands free of toys, away from other noises, etc.).

11. Provide your child with written directions and instructions to supplement verbal directions and instructions.

12. Emphasize or repeat word endings, key words, etc.

13. Speak clearly and concisely when delivering directions, explanations, and instructions.

14. Place your child near the source of information.

15. Reduce distracting stimuli (e.g., noise and motion in the room) in order to enhance your child's ability to listen successfully.

16. Use multiple modalities (e.g., auditory, visual, tactile, etc.) when presenting directions, explanations, and instructional content. Determine which modality is stronger and utilize the results.

17. Use concrete examples and experiences when teaching concepts and sharing information with your child.

18. Review, on a daily basis, those skills, concepts, tasks, etc., which have been previously introduced.

55 Does not hear all of what is said

1. Make certain your child's hearing has been checked recently.

2. Reward your child for hearing all of what is said. Possible rewards include verbal praise (e.g., "I like it when you listen and hear everything I say."), a kiss on the cheek, a hug, having a friend over to play, staying up late, watching a favorite TV show, and playing a game with a parent. (See Appendix for Reward Menu.)

3. Speak to your child to explain (a) what he/she is doing wrong (e.g., failing to listen to word endings, key words, etc.) and (b) what your child should be doing (e.g., listening for word endings, key words, etc.).

4. Reward your child for listening carefully based on the length of time your child can be successful. Gradually increase the length of time required for listening as your child demonstrates success.

5. Evaluate the difficulty of information to which your child is expected to listen (e.g., be sure information communicated is on your child's ability level).

6. Have your child question any directions, explanations, and instructions which are not understood.

7. Have your child repeat or paraphrase what is said to him/her in order to determine what was heard.

8. Give your child short directions, explanations, and instructions to follow. Gradually increase the length of directions, explanations, and instructions as the student demonstrates success.

9. Maintain consistency in the verbal delivery of information.

10. Make certain your child is attending to the source of information (e.g., making eye contact, hands free of toys, in a quiet area, etc.).

11. Provide your child with written directions and instructions along with verbal directions and instructions.

12. Emphasize or repeat word endings, key words, etc.

13. Speak clearly and concisely when delivering directions, explanations, and instructions.

14. Make certain your child is near the source of information when directions are being given.

15. Reduce distracting stimuli (e.g., noise and motion in the room) in order to increase your child's ability to listen successfully.

16. Stop at key points when delivering directions, explanations, and instructions in order to determine your child's comprehension.

17. Deliver directions, explanations, and instructions at an appropriate pace for your child.

18. Identify a list of word endings, key words, etc., that your child will practice listening for when someone is speaking.

19. Use multiple modalities (e.g., auditory, visual, tactile, etc.) when presenting directions, explanations, and instructional content. Determine which modality is stronger and utilize the results.

20. Stop at various points during the presentation of information to check your child's comprehension.

21. Teach your child listening skills (e.g., stop working, look at the person delivering questions and directions, have necessary note-taking materials, etc.).

22. Tell your child what to listen for when being given directions, receiving information, etc.

23. Make certain that all directions, questions, explanations, and instructions are delivered loud enough for your child to hear.

24. Play games to teach listening skills (e.g., *Mother May I? Red Light-Green Light, Simon Says,* etc.).

25. Have your child silently repeat information just heard to help him/her remember important facts.

56 Is unsuccessful in activities requiring listening

1. Make certain that your child's hearing has been checked recently.

2. Reward your child for listening. Possible rewards include verbal praise (e.g., "Thank you for listening to what I said."), a kiss on the cheek, a hug, having a friend over to play, staying up late, watching a favorite TV show, and playing a game with a parent. (See Appendix for Reward Menu.)

3. Speak to your child to explain (a) what your child is doing wrong (e.g., not listening to directions, explanations, and instructions) and (b) what your child should be doing (e.g., listening to directions, explanations, and instructions).

4. If there are other children or adolescents in the home, reward them for listening.

5. Write a contract with your child.

For example: I, William, for seven days in a row, will listen to my parents when they talk to me. When I accomplish this, I can buy a Matchbox car at the store.

The contract should be written within the ability level of your child and should focus on only one behavior at a time. (See Appendix for an example of a Behavior Contract.)

6. Evaluate the difficulty of information to which your child is expected to listen (e.g., be sure information communicated is on your child's ability level).

7. Identify a sibling or friend to act as a model for your child to imitate appropriate listening skills.

8. Have your child question any directions, explanations, and instructions which are not understood.

9. Make certain your child is near the source of information when listening is necessary.

10. Make certain your child is attending when you are speaking to your child (e.g., making eye contact, hands free of toys or other materials, etc.).

11. Make certain that competing sounds (e.g., talking, movement, noises, etc.) are silenced when you are speaking to your child.

12. Deliver a predetermined signal (e.g., calling your child by name, a hand signal, etc.) before beginning to speak to your child.

13. Stand directly in front of your child when speaking to your child.

14. Call your child by name prior to giving directions or instructions.

15. Have another child or adolescent in the home provide your child with the information he/she has missed.

16. Along with verbal directions, instructions, and explanations, give your child written directions, instructions, and explanations.

17. Maintain visibility to and from your child when you are speaking in order to ensure that your child is listening.

18. Reduce distracting stimuli in the immediate environment (e.g., call your child into the room to speak to him/her, leave a room where there are distractions, etc.). This is used as a means of reducing distracting stimuli and not as a form of punishment.

19. Have your child verbally repeat or paraphrase information.

20. Teach your child listening skills (e.g., listen carefully, write down important points, ask for clarification, wait until all directions are given before beginning a job, etc.).

21. Have your child practice activities designed to develop listening skills (e.g., following one-, two-, three-step directions; etc.).

22. Give directions in a variety of ways in order to enhance your child's ability to attend (e.g., verbally, in written form, etc.).

23. Stop at various points when speaking to your child in order to ensure that your child is attending.

24. Look at your child when speaking to him/her in order to ensure that your child is attending.

25. Demonstrate directions, explanations and instructions as they are given to your child (e.g., help your child od the first few homework problems, help your child get started cleaning the bedroom, etc.).

26. Use pictures, diagrams, and gestures when delivering information to your child.

27. Deliver information slowly to your child.

28. Present one concept at a time. Make certain your child understands each concept before presenting the next.

29. Rephrase directions, explanations, and instructions in order to increase the likelihood of your child understanding what is being presented.

30. Present directions, explanations, and instructions as simply and clearly as possible (e.g., ''Get your book bag and your lunch box and wait by the door for the bus.'').

31. When speaking to your child, be certain to use vocabulary that is within your child's level of comprehension.

32. Have your child practice listening skills by taking notes when directions, explanations, and instructions are presented.

33. Play games designed to teach listening skills (e.g., *Simon Says, Red Light-Green Light, Mother May I?*, etc.).

34. Have your child practice listening skills (e.g., ''Get your math homework and a pencil, open your book and get ready for us to review your math homework.'').

35. Teach your child when to ask questions, how to ask questions, and what types of questions to ask.

36. Have your child repeat to himself/herself information just heard to help your child remember the important facts.

37. Request listening or study guides form your child's teacher to use at home.

38. Along with a directive, provide an incentive statement (e.g., ''When you eat your peas, you may have dessert.'' ''You may watch TV after you get ready for bed.'' etc.).

39. Allow natural consequences to occur due to your child's failure to listen to directions or instructions (e.g., schoolwork not being done on time, missing out on going to the store when not ready on time, leaving his/her book bag at home, etc.).

40. Do not talk to your child from another room. Before beginning to talk, go to the room where your child is.

41. Make certain that games, activities, etc., in which your child participates are appropriate to your child's level of development.

42. Play games with your child that require listening in order to increase your child's ability to listen.

43. Use multiple modalities (e.g., auditory, visual, tactile, etc.) when presenting directions, explanations, and instructional content. Determine which modality is stronger and utilize the results.

44. Teach your child direction-following skills (e.g., stop doing other things, listen carefully, write down important points, wait until all directions are given, question any directions not understood, etc.).

45. Interact frequently with your child. Make certain that eye contact is being made in order to ensure that your child is attending.

46. Have your child tape record directions, explanations, and instructions in order that he/she may replay information as often as needed.

47. Identify your child's most efficient learning mode and use it consistently to increase the probability of understanding (e.g., if your child fails to understand directions or information given verbally, present it in written form).

57 Does not bring home notes about field trips, the book fair, etc.

1. Establish rules for taking care of responsibilities (e.g., bring notes home). These rules should be consistent and followed by everyone in the home, including the parents. Talk about the rules often.

2. Reward your child for "remembering" to bring notes home. Possible rewards include verbal praise (e.g., "You did a great job of remembering to bring your note home." etc.), a kiss on the cheek, a hug, having a friend over to play, staying up late, watching a favorite TV show, and playing a game with a parent. (See Appendix for Reward Menu.)

3. If there are other children or adolescents in the home, reward them for "remembering" to bring notes home.

4. Carefully consider your child's age and experience when expecting him/her to remember to bring notes home.

5. Make certain that your child sees the relationship between his/her behavior and the consequences which follow (e.g., forgetting to bring field trip notes home will result in not being able to go on the field trip).

6. When your child "forgets" to bring notes home, explain exactly what he/she did wrong, what should have been done, and why.

For example: "William, you need to put notes in your backpack and bring them home to me to sign and return."

7. Write a contract with your child indicating what behavior is expected (e.g., bringing notes home) and what reward he/she will earn when the terms of the contract have been met. The contract should be written within the ability level of your child and should focus on only one behavior at a time. (See Appendix for an example of a Behavior Contract.)

8. Allow natural consequences to occur due to your child's "forgetting" to take care of responsibilities (e.g., notes not being signed will result in your child not participating in activities, etc.).

9. Provide an incentive statement for your child to help him/her bring notes home (e.g., "When you bring notes home, you may stay up 10 minutes later in the evening." etc.).

10. Be consistent when expecting your child to bring notes home. Do not allow your child to fail to bring notes home one time and then expect him/her to bring them home the next time.

11. Do not punish your child for accidentally forgetting to bring notes home, for accidents that interfere with bringing notes home, etc.

12. Make certain to be specific when telling your child what you want him/her to do.

13. Make certain that the responsibilities given to your child are appropriate for your child's level of development and ability.

14. Provide your child with a book bag to carry notes to and from school.

15. Remind your child before leaving for school to bring home all notes that need to be signed.

16. Maintain open communications with school personnel in order to make certain that your child is putting notes in his/her book bag, to make certain that notes are getting back to school, etc.

17. Do not accept excuses. Your child must understand that, regardless of the reason, it is necessary that he/she takes responsibility for bringing notes home, getting notes back to school, etc.

58 Fails to remember sequences

1. Reward your child for remembering sequences. Possible rewards include verbal praise (e.g., "Thank you for remembering to do all the things that I asked you to do.") a kiss on the cheek, a hug, having a friend over to play, staying up late, watching a favorite TV show, playing a game with a parent. (See Appendix for Reward Menu.)

2. If there are other children or adolescents in the home, reward them for remembering sequences.

3. Reward your child for remembering sequencings based on the number of times your child can be successful. Gradually increase the length of the sequences required for reinforcement as your child demonstrates success.

4. Evaluate the appropriateness of what is required of your child to determine: (a) if the requirements are too difficult and (b) if the length of time scheduled to complete the task is appropriate.

5. Have your child question any directions, explanations, instructions not understood.

6. Break the sequence into units and have your child learn one unit at a time.

7. Give your child short sequences (e.g., two components, three components, etc.) to remember. Gradually increase the length of the sequences as your child demonstrates success.

8. Provide your child with environmental cues and prompts (e.g., lists of jobs to perform, sequence of daily events, bell, timer, etc.).

9. Maintain consistency in sequential activities in order to increase the likelihood of your child's success (e.g., your child has lunch every day at noon, nap time at one o'clock, etc.).

10. Teach your child associative cues or mnemonic devices to remember sequences.

11. Have your child maintain notes, written reminders, etc., in order to remember sequences.

12. Actively involve your child in learning to remember sequences by having your child physically perform sequential activities (e.g., operating equipment, following recipes, solving homework problems, etc.).

13. Have your child be responsible for helping a peer or sibling remember sequences.

14. Have your child practice remembering sequences by engaging in sequential activities which are purposeful to your child (e.g., operating equipment, following recipes, opening a combination lock, etc.).

15. Teach your child to use environmental resources to remember sequences (e.g., calendar, dictionary, etc.).

16. Have your child maintain a notebook for keeping notes regarding necessary sequential information (e.g., lists of things to do, schedule of events, days of the week, months of the year, etc.).

17. Provide your child with frequent opportunities to recite sequences throughout the day in order to increase memory skills.

18. Give your child additional activities which require the use of sequences in order to enhance your child's ability to remember sequences.

19. Practice sequential memory activities each day for those sequences your child needs to memorize (e.g., important telephone numbers, addresses, etc.).

20. Provide your child with a schedule of daily events for each day's activities at school. (See Appendix for Schedule of Daily Events).

21. Teach your child to make reminders for himself/herself (e.g., a reminder that today is a P.E. day and he/she will need gym shoes, a reminder that there is a field trip at school and he/she will need a sack lunch, etc.).

59 Has difficulty retrieving, recalling, or naming objects, persons, places, etc.

1. Reward your child for remembering things. Possible rewards include verbal praise (e.g., "You did a wonderful job of remembering to do your chores today."), a kiss on the cheek, a hug, having a friend over to play, staying up late, watching a favorite TV show, and playing a game with a parent. (See Appendix for Reward Menu.)

2. Reward your child for demonstrating accurate memory skills based on the length of time your child can be successful. Gradually increase the length of time for reinforcement as your child demonstrates success.

3. Have your child act as a messenger. Give your child a verbal message to deliver to a brother/sister, a parent, a friend, etc. Increase the length of the message as your child demonstrates success.

4. Review the sequence of the morning or afternoon activities with your child and have your child repeat the sequence. Increase the length of the sequence as your child demonstrates success.

5. At the end of the day, have your child recall the activities of the day. Gradually increase the number of activities your child is asked to recall as your child demonstrates success.

6. After a special activity or event, have your child recall what occurred.

7. After reading a short story, have your child recall the main characters, sequence the events, and recall the outcome of the story.

8. Give your child specific categories and have your child name the category to which they belong (e.g., objects, persons, places, etc.).

9. Give your child a series of words or pictures and have your child name the category to which they belong (e.g., objects, persons, places, etc.).

10. Help your child employ memory aids in order to recall words (e.g., a name might be linked to another word, for example, "Mr. Green" is a very colorful person).

11. Describe objects, persons, places, etc., and have your child name the items described.

12. Give your child a series of words describing objects, persons, places, etc., and have your child identify the opposite of each word.

13. Encourage your child to play word games such as *Hangman, Scrabble, Password,* etc.

14. Have your child complete "fill-in-the-blank" sentences with appropriate words (e.g., objects, persons, places, etc.).

15. Give your child a series of words (e.g., objects, persons, places, etc.) and have your child list all the words he/she can think of with similar meaning (synonyms).

16. Have your child compete against himself/herself by timing how fast he/she can name a series of pictured objects. Each time your child should try to increase his/her speed.

17. Have your child take notes in school in order to recall material needed to study at home.

18. Have your child make notes, lists, etc., of things he/she needs to be able to recall. Your child should carry these reminders in a purse, pocket, book bag, etc.

19. Have your child tape record important information that should be remembered.

20. Have your child outline, highlight, underline, or summarize information that needs to be remembered.

21. When your child is asked to recall information, help your child by giving clues about the information that should be recalled (e.g., "You remember when we were at Grandma's last week..." "Last week when we talked about going to Ann's house..." etc.).

22. Teach your child to recognize key words and phrases related to information in order to increase your child's memory skills.

23. Have your child practice repetition of information in order to increase accurate memory skills (e.g., repeating names, telephone numbers, dates of events, etc.).

24. Show your child an object or a picture of an object for a few seconds. Ask your child to recall specific attributes of the object (e.g., color, size, shape, etc.).

25. Label objects, persons, places, etc., in the environment in order to help your child be able to recall their names.

26. Make certain your child receives information from a variety of sources (e.g., in written form, verbally, through demonstrations, etc.) in order to enhance your child's memory/recall.

27. Make certain your child is attending to the source of information (e.g., eye contact is being made, hands are free of materials, your child is looking at his/her work, etc.).

28. Make certain your child has adequate opportunities for repetition of information through different experiences in order to enhance memory.

29. Review, on a daily basis, those skills, concepts, tasks, etc., which have been previously introduced.

30. Identify your child's most efficient learning mode and use it consistently to increase the probability of understanding (e.g., If your child fails to understand information presented verbally, present it in written form. If the child has difficulty understanding written information, present it verbally.).

60 Behaves inappropriately walking to school

1. Discuss rules for walking to and from school with your child on a daily basis (e.g., walk directly to and from school, stay on the sidewalk when possible, interact nicely with others, follow crosswalk rules, etc.).

2. Reward your child for following the rules. Possible rewards include verbal praise (e.g., ''I like the way you got home on time after school.''), having a friend over to play, staying up late, watching a favorite TV show, and playing a game with a parent. (See Appendix for Reward Menu.)

3. If there are other children or adolescents in the home, reward them for walking appropriately to and from school.

4. Speak with your child to let your child know what he/she is doing wrong, what should be done, and what the consequences are for the inappropriate behavior.

For example: Your neighbor complains that your child ''cuts through'' his yard every day after school. You should sit down and discuss this problem with your child. Let your child know that you realize that he/she is ''cutting through'' yards, that the sidewalk or street should be used, and that if the problem continues he/she will have to be escorted home after school.

5. Write a contract with your child.

For example: I, William, will walk directly to and from school, staying on the sidewalk when possible, for five days in a row. When I accomplish this, I can watch 30 extra minutes of TV.

The contract should be written within the ability level of your child and should focus on only one behavior at a time. (See Appendix for an example of a Behavior Contract.)

6. Determine whether or not your child is responsible enough to walk to and from school on his/her own. It may be necessary to have your child transported to school by you, a neighbor, a friend, etc., for a month, a semester, a year, etc.

7. Have a sibling or friend (someone older) walk with your child to and from school in order to model appropriate behavior for your child.

8. Allow natural consequences to occur as a result of your child's failure to demonstrate appropriate behavior while walking to and from school (e.g., his/her not walking directly to and from school may result in being tardy, throwing rocks may result in broken windows, etc.).

9. Maintain open communications with school personnel in order to make certain that your child is arriving and leaving school at the designated times.

10. Walk to and from school with your child in order to show your child how to use the sidewalk whenever possible, follow crosswalk rules, take the most direct route to and from school, etc.

11. Have your child perform ''jobs'' while walking to and from school (e.g., watching over a younger sibling or friend, picking up trash, etc.).

12. Encourage your child to tell you about problems that occur when walking to and from school (e.g., being ''bullied,'' approached by strangers, teased by others, chased by a dog, etc.).

13. Ask ''block parents'' to help you monitor your child's behavior while walking to and from school.

14. Do not allow your child to walk to and from school with children who cause your child to have difficulty walking to and from school.

15. Do not allow your child to take toys and materials with him/her on the walk to school. Allowing toys and materials may promote undesirable behavior on the way to school.

16. Post the rules for walking to and from school in a place where your child can read them frequently. (See Appendix for Posted Rules.)

17. Give your child a time limit in getting to and from school (e.g., have the school call if your child is not there by 8:15, the student must be home by 3:25, etc.).

61 Behaves inappropriately on the bus

1. Establish rules for riding the bus to and from school (e.g., sit quietly, keep your hands off of others and their belongings, talk in a quiet voice, keep objects inside of the bus, be friendly, etc.). These rules should be consistent and talked about often.

2. Reward your child for riding the bus appropriately. Possible rewards include verbal praise (e.g., "You did a super job on the bus today!", "Thank you for following the bus rules." etc.), a kiss on the cheek, a hug, having a friend over to play, staying up late, watching a favorite TV show, and playing a game with a parent. (See Appendix for Reward Menu.)

3. If there are other children or adolescents in the home, reward them for following the bus rules.

4. Determine whether or not your child is capable of riding the bus without close supervision. If your child is not, consider the possibilities of riding with your child or driving your child to school yourself.

5. Speak with your child to let him/her know what he/she is doing wrong, what should be done, and what the consequences are for inappropriate behavior.

For example: The bus driver tells you that your child is throwing objects out of the bus window. You should sit down and discuss this problem with your child, letting your child know that you are aware he/she has been throwing objects out of the bus window, that objects need to be kept inside the bus, and that if the problem continues he/she will not be allowed to sit by open windows while riding the bus.

6. Write a contract with your child.

For example: I, William, will not throw objects out of the bus windows for five days in a row. When I accomplish this, I can have a friend spend the night.

The contract should be written within the ability level of your child and focus on only one behavior at a time. (See Appendix for an example of a Behavior Contract.)

7. Allow natural consequences to occur as a result of your child's failure to demonstrate appropriate behavior while riding to and from school (e.g., fighting will cause him/her to be "kicked off" the bus, throwing objects out the windows may result in a littering fine, not staying seated will result in having to sit behind the bus driver, etc.).

8. Have a sibling or friend (someone older) sit next to your child on the bus in order to model appropriate behavior for your child.

9. Maintain open communication with school personnel in order to make certain that your child is riding the bus to and from school in an acceptable manner.

10. Ask that your child be given a special responsibility while on the bus (e.g., recording bus numbers, being bus monitor, giving the bus driver directions, etc.).

11. Have your child perform "jobs" while on the bus (e.g., watching over a younger sibling or neighbor).

12. Attempt to separate your child from those children who cause him/her to have difficulty riding the bus. Have your child sit at the opposite end of the bus, near the driver, etc.

13. Encourage your child to report problems that occur on the bus (e.g., being bullied, teased, etc.).

14. Do not allow your child to take toys or play materials on the bus. Allowing toys and play materials on the bus may promote undesirable behavior.

15. Post the bus rules in a place where your child can read them frequently. (See Appendix for Posted Rules.)

16. Have your child ride in the front of the bus until he/she earns the privilege of sitting with friends.

17. In the presence of the bus driver, with your child, review the rules for riding the bus.

18. Take your child to the bus stop and review all bus rules with your child before he/she gets on the bus in the morning before school.

19. Meet the bus at the end of the school day to check with the bus driver regarding your child's behavior on the bus that day.

20. Intervene early when you hear of your child having problems on the bus in order to prevent more serious problems from occurring.

A Reminder: If bus behavior is acceptable, a student can sit anywhere on the bus; if the bus behavior is not acceptable, a student may need to sit next to the bus driver.

62 Behaves inappropriately in others' homes

1. Establish rules for your child when he/she is at someone else's home (e.g., clean up after yourself, follow directions, be friendly, etc.). These rules should be consistent and you should talk about them often.

2. Reward your child for following the rules. Possible rewards include verbal praise (e.g., "Mrs. Jones said you picked up after yourself today when you were at her house. That's super!", "Johnny said that you were friendly today when you played at his house. Keep up the good job!" etc.), a kiss on the cheek, a hug, having a friend over to play, staying up late, watching a favorite TV show, and playing a game with a parent. (See Appendix for Reward Menu.)

3. If there are other children or adolescents in the home, reward them for following the rules.

4. Teach your child to respect others and their belongings by respecting your child's belongings.

5. Let your child know what he/she is doing wrong, what should be done, and why.

For example: Mrs. Jones calls to let you know that your child had trouble following her directions and was very rude while at her house. Sit down with your child and let him/her know that you are aware of his/her inappropriate behavior and that he/she needs to be able to follow directions and be nicer if he/she wants to play at Mrs. Jones' house again.

6. Allow natural consequences to occur as a result of your child's behavior (e.g., having to leave and not being able to return for a certain time period when he/she is unable to follow directions in someone else's home).

7. Do not allow your child to play at other people's homes until he/she can clean up after himself/herself, follow directions and be friendlier.

8. Be consistent. Reward good behavior at others' homes and deliver negative consequences for inappropriate behavior at others' homes.

9. Write a contract with your child.

For example: I, William, will follow directions when I go to a friend's house. When I accomplish this, I can go to Pizza Hut.

The contract should be written within the ability level of your child and should focus on only one behavior at a time. (See Appendix for an example of a Behavior Contract.)

10. Maintain open communication with those whom your child visits. Have them call you if any problems come up concerning your child's behavior in and around their home.

11. Make certain that the people in the homes your child visits are aware of the behavioral expectations that you have for your child (e.g., picking up, following directions, being friendly, etc.).

12. Prior to going to someone's house, remind your child to follow directions, pick up after himself/herself, and be friendly. Have your child report his/her behavior to you upon returning home.

13. Allow your child to call if he/she wants to come home early.

14. Encourage your child to report any problems, such as being bullied or teased at someone else's home.

15. Post a list of appropriate manners. Review the list with your child daily.

16. Make certain that your child understands that rules and consequences for inappropriate behavior will affect his/her going back to visit a friend's house another time.

17. Make sure your child knows that he/she should respect the adult in whose home your child is visiting.

18. Make certain there will be adult supervision at all times where your child is visiting.

19. Do not force your child to play/visit at someone's house with whom he/she is not completely comfortable.

20. Go in the house your child is visiting and review your rules and expectations with your child and the adult in charge.

21. Establish manners that should be followed both at home and in others' homes (e.g., using a tissue to blow your nose, chewing with your mouth closed, talking quietly, respecting the rights of others, etc.).

22. Set an example for your child by putting things back where they belong after you use them. Require your child to put things back where they belong in your home and when visiting other homes.

23. Get to know your child's friends and their parents and maintain open communication with them. Explain your expectations and ask them to provide an indication of your child's behavior when visiting them.

24. Share strategies for managing your child's behavior with adults where your child visits (e.g., when your child begins to get too excited, he/she must sit out for a few minutes; etc.).

25. Make certain there is consistency in the types of consequences delivered for behaving inappropriately in someone else's home (e.g., going to his/her room, sitting in a chair, making an apology, etc.).

26. Do not allow your child to go to others' homes until your child can behave appropriately.

27. Make certain your child does not become involved in overstimulating activities when visiting someone's home.

A Reminder: Children need to know that appropriate behavior determines whether or not we get to be a guest in someone's home again.

63 Plays with matches, cigarette lighters, etc.

1. Put all matches, cigarette lighters, etc., in a location where your child cannot get to them.

2. Make sure that all visitors in your home know to not leave matches, cigarette lighters, etc., where your child will have access to them.

3. Teach your child about the dangers of playing with matches, cigarette lighters, etc. Many local organizations (e.g., police and fire departments and hospitals) can provide you with information and may be willing to talk directly with your child about the dangers of playing with matches, cigarette lighters, etc.

4. Seek professional help from educators, social service workers, mental health workers, etc., in order to help your child better understand the dangers of playing with matches, cigarette lighters, etc.

5. Do not light matches, use cigarette lighters, etc., in front of your child.

6. Closely supervise your child when around fires (e.g., a barbecue, camp fire, fireplace, etc.).

7. Have a rule against playing with matches, cigarette lighters, etc., and reward your child for following the rule.

8. If there are other children or adolescents in the home, reward them for not playing with matches, cigarette lighters, etc.

9. Reward your child for not playing with matches, cigarette lighters, etc. Possible rewards include verbal praise (e.g., "I'm so proud of you for not playing with the matches you found!"), a kiss on the cheek, a hug, having a friend over to play, staying up late, watching a favorite TV show, and playing a game with a parent. (See Appendix for Reward Menu.)

10. Increase supervision of your child. Do not allow your child to be left alone, have friends in when you are not home, etc.

11. Do not leave your child unsupervised in your home or in others' homes.

12. When correcting your child, be sure to explain what he/she did wrong, what should have been done and why.

For example: You see your child playing with a book of matches. Go to your child and say, "You are playing with matches. You need to leave the matches alone because you could get burned. The next time you find some matches or a cigarette lighter, you need to leave them alone and tell an adult."

13. Write a contract with your child.

For example: I, William, will not play with matches, cigarette lighters, etc., for five days in a row. When I accomplish this, I can have a friend over to spend the night.

The contract should be written within the ability level of your child and should focus on only one behavior at a time. (See Appendix for an example of a Behavior Contract.)

14. Make certain your child knows what the consequences will be in your home for playing with matches (e.g., loss of freedom, loss of privileges, etc.).

15. Make teachers, baby-sitters, grandparents, etc., aware of your child's tendency to play with matches, cigarette lighters, etc.

16. Separate your child from other children, adolescents, etc., who play with matches, cigarette lighters, etc.

17. Make certain grandparents, baby-sitters, visitors in your home understand the importance of maintaining consistency in the discipline of your child.

18. Do not allow matches, cigarette lighters, etc., in your home.

19. Do not allow your child to visit in others' homes until you can be certain that he/she will not play with matches, cigarette lighters, etc.

20. Make certain your child understands the dangers involved in playing with matches, cigarette lighters, etc. (e.g., starting a fire in the home, hurting people, etc.).

A Reminder: If your child "plays" with matches, cigarette lighters, etc., remove every possible opportunity for your child to have access to matches, lighters, etc. Do not just hide them; remove them from your home.

64 Does not follow rules for behavior

1. Establish rules for behavior at home and in public places (e.g., be polite, follow rules, ask for assistance if necessary, etc.). These rules should be consistent and followed by everyone in the home. Talk about the rules often.

2. Before going to a public place, review the rules for appropriate behavior and explain why appropriate behavior in public is expected.

3. Reward your child for behaving appropriately at home and in public places. Possible rewards include verbal praise (e.g., "Thank you for following the rules at the pool today!"), a kiss on the cheek, a hug, having a friend over to play, staying up late, watching a favorite TV show, and playing a game with a parent. (See Appendix for Reward Menu.)

4. If there are other children or adolescents in the home, reward them for behaving at home and in public.

5. Supervise your child as much as necessary, both at home and in public places, in order to help your child follow the rules.

6. Encourage your child to play with other children or adolescents who behave appropriately in public places.

7. Do not allow your child to go to public places unless he/she can follow the rules.

8. Immediately remove your child from a public place when he/she begins to break rules, becomes loud, starts crying, etc.

9. When your child acts inappropriately at home or in public, explain exactly what he/she did wrong, what should have been done and why.

For example: You see your child dunking another child in the pool. Go to your child and say, "William, you are dunking someone! There is a rule against dunking people in the pool. You need to stop dunking and follow the rules or we will go home."

10. Make sure that you follow the rules in public places.

11. Show your child how to follow the rules posted in public places by reading the rules with him/her and then demonstrating how to follow the rules.

12. Write a contract with your child.

For example: I, William, will not run on the decks at the pool for two days in a row. When I accomplish this, I can take a friend to the pool.

The contract should be written within the ability level of your child and should focus on only one behavior at a time. (See Appendix for an example of a Behavior Contract.)

13. Make certain that your child sees the relationship between his/her behavior and the consequences which follow (e.g., failing to follow the rules at the skating rink may result in being "kicked out" for 1 week).

14. Allow natural consequences to occur due to your child's inability to follow the rules in public places (e.g., having to "sit out" at the pool, losing pool privileges, etc.).

15. Do not reinforce your child's inappropriate behavior by laughing when your child is silly, rude, etc.

16. Do not encourage your child to be silly and to entertain others and then scold your child when he/she begins to act too silly.

17. Always expect your child to behave at home and in public.

18. Have your child tell you the rules of the swimming pool, skating rink, etc., before going into a public place. Make sure your child understands the consequences of not following the rules.

19. Ask the employees of the public places that your child visits for a copy of the rules. Review the rules daily with your child.

20. Make certain that your child is individually supervised if he/she consistently fails to follow rules in public places.

21. Make certain that the employees of the public facility that your child is visiting know that you will deliver consequences if your child does not follow rules.

22. Do not allow your child to go to the pool, skating rink, etc., unaccompanied if there are other children there who stimulate inappropriate behavior, fight, etc.

23. Make certain your child knows what the consequences will be for not following rules at home or in public places (e.g., loss of privileges, loss of freedom to go places or be left alone, etc.).

24. Make certain baby-sitters, grandparents, visitors in your home, etc., are aware of the importance of maintaining consistency in the discipline of your child.

25. Help your child understand why it is important to follow rules at home and in public places (e.g., if you push Timmy off the slide, he may fall and break his arm; if you hold Molly under the water, she may panic, etc.).

26. Make certain your child knows what the reward will be for appropriate behavior each time he/she goes to the pool, skating rink, etc. (e.g., "For following the rules at the pool today, we will stop at Dairy Queen for a milk shake on the way home." etc.).

27. Make certain others who are involved with your child are aware of the consequences for your child when rules are not followed in your home or in public.

65 Has "bad" manners

1. Establish manners that should be followed both at home and in public (e.g., using a tissue to blow your nose, chewing with your mouth closed, talking quietly, respecting the rights of others, etc.).

2. Reward your child for demonstrating appropriate manners at home and in public. Possible rewards include verbal praise (e.g., "Your manners were excellent at dinner!", "I like the way you chewed your food with your mouth closed." etc.), a kiss on the cheek, a hug, having a friend over to play, staying up late, watching a favorite TV show, and playing a game with a parent. (See Appendix for Reward Menu.)

3. If there are other children or adolescents in the home, reward them for demonstrating appropriate manners at home and in public.

4. Carefully consider your child's age before expecting certain manners at home and in public.

5. Demonstrate appropriate manners for your child (e.g., chewing with your mouth closed, waiting quietly for others to stop talking before you talk, standing quietly in line at the movies, respecting the rights of others, etc.).

6. When your child does not demonstrate an appropriate manner, explain exactly what he/she did wrong, what should have been done and why.

For example: Your child is talking loudly during a movie. Tell your child that he/she needs to stop talking so that everyone else can hear and enjoy the movie.

7. Write a contract with your child.

For example: I, William, will wait quietly for others to stop talking before I talk during four out of five conversations. When I accomplish this, I can spend 20 minutes of one-to-one time with Mother.

The contract should be written within the ability level of your child and should focus on only one behavior at a time. (See Appendix for an example of a Behavior Contract.)

8. Talk about appropriate manners often, especially before going out in public.

9. Make certain that your child sees the relationship between his/her behavior and the consequences which follow (e.g., interrupting others will cause them to be annoyed).

10. Allow natural consequences to occur due to your child's inability to demonstrate appropriate behavior (e.g., he/she may not get to go to a restaurant because of inappropriate table manners).

11. Remove your child from a public place, such as the movies or a restaurant, until he/she can demonstrate appropriate manners.

12. Be consistent about expecting certain manners from your child. Do not laugh at your child for burping one time and then scold him/her the next time. This gives your child "mixed messages."

13. Avoid engaging your child in excessively long activities that are not geared for children (e.g., house hunting, furniture shopping, etc.).

14. Do not allow your child to bring to public places toys and materials which contribute to "bad" manners. Allow toys and materials which will promote desirable manners (e.g., books, paper and pencils, children's eating utensils, etc.).

15. Provide your child with a predetermined signal when he begins to display inappropriate manners.

16. Do not criticize. When correcting your child, be honest yet supportive. Never cause your child to feel bad about himself/herself.

17. Make your child aware of the number of times he/she behaved inappropriately (e.g., "You burped twice during dinner." "I had to ask you four times to quit talking during the movie." etc.).

18. Immediately remove your child from the situation when he/she begins to behave inappropriately. Do not allow your child to return unless he/she can demonstrate acceptable behavior.

19. Make certain that your child knows that he/she often embarrasses others when doing inappropriate things in public.

20. Do not encourage your child to be silly and to entertain others, then scold your child when he/she begins to act too silly and/or acts silly at a time you find inappropriate.

21. Always require your child to use appropriate manners at home and in public.

22. Practice using appropriate manners at all times (e.g., using a Kleenex, saying excuse me after burping, etc.).

23. Do not act shocked if your child is behaving inappropriately, simply remind your child of the rules and continue with what you are doing.

24. Do not inadvertently encourage your child's inappropriate behavior by laughing, encouraging, etc.

25. Talk to your child before going into a public place and remind your child of the importance of demonstrating appropriate manners.

26. Make certain that baby-sitters, grandparents, people visiting in your home, etc., are aware of the manners you expect your child to use and the consequences for not using them. Make certain they are aware of the importance of maintaining consistency in the discipline of your child.

27. Take time before going to visit at someone's home, going into the grocery store, etc., to review manners with your child.

66 Uses the telephone inappropriately

1. Do not allow your child to use the telephone if your child uses it inappropriately.

2. Establish rules for using the telephone (e.g., set time limits, use appropriate language, call only those individuals he/she knows, etc.). These rules should be consistent and followed by everyone in the home. Talk about the rules often.

3. Reward your child for using the telephone appropriately. Possible rewards include verbal praise (e.g., ''Thank you for using appropriate language on the phone!''), a kiss on the cheek, a hug, having a friend over to play, staying up late, watching a favorite TV show, and playing a game with a parent. (See Appendix for Reward Menu.)

4. If there are other children or adolescents in the home, reward them for using the telephone appropriately.

5. Supervise your child while he/she is using the telephone.

6. Show your child the proper way to use the telephone.

7. Immediately remove your child from the telephone when your child makes prank phone calls, uses bad language, etc.

8. When your child does not use the telephone appropriately, explain exactly what he/she is doing wrong, what should have been done and why.

For example: You overhear your child making prank phone calls. Go to your child and say, ''William, you are making prank phone calls! You must get off the phone until I know that you can use the telephone in an appropriate manner.''

9. Make certain someone is available to supervise your child during phone time until your child can be expected to talk appropriately on the phone.

10. Make certain baby-sitters and other adults who may be supervising your child are aware of your child's abuse of the phone.

11. Make sure that you do not use bad language when on the telephone.

12. Write a contract with your child.

For example: I, William, will not talk on the phone for more than 10 minutes at a time. When I accomplish this, I can play a game of basketball with Dad.

The contract should be written within the ability level of your child and should focus on only one behavior at a time. (See Appendix for an example of a Behavior Contract.)

13. Require that your child ask permission before using the phone.

14. Post telephone rules in a place where your child can read and review them daily. (See Appendix for Posted Rules.)

15. Make certain that your child understands the consequences of abusing the phone (e.g., people may put a trace on the line, someone may become very frightened, etc.).

16. Discuss telephone manners as a family (e.g., when someone is not available to come to the phone ask to take a message, answer the phone by saying ''Hello,'' etc.).

17. Make use of the telephone contingent upon using the telephone appropriately.

18. Make certain your child is aware of local and federal laws regarding the use of the telephone (i.e., harassment, obscenities, etc.).

19. Have your child earn extra time to use the phone by demonstrating appropriate behavior while on the phone.

20. Communicate with parents of your child's friends who are also using the telephone inappropriately (e.g., making prank phone calls, using bad language, etc.).

21. Limit your child's association with other children who are using the telephone inappropriately (e.g., making prank phone calls, using bad language, etc.).

22. Confront those children involved with your child's inappropriate use of the telephone (e.g., making prank phone calls, using bad language, etc.).

A Reminder: Your telephone company may be able to provide you with a means of "locking" your telephone when you do not want it to be used by a child.

67 Has difficulty with changes in routine

1. Sit down and explain changes in routine to your child a few days before they happen, if possible.

2. Encourage your child to tell you why he/she is upset about guests or a baby-sitter in the home. Make sure that your child is not being mistreated in any way.

3. Do not make your child go through changes that are upsetting.

4. Try to give your child as much structure and "sameness" in his/her life as possible.

5. Allow your child to participate in deciding when changes in routine will occur.

6. Have a calendar of family activities and indicate on the calendar when guests will visit, doctors' appointments will occur, baby-sitters will come, etc.

7. Plan things for your child to do when changes in routine occur (e.g., caring for a younger brother or sister, going to see a movie, having a friend spend the night, etc.).

8. Reward your child for accepting changes in routine. Possible rewards include verbal praise (e.g., "I'm proud of you for not getting mad when dinner was late."), a kiss on the cheek, a hug, having a friend over to play, staying up late, watching a favorite TV show, and playing a game with a parent. (See Appendix for Reward Menu.)

9. If there are other children or adolescents in the home, reward them for accepting changes in their routine.

10. Write a contract with your child.

For example: I, William, will not cry when I have to stay with a baby-sitter. When I accomplish this, I can have a friend spend the night.

The contract should be written within the ability level of your child and should focus on only one behavior at a time. (See Appendix for an example of a Behavior Contract.)

11. Try to remain calm and accept changes in your own routine. If you become upset by changes, your child will learn to do the same.

12. When your child has difficulty adjusting to a change in routine, explain exactly what he/she is doing wrong, what should have been done and why.

For example: You tell your child that dinner will be 15 minutes late and he begins to cry and stomp around. Go to your child and say, "William, you are crying. You need to stop crying and wash up so you'll be ready for dinner."

13. Remind your child, as often as possible, of changes that will occur in routine.

14. Try to limit the number of changes in your child's routine whenever possible.

15. Do not leave your child alone with others until your child has a feeling of comfort and safety.

16. Introduce your child to a new baby-sitter and let them spend some time getting acquainted before you leave your child alone with the baby-sitter.

17. Have your child try something new with peers with whom he/she feels uncomfortable (e.g., swim lessons, dancing, baseball, etc.).

18. If your child begins to use "afraid of doing it" as an excuse, take your child to the activity, see him/her into the location, leave, and come back when the activity is over. Make certain the person with whom you are leaving your child understands the situation.

19. Present changes in routine in the most attractive manner possible (e.g., "Rather than going to school this morning, we are going out to eat breakfast and see the dentist." etc.).

20. Allow your child to take part in changing the routine (e.g., let your child decide which day to visit Grandma, which baby-sitter he/she would like to have, etc.).

21. Be personally available when your child is dealing with changes in routine (e.g., take your child to the first day of swim lessons, have the new baby-sitter come over to play games with your child while you are home, etc.).

22. Do not reinforce your child's fears about changes in daily routine by allowing him/her to get out of participating in a situation because he/she is afraid of change.

23. Carefully consider your child's age and maturity level before expecting him/her to accept changes in routine.

24. Let your child know in advance of any change in the daily routine (e.g., identify the time dinner will be served, what time Dad will be home, what you will be doing for the day, etc.).

25. Help your child plan changes in routine (e.g., a slumber part, visiting relatives, etc.).

26. Have your child attend special events that may be a change in routine with peers with whom he/she feels comfortable (e.g., birthday parties, school, swim lessons, etc.).

27. Give your child a responsibility to perform at special events in order to participate, interact, etc., without experiencing the awkwardness of not knowing what to do or say to others (e.g., taking coats, serving refreshments, etc.).

28. Have your child help plan special events (e.g., family gatherings, parties, etc.) in your home by choosing refreshments, planning a schedule of daily events, etc.

29. Allow your child to attend special events without insisting that he/she socialize when feeling uncomfortable.

30. In order to help your child feel comfortable with a new situation, take your child to meet the new teacher, swim instructor, or dance instructor; visit the dentist before the actual appointment; etc.

31. Provide your child with a revised schedule of daily events which identifies the activities for the day and the time they will occur. (See Appendix for Weekday or Saturday Schedule.)

32. Attempt to limit the number of changes that need to occur in your child's routine.

33. Evaluate the significance of the change in routine in order to determine how much assistance your child will need in the change.

34. Make certain your child understands any directions, explanations, or instructions involved in changing to a new routine.

35. Provide your child with notes on the refrigerator, in his/her room, etc., to remember changes in routine.

36. Provide your child with a verbal reminder of changes in routine.

37. Provide your child with frequent opportunities to become accustomed to changes in the routine (e.g., having guests in your home, having a baby-sitter, etc.).

38. Limit the number of changes in your child's established routine. Gradually increase the number of changes in routine as your child demonstrates success.

39. Make certain that anyone who assumes responsibility in your home (e.g., grandparents, baby-sitter, etc.) is provided with rules, schedules, mealtimes, bedtimes, appropriate activities, consequences, etc., in order that their supervision will be as consistent with yours as possible.

40. Make certain your child understands that you will receive a report of behavior from baby-sitters, grandparents, etc., upon your return.

41. Make certain your child is rewarded for appropriate behavior during any change in routine (e.g., having guests in your home, having a baby-sitter, staying with grandparents, etc.).

A Reminder: Difficulty adjusting to changes in a routine often result from the excitement of doing something out of the ordinary. Make certain your child is well informed in advance of such changes and knows what the rules and expectations will be.

68 Is not able to eat, sleep, or concentrate because of personal or school problems

1. Talk to your family doctor, a school official, a social worker, or a mental health professional about your child's inability to eat, sleep, or concentrate.

2. Encourage your child to tell you when he/she is upset over personal or school problems.

3. Reward your child for talking to you about personal or school problems. Possible rewards include verbal praise (e.g., 'I'm so proud of you for coming to me to talk about your problem with your friend, Jamie.''), a kiss on the cheek, a hug, having a friend over to play, staying up late, watching a favorite TV show, and playing a game with a parent. (See Appendix for Reward Menu.)

4. If there are other children or adolescents in the home, reward them for talking about personal or school problems.

5. By maintaining an open and honest relationship with your child, he/she will feel comfortable coming to you for help in solving personal or school problems.

6. Make a point to ask your child how things are going each day.

7. Write a contract with your child.

For example: I, William, will tell Mother and/or Daddy when I am upset about something that happened in school. When I talk about my feelings I will earn a dime.

The contract should be written within the ability level of your child and should focus on only one behavior at a time. (See Appendix for an example of a Behavior Contract.)

8. Make certain that your child sees the relationship between his/her behavior and the consequences which follow (e.g., not eating and sleeping will cause illness).

9. Maintain trust and confidentiality with your child at all times.

10. Encourage your child to get involved in extracurricular activities (e.g., scouting, sports, clubs, etc.).

11. Encourage your child to talk with other individuals (e.g., guidance counselor, school nurse, social worker, teacher, relative, etc.) if your child is uncomfortable talking with you.

12. Before going to bed, read your child a pleasant bedtime story in order to help your child think about positive thoughts before going to sleep.

13. Have the family eat meals together in order to have conversation and to keep your child's mind off of school or personal problems.

14. Take time to listen so your child realizes that your concern is genuine.

15. Reduce the emphasis on competition. Repeated failures may heighten anxiety about performance.

16. Provide your child with as many enjoyable and interesting activities as possible.

17. Structure the home environment in such a way that time does not permit opportunities for your child to dwell on concerns or worries.

18. Discuss ways in which to practice self-improvement with your child.

19. Encourage your child to discuss problems with you instead of trying to handle problems alone.

20. Encourage your child to talk to a counselor at school about courses.

21. Explain that some concerns or worries, while legitimate, are not unusual for children (e.g., worrying about grades, popularity, dating, sex, etc.). Talking about concerns will only make it easier to deal with them.

22. Teach your child to be a problem-solver when encountering a personal or school problem:

Step 1: Identify the problem
Step 2: Identify goals and objectives
Step 3: Develop strategies
Step 4: Develop a plan for action
Step 5: Carry out the plan

23. Teach your child that the best way to deal with a problem is to confront it and solve it (e.g., if he/she is worried about an assignment, the best thing to do is to work on it; if he/she is worried about a test, study with a friend; etc.).

24. Be sensitive to your child's behavior in order to detect concern over personal or school problems and intervene early to help deal with them.

25. Spend time alone with your child in order to give him/her the opportunity to talk with you, share feelings, and feel comfortable sharing concerns over personal or school problems. Involve your child in your activities and get involved in your child's activities, getting to know your child's friends and their interests, concerns, etc.

26. Demonstrate to your child that you can be deliberate as a problem-solver and that you and your child together can solve personal or school problems (e.g., when your child has a problem with homework, help your child with it or communicate with the teacher in order to be able to complete the homework, turn it in on time, and have it accurate).

27. The way you react to your child's personal or school problems will determine whether or not he/she comes to you with a problem again (e.g., by being supportive and helping your child solve problems, your child will want to call upon you for help in the future).

28. Do not appear shocked or surprised by your child's problems. Be supportive and non-judgmental if your child comes to you with problems concerning drugs, sex, dating, boyfriends, girlfriends, etc.

A Reminder: Be sensitive to your child's worries and concerns. They are as real to him/her as yours are to you.

69 Leaves yard, is late for meals, stays out late

1. Establish rules for leaving the yard, being home on time for meals, etc. (e.g., leave a note with information such as where you will be, a phone number where you can be reached, and when you will be home; call when you will be late; ask permission to leave the yard; etc.). These rules should be consistent and followed by everyone in the home. Talk about the rules often and reward your child for following the rules.

2. Reward your child for asking permission to leave the yard, being home on time, etc. Possible rewards include verbal praise (e.g., ''Thank you for asking permission to leave the yard!'' ''I appreciate it when you get home in time for dinner.'' etc.), a kiss on the cheek, a hug, having a friend over to play, staying up late, watching a favorite TV show, and playing a game with a parent. (See Appendix for Reward Menu.)

3. If there are other children or adolescents in the home, reward them for asking permission to leave the yard, being on time for meals, etc.

4. Carefully consider your child's age before expecting him/her to ask permission to leave the yard, know when it is time to come home, etc. Supervise your child and know where he/she is at all times.

5. Let your child know what you are doing by leaving a note telling where you are, the number where you can be reached, and when you will be home. By doing this, your child will learn the importance of letting others know where he/she is at all times.

6. When your child leaves the yard without permission, explain exactly what he/she did wrong, what should have been done and why.

7. Make certain that your child sees the relationship between his/her behavior and the consequences which follow (e.g., getting home late for dinner results in having to eat food that is no longer warm).

8. Remind your child to keep track of time by asking an adult, looking at a watch, etc.

9. Write a contract with your child.

For example: I, William, will be home in time for dinner for four days in a row. When I accomplish this, I can have a friend over to spend the night.

The contract should be written within the ability level of your child and should focus on only one behavior at a time. (See Appendix for an example of a Behavior Contract.)

10. Allow natural consequences to occur due to your child's leaving the yard without permission, not coming home for dinner on time, etc. (e.g., not being able to leave the yard, missing dinner, having to eat leftovers, etc.).

11. After giving your child permission to leave the yard, make sure you know where your child will be and tell him/her what time to be home. Have your child repeat to you the time to be home.

12. Have your child keep track of the number of times he/she asks permission to leave the yard, is home on time for dinner, etc., by putting a star or check mark on a list by the behavior performed. Let your child trade in stars or check marks for rewards.

13. Make certain your child understands that the privilege of being away from home is dependent upon letting you know where he/she is at all times, coming home on time, etc.

14. Maintain a list of your child's friends and their telephone numbers in case you need to reach your child.

15. Establish a regular routine for meals and other family activities so that your child will know when to be home.

16. Be consistent in dealing with your child's behavior. Consequences must be delivered each time your child is late, goes somewhere he/she is not to go, etc.

17. Require your child to keep you informed by telephone where he/she is at all times.

18. Keep a notepad in a conspicuous place for your child to leave messages telling you where he/she will be and what time he/she will be home.

19. Make certain your child knows that coming home late without permission will result in loss of privileges (e.g., using the car, dating, etc.).

20. Increase supervision of your child (e.g., direct supervision by you, another adult, older adolescent, etc.).

21. Make certain your child understands that being late frightens and causes concern for the family.

22. Require your child to call home to tell you when and why he/she will be late.

23. If your child is late for a meal, have your child prepare his/her own meal, do without a meal, etc.

24. Make an agreement with your child to call you if the driver of a car in which he/she is riding has been drinking, if he/she has been drinking, if he/she is uncomfortable in a particular situation, etc. Make certain your child understands that there will be no negative consequences for calling, but if he/she does not call there could be negative consequences.

25. Offer your child the opportunity to have friends at your home to watch late movies, order pizza, spend the night, etc.

26. Make certain that baby-sitters, grandparents, visitors in your home, etc., are aware of your child's tendency to leave the yard without permission. Make certain they understand the importance of maintaining consistency in the discipline of your child when he/she leaves the yard without permission.

27. Make certain your child understands that people worry, become upset, etc., when he/she leaves the yard without permission.

28. Make certain that when consequences are delivered for inappropriate behavior, they are not extreme and are directly related to the inappropriate behavior (e.g., If your child leaves the yard without permission, he/she will be grounded to the yard for two hours, one day, etc.).

29. Make certain your child knows what the consequences will be in your home for leaving the yard without permission (e.g., loss of privileges, loss of freedom to be left alone, etc.).

A Reminder: Your child's behavior should determine how much freedom is given to come and go from day to day.

70 Cannot accept constructive criticism

1. Make sure that you criticize your child in a constructive and supportive manner. Do not "pick on your child" or make him/her feel "picked on."

2. Allow your child to make comments and be a part of the problem-solving process when there are behaviors that need to be changed.

3. Do not "make fun" of your child when he/she becomes angry, cries, etc., when others give constructive criticism.

4. Reward your child for accepting constructive criticism in an appropriate manner. Possible rewards include verbal praise (e.g., "I'm so proud of you for sitting and listening to me when I was trying to help you improve your English paper."), a kiss on the cheek, a hug, having a friend over to play, staying up late, watching a favorite TV show, and playing a game with a parent. (See Appendix for Reward Menu.)

5. If there are other children or adolescents in the home, reward them for accepting constructive criticism in an appropriate manner.

6. Show your child how to accept constructive criticism by listening, making appropriate comments, etc.

7. Be a model for accepting constructive criticism.

8. Write a contract with your child.

For example: I, William, for one week, will not cry when Mother tells me to clean my room. When I accomplish this, I can earn a model airplane.

The contract should be written within the ability level of your child and should focus on only one behavior at a time. (See Appendix for an example of a Behavior Contract.)

9. Do not become upset or angry when your child does something wrong. Help your child understand what he/she did wrong by talking calmly about the problem. If you get angry, your child will try to make excuses for the behavior.

10. Do not give your child constructive criticism in front of others. Discuss the need for behavioral changes in private.

11. When your child responds inappropriately to constructive criticism, explain exactly what he/she is doing wrong, what should be done and why.

For example: Your child begins crying when you are helping with an English assignment. Explain by saying, "I'm trying to help you with your English and you are crying. You need to stop crying so we can talk about your errors and discuss changes that need to be made."

12. Offer to help or provide assistance when you give your child constructive criticism.

13. Make sure that other individuals (e.g., teachers, parents of your child's friends, baby-sitters, etc.) are aware of your child's reaction to constructive criticism.

14. Help your child feel comfortable coming to you for assistance with a problem by listening to him/her and helping find a solution to the problem.

15. Make certain that your child sees the relationship between his/her behavior and the consequences which follow (e.g., others avoiding your child, not being allowed to participate in activities, etc.).

16. Help your child understand the intent of others when they say or do something that upsets him/her.

17. Teach your child to deal with feelings of sensitivity.

18. When your child reacts in an overly sensitive manner, explain what happened to cause your child to "overreact" and what could have been done in order to prevent the reaction.

19. Provide your child with a quiet place to go when he/she becomes upset or angry with a friend or friends.

20. Remove your child from a friend or group of friends who may be overly critical of your child.

21. Avoid allowing your child to engage in activities which may not prove successful and which may cause him/her to feel bad about himself/herself.

22. Encourage your child to pursue those activities with which he/she experiences the most success.

23. Make certain that your comments take the form of constructive criticism rather than criticism that can be perceived as personal, threatening, etc. (e.g., instead of saying, "You always make the same mistake." say "A better way to do that might be...").

24. Compliment your child whenever possible.

25. Encourage others to compliment your child.

26. Set up your child for success by finding activities that will result in success; then your child will feel more confident, self-assured, etc., and will likely find more success on his/her own.

27. Do not allow your child to remain in those activities, situations, etc., where there is not a chance of success. Continued failures can be a destructive influence.

28. Do not reinforce your child's sensitivity by feeling sorry for him/her, putting others down, involving yourself in the situation, etc., when your child comes to you saying someone laughed at or made fun of him/her.

29. Identify those things about which your child appears to be overly sensitive. Talk to your child and help overcome the sensitivity by getting a tutor, cutting your child's hair, playing catch, helping to lose weight, etc.

30. Do not tease your child about weight, color of hair, abilities, etc.

31. Talk to peers, brothers/sisters, etc., about being sensitive to your child's feelings.

32. When giving your child constructive criticism, deliver a positive comment before offering criticism (e.g., "Your room looks great, but you need to spend a few extra minutes cleaning your closet." "You did a great job in the baseball game today. Next time you may want to play closer to first base." etc.).

33. Make certain the criticism you are giving your child is constructive in nature.

34. Make certain that others offering your child criticism are doing it in a constructive way.

35. Explain to your child how to take constructive criticism (e.g., say, "OK, thanks for the advice." "Thanks for helping me out." "Great idea." etc.).

36. Explain to your child that constructive criticism is not a put-down, but rather a way to help him/her improve.

37. Use language that reflects support rather than language that proves threatening (e.g., "Another way to do that might be..." rather than "That's not the right way to do that. Do it over." etc.).

38. Anytime that constructive criticism is given, begin by saying to your child, "Let me help you."

39. Review those things you are going to say to your child to make certain they are constructive and positive.

40. Make certain your child is receiving adequate, positive reinforcement anytime it is appropriate.

41. Provide constructive criticism when your child is most likely to demonstrate an appropriate response (e.g., instead of giving constructive criticism at the end of a ball game, wait until the next day; etc.).

42. Ask your child if he/she would like to have some constructive criticism. Respect his/her decision.

43. Avoid using such phrases as "don't take this the wrong way, but... ", "Don't take this personally, but...", "I don't mean to hurt your feelings, but... ", when approaching your child with constructive criticism.

A Reminder: We are all sensitive to criticism; be certain to be as positive as possible.

71 Is impatient

1. Establish a rule (e.g., be patient with others). This rule should be consistent and followed by everyone in the home. Talk about the rule often and reward your child for following the rule.

2. Attempt to be patient. If you are impatient, your child will learn to be impatient also.

3. Reward your child for being patient. Possible rewards include verbal praise (e.g., "Thanks for waiting patiently until I was finished talking on the phone!"), a kiss on the cheek, a hug, having a friend over to play, staying up late, watching a favorite TV show, and playing a game with a parent. (See Appendix for Reward Menu.)

4. If there are other children or adolescents in the home, reward them for being patient.

5. Give your child suggestions of things to do (e.g., counting to 10, saying the alphabet, walking away from the situation and then returning, etc.) in order to help teach more patience.

6. When your child is impatient, explain exactly what he/she is doing wrong, what he/she should be doing and why.

For example: You overhear your child yelling at a friend to hurry. Go to your child and say, "William, you are yelling at Matt. You need to wait patiently until he is ready to play, or he may not want to play with you."

7. Write a contract with your child.

For example: I, William, for two days in a row, will wait patiently for my turn to use the telephone. When I accomplish this, I can go to the movies on Saturday.

The contract should be written within the ability level of your child and should focus on only one behavior at a time. (See Appendix for an example of a Behavior Contract.)

8. Provide supervision when your child interacts with others.

9. Immediately remove your child from interacting with others when he/she begins to be impatient.

10. Make certain that your child sees the relationship between his/her behavior and the consequences which follow (e.g., hurting others' feelings, others avoiding your child, etc.).

11. Teach your child how to deal with feelings of frustration in an appropriate manner.

12. Carefully consider your child's age and experience before expecting him/her to always be patient.

13. Encourage your child to ask for help when necessary.

14. Do not make your child wait for long periods of time to get your attention.

15. Make sure that there is something to do if your child has to wait on others (e.g., reading, playing a game, listening to music, etc.).

16. Encourage your child to find something to do when waiting for others.

17. Remind your child how it felt when he/she was learning something new, attempting something new, etc., and help your child see how others might feel in the same situation and that he/she should use patience when around such situations.

18. Do not allow your child to play with children with whom he/she has little patience.

19. Have your child spend short periods of time with younger brothers and/or sisters and friends in order to learn to be more patient with them. Gradually increase the amount of time your child spends with younger brothers and/or sisters and friends as he/she demonstrates increased patience.

20. Identify the thing with which your child is impatient (e.g., younger brothers/sisters or friends, games, homework, etc.). Remind your child to try to use patience before doing something with which he/she is impatient.

21. Make certain that your child is able to get those things that are needed without having to ask others for help. Your child should be able to reach food, dishes, shampoo, clothes, etc., without needing someone's help.

22. Talk to your child in the manner in which you want them to talk to you. Treat them with respect and do not "talk down" to them.

23. Provide your child with a place to go when he/she becomes impatient (e.g., a quiet corner, a room, etc.).

24. When your child begins to get impatient, provide reminders for self-control (e.g., by saying, "You need to count to 10." "Calm down, you're becoming impatient." etc.).

25. After telling your child that he/she cannot do or have something, explain the reason.

26. Teach your child alternative ways to communicate unhappiness (e.g., talking about a problem, asking for help, etc.).

27. Give your child additional responsibilities (e.g., chores, errands, privileges, etc.) in order to provide alternative activities if your child does not get to do what he/she wants.

28. Discourage your child from engaging in those activities which cause unhappiness.

29. Help your child to be able to identify when he/she is beginning to get upset in order to do something to calm down (e.g., walk away, talk about feelings in a socially acceptable way, seek help from an adult, etc.).

30. Involve your child in activities that are likely to result in success and which will help your child feel good about himself/herself. Repeated failures result in frustration and impatience.

31. Do not place emphasis on perfection. If your child feels he/she must meet up to your expectations and cannot, it may cause your child to become impatient with himself/herself.

32. Talk to your child's teacher to make certain that the child is not having trouble in school and becoming impatient with schoolwork.

33. Make necessary adjustments in the environment to prevent your child from experiencing stress, impatience, frustration, etc.

34. Reinforce your child for demonstrating self-control based on the length of time he/she can be successful. Gradually increase the length of time required for reinforcement as your child demonstrates success.

35. Prevent frustrating or anxiety-producing situations from occurring (e.g., only give your child chores, responsibilities, etc., on the appropriate ability level).

36. Teach your child to verbalize feelings before losing control (e.g., "I'm getting tired of doing this." "I'm getting bored standing here." etc.).

37. Monitor the behavior of others (e.g., brothers, sisters, friends, etc.) to make certain they are not teasing or otherwise stimulating your child to become upset or angry.

38. Look for the warning signs (e.g., arguing, loud voices, etc.) that your child is getting upset or angry and intervene to change the activity.

39. Before competitive activities, discuss how your child should react if he/she becomes impatient.

40. Do not allow your child to participate in a situation unless he/she can demonstrate self-control.

41. Make certain that the activities, situations, etc., in which your child is involved are appropriate for your child's age, maturity, developmental level, etc. It may be that your child is not ready for such activities at this particular time.

42. Reduce the emphasis on competition. Highly competitive activities may cause your child to be impatient to win, "beat" someone, etc.

43. Help your child perform those activities which cause him/her to be impatient (e.g., putting a model together, making the bed, etc.). Provide less assistance as your child experiences success.

44. Prevent your child from becoming overly frustrated by activities or situations. Intervene to keep your child from becoming too upset. Repeated frustration/impatience only contributes to more frequent impatience occurring at shorter intervals.

A Reminder: Impatience to participate, get things done, etc., while annoying, is a characteristic of youth. Patience is learned with personal success and by satisfaction with our accomplishments.

1. Teach your child how to respond to friendly teasing (e.g., laugh, tease in return, etc.).

2. Act as a model for friendly teasing by joking with others and dealing with friendly teasing in an appropriate manner.

3. Teach your child how to deal with friendly teasing which upsets him/her (e.g., avoid those individuals who do the teasing, walk away from the situation, move to another location, etc.).

4. Explain to your child that friendly teasing is a positive means by which people show others that they like them and enjoy their company.

5. Reward your child for dealing with friendly teasing in an acceptable manner. Possible rewards include verbal praise (e.g., "I'm glad that you didn't get angry when Lisa was teasing you today!"), a kiss on the cheek, a hug, having a friend over to play, staying up late, watching a favorite TV show, and playing a game with a parent. (See Appendix for Reward Menu.)

6. If there are other children or adolescents in the home, reward them for dealing with friendly teasing in an acceptable manner.

7. When your child has difficulty dealing with friendly teasing, explain exactly what he/she is doing wrong, what should be done and why.

For example: You overhear your child yelling at his sister because she is teasing him. Go to you child and say, "William, Kim is teasing you and you are yelling at her. She is trying to make you laugh and wants you to tease her in return. If you don't like the teasing, then you need to ask her to stop in a friendly manner or walk away from her. If you start yelling, others will not want to be around you."

8. Supervise your child's interactions with others in order to be sure that the teasing is friendly and to help your child respond in an acceptable manner.

9. Write a contract with your child.

For example: I, William, for three days in a row, will not cry when Kim teases me. When I accomplish this, I can earn a Matchbox car.

The contract should be written within the ability level of your child and should focus on only one behavior at a time. (See Appendix for an example of a Behavior Contract.)

10. Talk with your child about choosing friends who are friendly and sincere.

11. Talk with school personnel and other individuals who spend time with your child in order to make them aware of your child's response to friendly teasing.

12. Point out to your child, when you are teasing others, that no harm is meant and that the same holds true when others tease your child.

13. Make certain that your child sees the relationship between his/her behavior and the consequences which follow (e.g., others avoiding your child, being removed from interacting with others, not being able to participate in special activities, etc.).

14. Immediately remove your child when he/she has difficulty dealing with friendly teasing.

15. Allow natural consequences to occur as a result of your child's inability to deal with friendly teasing (e.g., being removed from interacting with others when reacting inappropriately).

16. Help your child understand the intent of others when they say or do something that is upsetting.

17. Treat your child in a sensitive manner. Do not tease, make fun of, or "talk down" to your child.

18. Help your child feel good about himself/herself by making positive comments and spending one-to-one time with him/her.

19. Do not punish or make fun of your child when he/she reacts in an overly sensitive manner.

20. Encourage your child to play with others who are friendly, cooperative, and kind.

21. Make certain that you accept teasing, joking, etc., in an acceptable way.

22. Do not put your child in a situation where he/she may feel bad about himself/herself (e.g., playing football if unwilling and noncompetitive, dancing if not good at it, etc.).

23. Do not reinforce your child's sensitivity by feeling sorry for him/her, putting others down, involving yourself in the situation, etc., when your child comes to you saying someone laughed at or made fun of him/her.

24. Do not tease your child about weight, color of hair, abilities, etc.

25. Talk to peers, brothers/sisters, etc., about being sensitive to your child's feelings.

26. Make certain your child has many successes in order to feel satisfied with himself/herself.

27. Explain to your child that people often tease in a friendly manner because they like the person they are teasing.

28. Teach your child the difference between ''friendly teasing'' and ''unfriendly teasing.''

29. Remove your child from a friend or group of friends who may be overly critical of your child.

30. Encourage others to compliment your child.

31. Pair your child with a younger brother/sister, younger children, etc., in order to enhance your child's feelings of success or accomplishment.

32. Discuss with others your child's sensitivity and difficulty in dealing with friendly teasing in order that they may adjust their behavior accordingly.

33. Discuss with your child topics which are not appropriate for friendly teasing (e.g., death, disease, handicaps, poverty, etc.).

34. Help your child understand that if he/she cannot accept friendly teasing, then it would be best if your child avoided certain situations (e.g., do not join in friendly teasing if you cannot handle the situation when the teasing turns to you).

35. Act as a model for friendly teasing by joking with others and your child and laughing when they tease you.

36. Make certain your child understands that friendly teasing is an accepted means of communication and interaction in our society. If your child can accept friendly teasing and also practice it, he/she will have learned a valuable communication skill.

37. Make certain your child understands that when friends tease, it is ''friendly teasing'' (i.e., even sarcasm, one-upmanship, etc., constitute ''friendly teasing'' when it is among ''friends'').

A Reminder: Impress upon your child that ''friendly teasing'' is a part of having ''friends.''

1. Reward your child for reacting in an acceptable manner to things others say or do. Possible rewards include verbal praise (e.g., "I am so proud of you for not crying when your friend did not want to play with you today."), a kiss on the cheek, a hug, having a friend over to play, staying up late, watching a favorite TV show, and playing a game with a parent. (See Appendix for Reward Menu.)

2. If there are other children or adolescents in the home, reward them for reacting in an acceptable manner to things others say or do.

3. Help your child understand the intent of others when they say or do something that may be upsetting.

4. Teach your child to deal with his/her feelings of sensitivity.

5. When your child reacts in an overly sensitive manner, explain what happened to cause your child to "overreact" and what could have been done to prevent the reaction.

6. Make certain that your child sees the relationship between his/her behavior and the consequences which follow (e.g., others making fun, others avoiding your child, not being invited to do things with others, etc.).

7. Treat your child in a sensitive manner. Do not tease, make fun of, or "talk down" to your child.

8. Help your child feel good about himself/herself by making positive comments and spending one-to-one time with him/her.

9. Encourage your child to play with others who are friendly, cooperative, and kind.

10. Help your child choose activities that make him/her feel good about himself/herself.

11. Do not put your child in a situation where he/she may feel bad about himself/herself (e.g., playing football if unwilling and noncompetitive, dancing if not good at it, etc.).

12. Do not punish or make fun of your child when he/she is reacting in an overly sensitive manner.

13. Make certain that you accept teasing, joking, change, etc., in an acceptable way.

14. Treat your child with respect. Talk in an objective manner at all times and use a calm, quiet voice without losing your temper.

15. Provide your child with a quiet place to go when he/she becomes upset or angry with a friend or friends.

16. Encourage your child to play with children who do not laugh at and/or make fun of others.

17. Increase supervision of your child when playing with others.

18. Talk to your child about ways to handle feelings when someone laughs at or makes fun of him/her (e.g., laughing along, walking away, counting to 10, etc.).

19. Help your child to see his/her good points and talk about them often in an attempt to help your child feel better about himself/herself.

20. Do not put an emphasis on competition. Repeated failures may cause your child to criticize himself/herself.

21. Talk with your child about individual differences, and discuss strengths and weaknesses of individuals your child knows.

22. Make certain you do not contribute to your child being critical of himself/herself by discussing weight, grades, looks, etc., in public or in front of your child.

23. Make certain that your comments take the form of constructive criticism rather than criticism that can be perceived as personal, threatening, etc. (e.g., instead of saying, "You always make the same mistake." say, "A better way to do that might be...").

24. Remove your child from a friend or group of friends who may be overly critical of your child.

25. Avoid engaging your child in activities in which he/she may not succeed and which may cause your child to have bad feelings about himself/herself.

26. Encourage your child to pursue those activities with which he/she experiences the most success.

27. Encourage your child to learn to accept improvement rather than insisting on excellence (e.g., getting one hit during a game is an improvement over striking out four times, etc.).

28. Encourage others to compliment your child.

29. Set up your child for success by finding activities that will result in success; then your child will feel more confident, self-assured, etc., and will likely find more success on his/her own.

30. Do not reinforce your child's sensitivity by feeling sorry for him/her, putting others down, involving yourself in the situation, etc., when your child comes to you saying someone laughed at or made fun of him/her.

31. Do not allow your child to remain in those activities, situations, etc., where there is no chance of success. Continued failures can be a destructive influence.

32. Talk to teachers at school to make certain that your child is successful in school and to see if there are any problems with schoolwork.

33. Identify those things about which your child appears to be overly sensitive. Talk to your child and help to overcome the sensitivity by getting him/her a tutor, cutting your child's hair, playing catch, helping to lose weight, etc.

34. Do not tease your child about weight, color of hair, abilities, etc.

35. Talk to peers, brothers/sisters, etc., about being sensitive to your child's feelings.

36. Remove your child from others who may make fun of him/her.

37. Make certain your child has many successes in order to feel satisfied with himself/herself.

A Reminder: We are all sensitive to others making fun of or laughing at us. We need to be careful that we afford our children the same respect for their feelings as we do for the feelings of adults.

1. Establish rules (e.g., wait your turn, share, ask for help when necessary, treat others in a friendly manner, walk away from a situation when you are getting upset, etc.). These rules should be consistent and followed by everyone in the home. Talk about the rules often and reward your child for following the rules.

2. Reward your child for not throwing temper tantrums. Possible rewards include verbal praise (e.g., "I am so proud of you for waiting your turn!"), a kiss on the cheek, a hug, having a friend over to play, staying up late, watching a favorite TV show, and playing a game with a parent. (See Appendix for Reward Menu.)

3. If there are other children or adolescents in the home, reward them for not throwing temper tantrums.

4. Help your child understand why he/she is throwing temper tantrums and teach an acceptable way to show anger, frustration, anxiety, etc.

5. Do not "give in" to your child's demands when he/she throws a temper tantrum. If you do, your child will learn to throw temper tantrums in order to get his/her own way.

6. Immediately remove your child when he/she begins to throw a temper tantrum.

7. When possible, walk away from your child until he/she can calm down and express his/her feelings in a socially acceptable way.

8. Remain calm when your child throws a temper tantrum.

9. Make sure that you express your feelings in a socially acceptable way.

10. When your child throws a temper tantrum, explain exactly what he/she is doing wrong, what should be done and why.

For example: Your child is crying because he/she cannot have a piece of candy. Go to your child and say, "William, you are screaming. You need to calm down and talk about your anger in an appropriate manner."

11. Write a contract with your child.

For example: I, William, will not throw temper tantrums for five days in a row. When I accomplish this, I can stay up late on Saturday night.

The contract should be written within the ability level of your child and should focus on only one behavior at a time. (See Appendix for an example of a Behavior Contract.)

12. Make sure that your child sees the relationship between his/her behavior and the consequences which follow (e.g., others avoiding your child, losing friends, not being able to participate in activities, property is damaged, feelings getting hurt, etc.).

13. Teach your child how to deal with his/her feelings in a socially acceptable manner (e.g., compromising, walking away from the situation, talking with an adult, problem-solving, etc.).

14. Help your child choose activities that do not cause anger, frustration, anxiety, etc.

15. Help your child identify when he/she is getting upset so something can be done to calm down (e.g., walk away, talk about feelings in a socially acceptable way, seek help from an adult, etc.).

16. Ignore your child's temper tantrums. Do not let your child have his/her way when crying.

17. Be consistent. Try to deal with your child and the behavior in a manner that is as fair as possible.

18. Walk away from your child when he/she throws temper tantrums.

19. Carefully consider your child's age and maturity level before expecting him/her to not throw temper tantrums.

20. Decide on one consequence for throwing a temper tantrum (e.g., sitting in a chair for 15 minutes, standing in the corner, going to his/her room, etc.). Make certain that you always maintain consistency in delivering the consequence.

21. Tape record your child when he/she throws a temper tantrum, let him/her listen to the tape, and discuss the reaction to the tape.

22. Show your child how to control angry feelings when things do not go his/her way (e.g., count to 10, say the alphabet, etc.).

23. Immediately remove your child from the attention of others when throwing a temper tantrum.

24. Make certain you do not "give in" to your child's temper tantrums because others are present. Maintain consistency at all times.

25. Remind your child of the consequences of throwing a temper tantrum before going into a grocery store, shopping mall, friend's house, etc.

26. Make certain that your child does not go to another adult after you have said "no."

27. After telling your child that he/she cannot do or have something, explain the reason.

28. Offer another suggestion to your child after you have said "no" to something (e.g., if your child wants to spend the night at someone else's house and cannot do that, suggest that your child have the friend come to your house; if your child wants a new toy but cannot get one, suggest getting it for a birthday or earning it for good behavior; etc.).

29. Be consistent in expecting your child to ask for things and react to disappointment without throwing a temper tantrum. Do not "give in" one time and expect appropriate behavior the next time.

30. Make certain your child knows beforehand what to expect in various situations (e.g., how much money to spend at the store, how long your child can visit a friend, when to come home, etc.).

31. If your child throws a temper tantrum about such things as not getting to go to a movie or not getting a new toy, have him/her earn such items/activities for appropriate behavior. Do not "give in" to your child if he/she is throwing a temper tantrum.

32. Separate your child from peers who throw temper tantrums when they do not get their own way.

33. Make certain that baby-sitters, grandparents, teachers, etc., understand the importance of maintaining consistency in discipline with your child.

34. Encourage your child to use problem-solving skills: (a) identify the problem, (b) identify goals and objectives, (c) develop strategies, (d) develop a plan for action, and (e) carry out the plan.

35. Teach your child alternative ways to communicate unhappiness (e.g., talking about a problem, asking for help, etc.).

36. Reduce the emphasis on competition. Repeated failure may cause your child to throw temper tantrums.

37. Provide your child with alternative activities, games, etc., in case some activities prove upsetting.

38. Give your child additional responsibilities (e.g., chores, errands, privileges, etc.) so that there will be alternative activities if your child does not get to do what he/she wants.

39. Discourage your child from engaging in those activities which cause unhappiness.

40. Avoid those situations which are likely to stimulate your child's temper tantrums (e.g., highly competitive activities, extreme disappointment, quarreling with brothers and sisters, etc.).

41. Intervene early when your child begins to get upset in order to prevent a tantrum from getting out of control (e.g., take your child out of the store, leave the checkout line, etc.).

A Reminder: Your child will stop throwing temper tantrums in order to get his/her own way if you do not "give in" to the tantrums.

1. Talk to your family doctor concerning your child's eating habits.

2. Monitor at all times the amount of food your child eats.

3. Encourage your child to eat fruit for snacks.

4. Do not allow your child to serve himself/herself.

5. Reward your child for eating an appropriate amount of food. Possible rewards include verbal praise (e.g., "I'm proud of you for not eating all of the cookies."), a kiss on the cheek, a hug, having a friend over to play, staying up late, watching a favorite TV show, and playing a game with a parent. (See Appendix for Reward Menu.)

6. If there are other children or adolescents in the home, reward them for not eating too much.

7. Do not leave food where your child can get to it.

8. Make sure that you have good eating habits in order to set an example for your child.

9. Show your child how to take and eat appropriate amounts of food.

10. Write a contract with your child.

For example: I, William, will not eat between meals this week. When I accomplish this, I can go roller skating Saturday afternoon.

The contract should be written within the ability level of your child and should focus on only one behavior at a time. (See Appendix for an example of a Behavior Contract.)

11. Do not direct a lot of attention toward your child's eating habits. If you do, your child may eat too much in order to get your attention.

12. Keep healthy snacks around the house (e.g., fruit, vegetables, Fun Fruits, granola bars, etc.) rather than candy, cookies, ice cream, etc.

13. Talk with a professional before putting your child on any eating program.

14. Make lower-calorie snacks available for your child (e.g., vanilla wafers, graham crackers, frozen yogurt, etc.).

15. Plan menus using lower-calorie foods for your family (e.g., chicken, fish, ground turkey) rather than higher-calorie foods (e.g., ground beef, steak, pork, etc.).

16. Encourage your child to take sack lunches rather than buy school lunches.

17. Make baby-sitters, grandparents, people whose homes your child visits, etc., aware of your child's eating habits and the amount of food, snacks, etc., you allow your child to have.

18. Send "special" snacks to school for your child on days of birthday parties, field trips, holiday parties, field days, etc. "Special" snacks may include yogurt-covered raisins, pretzels, fruit, sugarless candy, etc.

19. Let your child help you plan a weekly menu for the family. Encourage your child to include all of the food groups, pay attention to calories, etc., when planning.

20. Have your child go to the grocery store with you in order to look at labels and decide which products offer the most nutritional value.

21. Develop good eating habits when your child is young.

22. Do not allow eating in front of the TV.

23. Make certain your child eats all meals and snacks at the kitchen or dining room table.

24. Maintain consistency in times when meals and snacks are served (e.g., breakfast at 8:00 a.m., lunch at noon, snack time after nap time or school, dinner at 6:00 p.m., bedtime snack at 8:30 p.m.). Follow the same schedule as often as possible.

25. Encourage your child to become involved in extra activities (e.g., sports, dancing, crafts, etc.).

26. Remove fattening snacks from your home (e.g., fruits canned in heavy syrup, glazed fruits, commercial cakes, cookies, pies, candy, ice cream, soda, potato and corn chips, salted peanuts, etc.).

27. Prepare healthy/low calorie snacks for your family for between meals or in the evening (e.g., sliced apples, pear slices, orange slices, carrot sticks, celery sticks, etc.).

28. Do not put too much emphasis on food, being overweight, eating too much, etc. Your child may learn to not feel good about himself/herself, stop eating altogether, etc.

A Reminder: Your physician will be able to provide you with nutritional information, calorie-intake guidelines, general health requirements, etc. More food than what is required for good health is unnecessary.

76 Is a bad loser

1. Establish rules for playing games (e.g., share materials, take turns, follow game rules, problem-solve, talk nicely, etc.). These rules should be consistent and followed by everyone in the home. Talk about the rules often.

2. Reward your child for following the rules. Possible rewards include verbal praise (e.g., "I'm proud of you for not getting angry when you lost the game!"), a kiss on the cheek, a hug, having a friend over to play, staying up late, watching a favorite TV show, and playing a game with a parent. (See Appendix for Reward Menu.)

3. If there are other children or adolescents in the home, reward them for sharing, taking turns, following the rules, being a good loser, etc.

4. When your child is a bad loser, explain exactly what he/she is doing wrong, what should have been done and why.

For example: Your child is crying because he/she lost a game. Go to your child and say, "William, you are crying because you lost the game. You need to stop crying or others will not want to play with you."

5. Be a good role model for your child by being a good loser.

6. Limit your child's participation in activities that cause him/her to act like a bad loser.

7. Teach your child appropriate ways in which to deal with anger, frustration, disappointment, etc.

8. Write a contract with your child.

For example: I, William, will not be a poor loser today when I play Monopoly with Kim. When I accomplish this, I can stay up until 11:00 p.m. Friday night.

The contract should be written within the ability level of your child and should focus on only one behavior at a time. (See Appendix for an example of a Behavior Contract.)

9. Immediately remove your child from an activity when he/she begins to behave like a bad loser.

10. Make certain that your child sees the relationship between his/her behavior and the consequences which follow (e.g., being made fun of, being avoided by others, being removed from the activity, etc.).

11. Reduce the emphasis on competition and "winning." Emphasize working together, having fun, making new friends, etc.

12. Supervise your child closely when engaging in competitive activities in order to provide alternative ways in which to behave when losing a game.

13. Allow natural consequences to occur as a result of your child's behavior (e.g., others not wanting to play with him/her, being made fun of by others, etc.).

14. Before your child begins a game or competitive activity, discuss the ways in which your child should behave when losing the game.

15. Before beginning a game or competitive activity, make sure your child knows the rules, is familiar with the game, and will be compatible with the other individuals who will be playing.

16. Be a model for participating for enjoyment rather than always needing to "win" or "beat" someone else.

17. Encourage your child to engage in less competitive activities (e.g., reading, clubs, scouting, student council, etc.).

18. Encourage your child to participate in activities, sports, etc., for self-improvement rather than to "win" or "beat" someone else (e.g., try to improve a batting average or defensive skills rather than being disappointed if the team does not win).

19. Encourage your child to participate in more individualized sports (e.g., aerobics, swimming, track and field, golf, etc.).

20. Encourage your child to play and interact with friends who are not highly competitive.

21. Reduce the emphasis on competition among brothers and sisters in your family. Competitiveness learned in the home will be demonstrated at school and elsewhere.

22. Use natural consequences which will demonstrate to your child that when he/she is overly competitive to the extent of making participation unpleasant, participation will need to be discontinued for awhile (e.g., becoming angry and abusive during a game will result in sitting out for the rest of the game, arguing with officials will result in being thrown out of a game, etc.).

23. Encourage your child to refrain from "one-upmanship" with friends (e.g., when friends talk about a new possession, it may be more desirable to say "You're lucky." or "That's great." rather than "That's nothing, my dad's going to buy me a....").

24. Be consistent. Try to deal with your child and his/her behavior in a fair manner.

25. Carefully consider your child's age before expecting him/her to be a good sport about winning.

26. Show your child how to accept angry feelings when things do not go a certain way (e.g., count to 10, say the alphabet, etc.).

27. Make certain that baby-sitters, grandparents, teachers, etc., understand the importance of maintaining consistency in discipline.

28. Provide your child with alternative activities, games, etc., in case some activities prove upsetting.

29. Discourage your child from engaging in those activities which cause unhappiness.

30. Encourage your child to participate in activities in which winning is not the object of the game (e.g., *Hide and Seek, Kick the Can,* etc.).

31. If your child does not win awards (e.g., a trophy, plaque, certificate, etc.) in competition provide a trophy, plaque or certificate at home for good sportsmanship, improvement, finishing a season, etc.

32. Support your child when losing occurs instead of becoming upset or angry.

33. Before a competitive activity, remind your child of the importance of personal improvement, putting forth the best effort, contributing to team success, etc.

34. Your child needs to understand that participation depends on the ability to deal with losing.

35. Make certain you agree with the emphasis your child's coaches place on winning and losing.

36. If your child needs improvement in particular skill areas in order to be competitive, help him/her improve in those areas with more practice, additional coaching, etc.

37. Make certain your child understands that being a bad loser in competitive activities may result in others not wanting to interact, play or compete with him/her again.

38. Make certain your child understands that if it really bothers him/her to lose, then your child may want to channel that feeling into more effort for practice, self-improvement, etc.

39. Make certain that competitive situations are appropriate for your child's age, maturity, developmental level, etc. It may be that your child is not ready for such activities at this time.

40. Teach your child appropriate ways to react to losing (e.g., compliment your opponent by saying, "Great game." "You really did well." "Good luck next game." etc.).

41. Encourage your child to "play the game in such a manner that it can be played again tomorrow" (e.g., do not behave foolishly or upset your opponent so that he/she will not want to compete against you again).

42. Identify, for your child, someone who is a model for good sportsmanship for your child to imitate in winning, playing the game, and losing.

A Reminder: Stress to your child that winning is not nearly as important as personal integrity and strong character.

77 Yells when angry or told to do something

1. Establish rules for doing what you are told (e.g., listen quietly, do not yell or argue, ask questions if you do not understand, do what you are told, etc.). These rules should be consistent and followed by everyone in the home. Talk about the rules often and reward your child for doing what is expected.

2. Reward your child for handling anger in an appropriate manner. Possible rewards include verbal praise (e.g., "Thank you for not yelling when I told you to take out the trash!"), a kiss on the cheek, a hug, having a friend over to play, staying up late, watching a favorite TV show, and playing a game with a parent. (See Appendix for Reward Menu.)

3. If there are other children or adolescents in the home, reward them for handling their anger in an appropriate manner.

4. Show your child how to handle anger in an appropriate manner (e.g., compromising, walking away from the situation, talking with an adult, problem-solving, etc.).

5. Make sure that you do not yell when you are angry or told to do something. If you do, your child will learn to do the same.

6. When your child yells, explain exactly what he/she is doing wrong, what should be done and why.

For example: You tell your child to feed the dog and he/she starts yelling at you. Get your child's attention and say, "William, you are yelling. You need to stop yelling and feed the dog."

7. Write a contract with your child.

For example: I, William, for one week, will not yell when I do not get my way. When I accomplish this, I can ask a friend to go roller skating on Saturday.

The contract should be written within the ability level of your child and should focus on only one behavior at a time. (See Appendix for an example of a Behavior Contract.)

8. Remain calm if your child yells when he/she is angry or told to do something.

9. Make certain that your child sees the relationship between his/her behavior and the consequences which follow (e.g., others avoiding your child, being removed from activities, not being able to attend special activities, etc.).

10. Allow natural consequences to occur due to your child's yelling when angry or told to do something (e.g., being removed from activities, being avoided by others, etc.).

11. Immediately remove your child from an activity or the attention of others when he/she begins to yell.

12. Deliver directions in a supportive rather than a threatening manner (e.g., "Please take out the trash." rather than "You had better take out the trash or else!").

13. Do not "give in" to your child's yelling. If you do, your child will learn to yell in order to get his/her own way.

14. When possible, walk away until your child can calm down and express his/her feelings in a socially acceptable way.

15. Help your child choose activities that do not cause anger, frustration, anxiety, etc.

16. Help your child identify when he/she is getting angry so steps can be taken to calm down (e.g., walk away, talk about feelings in a socially acceptable way, seek help from an adult, etc.).

17. Do not yell in return when your child yells at you or others.

18. When your child yells in public (e.g., at the grocery store, in the mall, playing with friends, etc.), remove your child from the situation until he/she can demonstrate self-control and refrain from arguing.

19. Be consistent when your child yells. Decide on an appropriate consequence for yelling (e.g., going to his/her room for five minutes) and use the consequence every time your child yells.

20. Encourage your child to express feelings and teach him/her how to talk about feelings in a controlled manner.

21. Make certain you ask people to do things for you in a polite way (e.g., "Would you please get me a drink of water?" "Please water the dog." etc.).

22. Talk to your children in the manner in which you want them to talk to you. Treat them with respect and do not "talk down" to them.

23. Remind your child before going shopping, going to a friend's house, friends come to visit, etc., that he/she should follow directions when they are given, and remind your child of the consequences that follow yelling and becoming angry when told to do something.

24. Make certain that baby-sitters, grandparents, neighbors, etc., understand the importance of maintaining consistency in discipline with your child.

25. Tape record your child yelling and arguing after being told to do something. Let your child listen to the tape, and then discuss the reaction to the tape.

26. Show your child how to accept and deal with angry feelings when things do not go his/her way (e.g., count to 10, say the alphabet, etc.).

27. Make certain you do not "give in" to your child because others are present when he/she is arguing and upset. Maintain consistency at all times.

28. Make certain your child does not go to another adult after you have already given directions or dealt with the situation.

29. After asking your child to do something, explain why it needs to be done and your reason for asking your child to do it.

30. Have your child do those things that need to be done when it is discussed instead of later (e.g., put swimsuits in the car now so that when you go to the pool later this afternoon, they will not be forgotten, etc.).

31. Offer another suggestion to your child after you have said "no" to something (e.g., if your child wants to spend the night at someone else's house and cannot do that, suggest that your child have the friend to your house; if your child wants a new toy but cannot get one, suggest getting it for a birthday present or earning it for good behavior; etc.).

32. Make certain that baby-sitters, grandparents, teachers, etc., understand the importance of maintaining consistency in discipline with your child.

33. Teach your child alternative ways to communicate unhappiness (e.g., talking about a problem, asking for help, etc.).

34. Reduce the emphasis on competition. Repeated failure may cause your child to become upset or cry.

35. Along with a directive, provide an incentive statement when asking your child to do something (e.g., "Since you do such an excellent job of setting the table, would you please set it tonight?" "If you clean your room, you can go to a friend's house to play." etc.).

36. Demonstrate the appropriate way to follow directions (e.g., give your child directions to feed the dog, then you feed the dog with your child).

37. When your child has difficulty following directions in front of others (e.g., at the grocery store, in the mall, playing a game with family members, etc.), remove your child from the situation until he/she can demonstrate self-control and follow directions.

38. In order to help your child follow directions, reduce distractions (e.g., turn off the TV, give directions in a room away from his/her friends, etc.).

39. Establish a certain time each day for your child to take care of responsibilities (e.g., feeding the dog, completing homework, etc.).

40. Sit down with your child and discuss a list of chores he/she would like to do.

41. Make certain that the responsibilities given to your child are appropriate for your child's level of development and ability.

42. Assist your child in performing responsibilities. Gradually require your child to independently assume more responsibilities as he/she demonstrates success.

43. Monitor the behavior of others (e.g., brothers, sisters, friends, etc.) to make certain they are not teasing or otherwise stimulating your child to become upset or angry.

44. Teach your child ways to deal with conflict situations (e.g., talking, reasoning, asking an adult to intervene, walking away, etc.).

45. Look for the warning signs (e.g., arguing, loud voices, etc.) that your child is getting upset or angry and intervene to change the activity.

46. Reinforce your child for demonstrating self-control based on the length of time he/she can be successful. Gradually increase the length of time required for reinforcement as he/she demonstrates success.

47. Prevent frustrating or anxiety-producing situations from occurring (e.g., only give your child chores, responsibilities, etc., on the appropriate ability level).

48. Make necessary adjustments in the environment to prevent your child from experiencing stress, frustration, and anger.

49. Teach your child to verbalize feelings before losing control (e.g., "The work is too hard." "Please leave me alone, you're making me angry." etc.).

50. Maintain a regular routine of chores, meals, bedtime, TV, sports, etc., so your child knows what is expected at all times.

51. Make certain you approach your child with words and phrases that offer support rather than stimulating antagonism, anger, etc. (e.g., "I'll help you make your bed." rather than "If that bed isn't made in 10 minutes, you're not going over to Matt's." "Let me help you get out the mower." rather than "If that grass isn't mowed you can forget about going out this weekend.").

52. Repeat rules and expectations before activities which might result in your child becoming upset or angry (e.g., in the car before going into a store to shop, before entering a movie theater, at home before friends come over to go to a ball game or party, etc.).

53. Be careful to avoid embarrassing your child by giving orders, demands, etc., in front of others.

54. Speak to your child quietly in private to provide reminders about behavior, when to come home, etc.

A Reminder: Always treat your child with respect for his/her feelings. Talk quietly; remain calm; and, when appropriate, privately.

78 Eats junk food between meals

1. Do not allow your child to serve himself/herself between meals.

2. Do not buy junk food. Have fruit and vegetables available for your child's snack between meals.

3. Monitor the amount of food your child eats at all times.

4. Talk with your family doctor concerning your child's eating habits.

5. Put all snacks out of your child's sight and reach.

6. Evaluate meals you serve your child in order to see that your child is getting enough to eat, as well as the correct amounts of nutrients that are needed.

7. Reward your child for not eating junk food between meals. Possible rewards include verbal praise (e.g., "I'm proud of you for choosing an apple for your snack!"), a kiss on the cheek, a hug, having a friend over to play, staying up late, watching a favorite TV show, and playing a game with a parent. (See Appendix for Reward Menu.)

8. If there are other children or adolescents in the home, reward them for not eating junk food between meals.

9. Make sure that you have good eating habits in order to set an example for your child.

10. Write a contract with your child.

For example: I, William, for three days in a row, will choose a healthy snack (e.g., apple, banana, broccoli, etc.) when I am hungry. When I accomplish this, I can have a friend spend the night.

The contract should be written within the ability level of your child and should focus on only one behavior at a time. (See Appendix for an example of a Behavior Contract.)

11. Talk with a professional before putting your child on any eating program.

12. Do not direct a lot of attention toward your child's eating habits. If you do, your child may eat junk food between meals in order to get your attention.

13. Encourage your child to engage in activities (e.g., bike riding, playing with friends, etc.) in order to help occupy time. If your child is busy, he/she will not eat as much between meals.

14. Make lower-calorie snacks available for your child (e.g., vanilla wafers, graham crackers, frozen yogurt, etc.).

15. Make baby-sitters, grandparents, people in whose homes your child visits, etc., aware of your child's eating habits and the amount of food, snacks, etc., that you will allow your child to have.

16. Send "special" snacks to school for your child on days of birthday parties, field trips, holiday parties, field days, etc. "Special" snacks may include yogurt-covered raisins, pretzels, fruit, sugarless candy, etc.

17. Have your child go to the grocery store with you in order to look at labels and decide which products offer the most nutritional value.

18. Make certain your child develops good eating habits at the earliest age.

19. Do not allow eating in front of the TV.

20. Make certain your child eats all meals and snacks at the kitchen or dining room table.

21. Maintain consistency in the times when meals and snacks are served (e.g., breakfast at 8:00 a.m., lunch at noon, snack time after nap time or school, dinner at 6:00 p.m., bedtime snack at 8:30 p.m.). Follow the same schedule as often as possible.

22. Remove fattening snacks from your home (e.g., fruit canned in heavy syrup, glazed fruits, commercial cakes, cookies, pies, candy, ice cream, soda, potato and corn chips, salted peanuts, etc.).

23. Make certain, when your child is visiting in other people's homes, that he/she is not given the types of snacks that are forbidden.

24. Prepare healthy/low calorie snacks for your family to eat between meals or in the evening (e.g., sliced apples, pear slices, orange slices, carrot sticks, celery sticks, etc.).

25. Collect recipes of fun ways to prepare healthy snacks for your child (e.g., peanut butter on apple slices; trail mix using unsalted nuts, raisins, etc.). Bookstores have cookbooks of children's snacks.

26. Encourage your child to eat the entire meal, reducing the need for between-meal snacks.

27. Keep apples, oranges, bananas, etc., out in plain view for your child at all times.

28. Make certain the entire family is eating healthy snacks between meals. You cannot expect your child to refrain from junk food if it is available to others.

29. If you have junk food in your home, use it only as a desert.

A Reminder: Junk food in your house is likely to end up in your child.

79 Curses

1. Talk to your children in the manner in which you want them to talk to you. Treat them with respect and do not curse at them.

2. Make sure that you do not curse. If you curse, your child will learn to do the same.

3. Establish a rule (e.g., no cursing). This rule should be consistent and followed by everyone in the home. Talk about the rule often.

4. Reward your child for not cursing. Possible rewards include verbal praise (e.g., "I'm really proud of you for not cursing when your team lost the game!"), a kiss on the cheek, a hug, having a friend over to play, staying up late, watching a favorite TV show, and playing a game with a parent. (See Appendix for Reward Menu.)

5. If there are other children or adolescents in the home, reward them for not cursing.

6. When your child curses, explain exactly what he/she is doing wrong, what should be done and why.

For example: You hear your child cursing at his sister. Go to your child and say, "William, you are cursing at Kim. You need to use appropriate language when you are angry at someone or you will offend them."

7. Write a contract with your child.

For example: I, William, for one week, will not curse when I get angry at others. When I accomplish this, I can stay up until 11:30 p.m. Saturday night.

The contract should be written within the ability level of your child and should focus on only one behavior at a time. (See Appendix for an example of a Behavior Contract.)

8. Allow natural consequences to occur as a result of your child's cursing (e.g., not being able to participate in special activities, being removed from interacting with others, being avoided by others who do not curse, etc.).

9. Make certain that your child sees the relationship between his/her behavior and the consequences which follow (e.g., being removed from activities).

10. Immediately remove your child from interacting with others when cursing.

11. Teach your child acceptable ways to express anger, frustration, anxiety, etc.

12. Be consistent when your child curses. Decide on an appropriate consequence for cursing (e.g., sitting in a certain chair for five minutes) and use it every time your child curses.

13. Separate your child from those individuals who encourage or stimulate him/her to curse.

14. Do not appear shocked or surprised when your child curses. Deal with the behavior in a calm and deliberate manner.

15. Make certain that you and other adults with whom your child associates do not use inappropriate language.

16. Separate your child from the peer(s) who stimulate inappropriate language.

17. Inform teachers, baby sitters, etc., of your child's use of inappropriate language in order to make certain they follow through with discipline.

18. Remind your child of the consequences of swearing before going to a friend's house, in a store, to school, etc.

19. Separate your child from children who curse.

20. Avoid those situations which are likely to stimulate your child's swearing (e.g., highly competitive activities, extreme disappointment, quarreling with brothers and/or sisters, etc.).

21. Teach your child to recognize when he/she is becoming upset or angry and ways, other than cursing, to express feelings.

22. Closely supervise your child in order to monitor his/her behavior at all times.

23. Discuss your child's behavior in private, rather than in front of others.

24. Do not allow your child to participate in a situation unless he/she can demonstrate self-control.

25. Provide your child with a place to go when he/she gets upset or angry (e.g., a quiet chair, a room, a corner, etc.).

26. Teach your child what to do when becoming upset or angry (e.g., count to 10, say the alphabet, leave the room, etc.).

27. Make certain you deal in a socially acceptable way with situations that may be upsetting.

28. Teach your child to verbalize feelings before losing control (e.g., "The work is too hard." "Please leave me alone, you're making me angry." etc.).

29. Monitor the behavior of others (e.g., brothers, sisters, friends, etc.) to make certain they are not teasing or otherwise stimulating your child to become upset or angry.

30. Teach your child ways to deal with conflict situations (e.g., talking, reasoning, asking an adult to intervene, walking away, etc.).

31. Look for the warning signs (e.g., arguing, loud voices, etc.) that your child is getting upset or angry and intervene to change the activity.

32. Make certain you approach your child with words and phrases that offer support rather than stimulating antagonism, anger, etc. (e.g., "I'll help you make your bed." rather than "If that bed isn't made in 10 minutes you're not going over to Matt's." "Let me help you get the mower out." rather than "If that grass isn't mowed, you can forget about going out this weekend.").

33. Repeat rules and expectations before activities occur which might result in your child becoming upset or angry (e.g., in the car before going into a store to shop, before entering a movie theater, at home before friends come over to go to a ball game or party, etc.).

34. Make certain to intervene early when your child does curse, before cursing becomes an established part of your child's speech.

35. Make certain your child knows the consequences of cursing that will be delivered in your home (e.g., loss of privileges, loss of opportunity to associate with those with whom he curses, loss of freedom to be left alone with friends, etc.).

36. Make certain your child understands that other parents will not stand for cursing, your child should expect to be embarrassed, may be prevented from interacting with others whose parents will not tolerate cursing, may be prevented from entering friends' homes, etc.

37. Reduce the emphasis on competition. Highly competitive activities may cause your child to become upset, angry, frustrated, etc., and curse.

38. Do not inadvertently reinforce your child's cursing by laughing, smiling, ignoring, etc.

39. Prevent your child from becoming frustrated to the extent that cursing results. Intervene to help your child in those situations which may result in frustration and cursing.

40. If highly competitive activities contribute to your child's cursing, either reduce your child's involvement in those activities, or make certain your child understands that cursing will result in loss of opportunities to participate in those activities.

41. Point out to your child those successful persons you know who actively participate in a variety of activities without cursing.

42. Make certain your child is taught those words which are socially appropriate to use in place of cursing (e.g., "dang," "shoot," "darn," "heck," etc.).

43. If the language in movies contributes to your child's cursing, opportunities to view those movies may need to be restricted.

44. Cursing is not a behavior that should be ignored. By ignoring your child's cursing, you send the message that it is acceptable.

A Reminder: Your child will repeat what he/she hears.

80 Does not work out problems with others

1. Establish rules for getting along with others (e.g., be friendly, play cooperatively, share, problem-solve, talk in an acceptable manner, do not fight). These rules should be consistent and followed by everyone in the home. Talk about the rules often.

2. Reward your child for working out problems with others. Possible rewards include verbal praise (e.g., ''I'm so proud of you for compromising with Lori when you were deciding which game to play!''), a kiss on the cheek, a hug, having a friend over to play, staying up late, watching a favorite TV show, and playing a game with a parent. (See Appendix for Reward Menu.)

3. If there are other children or adolescents in the home, reward them for working out problems with others.

4. Carefully consider your child's age and experience in interacting and working out problems with others before expecting him/her to work out problems with others in an acceptable manner.

5. Show your child how to work out problems with others in an acceptable manner (e.g., by playing cooperatively, sharing, talking in an acceptable manner, seeking help from an adult, etc.).

6. Make sure that you work out problems with others in an acceptable manner. If you resort to fighting, crying, arguing, threatening, etc., your child will learn to do the same.

7. When your child has difficulty working out problems with others, explain exactly what he/she is doing wrong, what should be done and why.

For example: You overhear your child threatening a friend who does not want to share. Go to your child and say, ''William, you are threatening Pat. You need to stop threatening Pat. If he does not want to share with you, that is his choice. If you do not like it, then you need to stop playing with him and find someone else with whom to play. Others will not want to play with you if you threaten them.''

8. Write a contract with your child.

For example: I, William, will play cooperatively with others. When I accomplish this, I can pick out a video to watch tonight.

The contract should be written within the ability level of your child and should focus on only one behavior at a time. (See Appendix for an example of a Behavior Contract.)

9. Make certain that your child sees the relationship between his/her behavior and the consequences which follow (e.g., others not wanting to play, being removed from interacting with others, etc.).

10. Immediately remove your child from interacting with others when there is difficulty working out problems.

11. Have your child watch an older brother and/or sister work out problems with others. This will help your child learn to work out problems with others in an acceptable manner.

12. Do not allow interaction with other individuals with whom your child has difficulty working out problems.

13. Supervise your child's interactions with others in order to stop inappropriate behavior and model appropriate behavior.

14. When your child has had difficulty working out a problem with someone, sit down with your child and talk about the alternative things that could have been done to help solve the problem.

15. Talk with your child about appropriate ways to deal with anger and frustration (e.g., compromising, talking about the problem with an adult, etc.).

16. Do not emphasize competition. Competitive activities may cause your child to have difficulty working out problems with others.

17. Arrange for your child to be involved in many activities with others in order to help him/her learn the skills necessary to interact and successfully work out problems.

18. Show your child how to ask permission to use something and how to react whether he/she is told "yes" or "no."

19. Teach your child to avoid becoming involved in conflicts with others (e.g., by moving away from the situation, changing his/her behavior, etc.).

20. Do not allow your child to engage in stimulating activities which cause him/her to have trouble getting along with friends.

21. Do not make your child play with a certain child or group of children. Allow your child to pick his/her own friends.

22. Be consistent. Try to deal with your child and the behavior in a manner that is as consistent as possible (e.g., react in the same manner each time, use the same consequences, etc.).

23. Provide your child with a quiet place to go when becoming upset or angry with a friend or friends.

24. Help your child choose activities to play when friends are over that do not cause him/her to become angry, frustrated, anxious, etc.

25. Arrange for your child to be involved in many activities with other children in order to help him/her learn the skills necessary to interact appropriately with others.

26. Make sure your child understands that the privilege of having a friend over or going to a friend's house will be taken away if he/she is not nice to friends.

27. Get to know your child's friends and their parents and maintain open communications with them.

28. Encourage your child to participate in supervised extracurricular activities at school (e.g., Chess Club, Math Club, team sports, etc.) in order to help learn appropriate interaction skills.

29. Discourage your child from engaging in those activities which cause unhappiness.

30. Allow natural consequences to occur due to your child's inappropriate behavior (e.g., fighting with friends results in not being able to have them over, visit in their homes, play with them outside of the home, etc.).

31. Inform the parents of your child's friends of the tendency of your child to have trouble getting along with friends in order that they may increase supervision when your child is at their houses.

32. Ask your child's teacher to have your child participate in group activities, act as a peer tutor, etc., in order to help learn interaction skills with others.

33. Be consistent in expecting your child to work out problems with friends and react to disappointment without fighting, arguing, threatening, etc. Do not allow your child to fight, argue, threaten, etc., one time and expect appropriate behavior the next time.

34. Make certain there is consistency in the types of consequences delivered when your child cries because he/she does not get his/her own way (e.g., going to a room, sitting in a chair, etc.).

35. Make certain that baby sitters, grandparents, teachers, etc., understand the importance of maintaining consistency in discipline with your child.

36. Make certain your child understands that things may be earned (for appropriate behavior) that he/she sees that others have, but you will not "give in" to those things when your child does not behave appropriately with friends.

37. Encourage your child to use problem-solving skills: (a) identify the problem, (b) identify goals and objectives, (c) develop strategies, (d) develop a plan for action, and (e) carry out the plan.

38. Teach your child alternative ways to communicate unhappiness (e.g., talking about a problem, asking for help, etc.).

39. Provide your child with alternative activities, games, etc., in which to engage in case some activities prove upsetting.

40. Avoid those situations which are likely to stimulate your child's problem of getting along with friends (e.g., highly competitive activities, extreme disappointments, quarreling with brothers and sisters, etc.).

41. Intervene early when your child begins to have problems with friends in order to prevent the problems from getting out of control (e.g., send your child to a room, send friends home, etc.).

42. Teach your child to recognize when he/she is becoming upset or angry and ways in which to deal with those feelings.

43. Reinforce your child for demonstrating self-control based on the length of time he/she can be successful. Gradually increase the length of time required for reinforcement as your child demonstrates success.

44. Teach your child to verbalize feelings before losing control (e.g., ''You're making me angry.'' ''Please put down my toy before I get angry.'' etc.).

45. Monitor the behavior of others (e.g., brothers, sisters, friends, etc.) to make certain they are not teasing or otherwise stimulating your child to become upset or angry.

46. Look for the warning signs (e.g., arguing, loud voices, etc.) that your child is getting upset or angry and intervene to change the activity.

47. Teach your child how to resolve conflict situations (e.g., do not get angry, compromise by letting a friend have the first turn, let a friend have his/her way if it is that important, ask an adult for assistance, discuss alternative ways to do things, etc.).

48. Reduce the emphasis on competition. Highly competitive activities may result in frustration, failure, etc., which may lead to inappropriate behavior (e.g., fighting, crying, arguing, threatening, etc.).

49. Make certain others are not taking advantage of your child's age, size, etc. Provide supervision to determine that the behavior of others is appropriate and not the cause of your child's inappropriate behavior.

A Reminder: Learning to work out problems with others is a chore for all of us. It is especially difficult for children and requires years of practice.

81 Is afraid of the doctor or dentist

1. Take your child to see the doctor, dentist, etc., before the actual appointment in order to let your child look around and become familiar with the surroundings.

2. Encourage your child to talk about concerns, and answer questions with complete honesty (e.g., if your child asks if a shot hurts, be honest and say that it will sting, but it won't hurt for long).

3. Talk with your child about the reasons we go to the doctor, dentist, etc.

4. Choose a doctor, dentist, etc., who works well with children and makes them feel comfortable.

5. Do not talk negatively about doctors, dentists, etc., around your child. When your child is within hearing distance, say only positive things about doctors, dentists, etc.

6. Let your child go with you when you visit the doctor, dentist, etc.

7. Stay with your child at all times when visiting the doctor, dentist, etc., in order to provide a feeling of security.

8. Do not "make fun" when your child cries about going to the doctor, dentist, etc.

9. Discuss your child's fears with the doctor, dentist, etc., before taking your child to the doctor, dentist, etc.

10. Read books about visiting the doctor, dentist, etc., in order to help your child feel more comfortable.

11. Write a contract with your child.

For example: I, William, will go to the dentist's office on Wednesday. When I accomplish this, I can earn a new toy.

The contract should be written within the ability level of your child and should focus on only one behavior at a time. (See Appendix for an example of a Behavior Contract.)

12. Reward your child for going to the doctor's office, dentist's office, etc. Possible rewards include verbal praise (e.g., "I'm so proud of you for going to the doctor today. You were very brave!"), a kiss on the cheek, a hug, having a friend over to play, staying up late, watching a favorite TV show, and playing a game with a parent. (See Appendix for Reward Menu.)

13. If there are other children or adolescents in the home, reward them for going to the doctor's office, dentist's office, etc.

14. Allow your child plenty of time to prepare himself/herself for going to the doctor, dentist, etc. Make appointments several weeks in advance, allow your child to select the appointment time, etc.

15. Allow your child to invite a friend to go to see the doctor, dentist, etc.

16. Take a few of your child's favorite toys and books to the doctor's office, dentist's office, etc., and allow your child to play with them while waiting.

17. Take your child to the dentist, doctor, etc. a few days before the appointment to meet the doctor, nurses, etc.

18. Make an appointment for yourself or a brother/sister on the same day your child is to visit the doctor, dentist, etc.

19. Make certain your child feels comfortable with the dentist, doctor, etc. After an appointment, ask your child if he/she felt comfortable, liked the dentist or doctor, etc.

20. Do not convey your own personal fears or dislikes to your child (e.g., fear of going to the doctor, not enjoying going to the dentist, etc.).

21. Provide your child with rewards or treats for visiting the doctor or dentist.

22. Remind your child before visiting the doctor or dentist that there are rewards and treats from the doctor or dentist after the visit.

23. Make your doctor or dentist aware of your child's fear in order that the doctor or dentist will help make your child feel comfortable.

24. Find a doctor or dentist who specializes in children's services.

25. Stay in the room with your child when the doctor or dentist is in the room.

26. Choose a doctor or dentist who is known for a good "bedside manner."

A Reminder: It may be necessary to find another doctor or dentist your child will be comfortable visiting.

82 Gets upset when bumped or touched

1. Establish rules for making physical contact with others (e.g., be friendly, move away if you feel uncomfortable, talk in an acceptable manner, etc.). These rules should be consistent and followed by everyone in the home. Talk about the rules often and reward your child for following the rules.

2. Reward your child for reacting appropriately when bumped, touched, brushed against, etc. Possible rewards include verbal praise (e.g., "I'm proud of you for walking away when Lisa bumped against you!"), a kiss on the cheek, a hug, having a friend over to play, staying up late, watching a favorite TV show, and playing a game with a parent. (See Appendix for Reward Menu.)

3. If there are other children or adolescents in the home, reward them for reacting appropriately when bumped, touched, brushed against, etc.

4. Teach your child to recognize the difference between accidental physical contact and intentional physical contact.

5. Show your child how to react appropriately when bumped, touched, brushed against, etc.

6. When your child becomes upset when bumped, touched, brushed against, etc., explain exactly what he/she is doing wrong, what should be done and why.

For example: Your child starts yelling when his sister brushes against him. Go to you child and say, "William, you need to stop yelling. Kim accidentally brushed against you and you are yelling at her. If you do not like her touching you, then you need to move away from her. Yelling at her will hurt her feelings and she will not want to play with you."

7. Write a contract with your child.

For example: I, William, for five days in a row, will not get upset when someone bumps, touches, and/or brushes against me. When I accomplish this, I can have a friend spend the night.

The contract should be written within the ability level of your child should focus on only one behavior at a time. (See Appendix for an example of a Behavior Contract.)

8. Encourage your child to tell you when he/she feels uncomfortable being around others. Do not "force" your child to be around those individuals who cause him/her to feel uncomfortable.

9. Make certain that your child sees the relationship between the behavior and the consequences which follow (e.g., others avoiding your child, being removed from activities, not being able to participate in special activities, etc.).

10. Allow natural consequences to occur as a result of your child's becoming upset when bumped, touched, brushed against, etc., (e.g., not being able to participate in special activities, being avoided by others, etc.).

11. Immediately remove your child from interacting with others when he/she becomes upset over being bumped, touched, brushed against, etc.

12. Make sure that you do not get upset when you are bumped, touched, brushed against, etc.

13. Make sure that others are, in fact, accidentally bumping, touching or brushing against your child and not doing so purposely.

14. Have your child sit near you or another adult in order to reduce the frequency of being bumped, touched, brushed against, etc.

15. Have your child walk beside you, hold your hand, ride in the shopping cart, etc., to avoid others bumping, touching or brushing against him/her.

16. Have your child avoid crowded areas. Gradually allow your child access to crowded areas as he/she develops the ability to deal with being bumped, touched, brushed against, etc., and learns to accept exchanges with other people in an appropriate manner.

17. Call attention to those times when your child bumps, touches, or brushes against other people. Point out and help your child realize that those physical exchanges were typical and accidental.

18. Have your child practice appropriate verbal exchanges which should be made when typical physical exchanges take place (e.g., ''Excuse me.'' ''I'm sorry.'' etc.).

19. Teach your child to avoid being bumped, touched, or brushed against by giving others room to pass, taking turns, watching the movement of others around, etc.

20. Increase supervision of your child when he/she plays with others.

21. Teach your child to verbalize feelings when someone has bumped, touched, or brushed against him/her (e.g., ''Would you please move over a little?'' ''Can you allow a little more room for me?'' etc.).

22. Provide your child with a place to go when upset or angry (e.g., a quiet chair, a room, a corner, etc.).

23. Teach your child what to do when he/she becomes upset or angry (e.g., count to 10, say the alphabet, leave the room, etc.).

24. Reinforce your child for demonstrating self-control based on the length of time he/she can be successful. Gradually increase the length of time required for reinforcement as your child demonstrates success.

25. Immediately remove your child from the attention of others when he/she gets upset or angry.

26. Prevent frustrating or anxiety-producing situations from occurring (e.g., avoid overly crowded areas, long lines, etc.).

27. Make necessary adjustments in the environment to prevent your child from experiencing stress, frustration, and anger.

28. Reinforce your child for demonstrating self-control based on the length of time he/she can be successful. Gradually increase the length of time required for reinforcement as your child demonstrates success.

29. Make certain your child understands that being bumped, touched, brushed against, etc., is usually accidental.

30. Encourage your child to determine whether he/she was bumped, touched, brushed against, etc., on purpose, and if not, accept it as unintentional and go on doing what he/she was doing.

A Reminder: Be sensitive to your child's size and age when in situations where he/she is bumped, touched, or brushed against.

83 Has inappropriate table manners

1. Establish rules for eating at the table (e.g., keep elbows off the table, chew with your mouth closed, do not talk with food in your mouth, ask to be excused, keep feet under the table, etc.). These rules should be consistent and followed by everyone.

2. Reward your child for demonstrating appropriate manners at the table. Possible rewards include verbal praise (e.g., "Your manners were excellent at dinner!" "I like the way you chewed your food with your mouth closed." etc.), a kiss on the cheek, a hug, having a friend over to play, staying up late, watching a favorite TV show, and playing a game with a parent. (See Appendix for a Reward Menu.)

3. If there are other children or adolescents in the home, reward them for demonstrating appropriate manners at the table.

4. Carefully consider your child's age before expecting certain table manners out of him/her.

5. Demonstrate appropriate table manners while you are eating.

6. When your child does not demonstrate an appropriate manner, explain exactly what he/she did wrong, what should be done and why.

For example: Your child is chewing with his mouth open. Tell your child that he/she is chewing with his/her mouth open and that he/she needs to stop so everyone else can enjoy the meal.

7. Write a contract with your child.

For example: I, William, for three nights in a row, will chew with my mouth closed. When I accomplish this, I can choose a movie at the video store to watch on Friday night.

The contract should be written within the ability level of your child and should focus on only one behavior at a time. (See Appendix for an example of a Behavioral Contract.)

8. Allow natural consequences to occur due to your child's inability to demonstrate appropriate behavior (e.g., your child may not get to go to a restaurant because of inappropriate table manners.)

9. Make certain that your child sees the relationship between his/her behavior and the consequences which follow (e.g., others refusing to eat with your child).

10. Talk about inappropriate manners often, especially before going out in public.

11. Remove your child from a public place, such as the movies or a restaurant, until he/she can demonstrate appropriate manners.

12. Be consistent about expecting certain manners from your child. Do not laugh when your child burps one time and then scold the next time. This gives your child "mixed messages."

13. Avoid engaging your child in excessively long dinners that are not geared for children (e.g., adult dinner parties, eating at a restaurant geared for adults, etc.).

14. Do not allow your child to bring to public places toys and materials which contribute to "bad" manners. Allow toys and materials which will promote desirable manners (e.g., books, paper and pencils, children's eating utensils, etc.).

15. Provide your child with a predetermined signal when he/she begins to display inappropriate manners.

16. Do not criticize. When correcting your child, be honest yet supportive. Never cause your child to feel bad about himself/herself.

17. Make your child aware of the number of times he/she behaved inappropriately (e.g., "You burped four times during dinner." "You had to be asked three times to get your elbows off the table." etc.).

18. Immediately remove your child from the situation when beginning to behave inappropriately. Do not allow your child to return unless he/she can demonstrate acceptable behavior.

19. Always require your child to use appropriate manners at home and in public.

20. Make certain your child knows that he/she often embarrasses others when using inappropriate table manners.

21. Do not encourage your child to be silly and to entertain others, then scold your child when he/she begins to act too silly and/or acts silly at a time you find inappropriate.

22. Do not act shocked if your child is using inappropriate table manners, simply remind him/her of table rules and continue with the meal. If he/she does not respond by using appropriate manners, remove your child from the situation.

23. Do not inadvertently encourage your child's inappropriate behavior by laughing, encouraging, etc.

24. Talk to your child before going into a public place and explain the importance of demonstrating appropriate manners.

25. Make certain that baby-sitters, grandparents, people visiting in your home, etc., are aware of table rules and the consequences for not following them. Make certain they are aware of the importance of maintaining consistency in the discipline of your child.

26. Practice using appropriate manners at all times.

27. Post a list of table manners in a place where your child can review them daily. (See Appendix for Sample List.)

28. Take a few minutes at each meal to teach appropriate table manners (using utensils; chewing food; using a napkin; passing the salt, pepper, bread, butter; etc.).

29. Set aside ''special'' evenings when the family dresses for dinner and ''practices'' the very best table manners. (Note: This does not mean that good table manners are ignored at regular meals.)

30. Make sure your child is not hurried through a meal.

31. Check with your child's school to determine the circumstances for eating lunch. More appropriate supervision, time, etc., may be required of your child and his/her friends at lunch.

A Reminder: If your child is to learn to use good table manners, everyone in the family will need to practice good table manners at all times.

84 Does what others do even if it is wrong

1. Establish rules for appropriate behavior (e.g., act responsible, respect others' property, respect the rights of others, etc.). Talk about the rules often and reward your child for following the rules. The rules should be consistent and followed by everyone in the family.

2. Reward your child for acting responsible and respecting others. Possible rewards include verbal praise (e.g., "I'm very proud of you for not throwing rocks with your friends!"), a kiss on the cheek, a hug, having a friend over to play, staying up late, watching a favorite TV show, and playing a game with a parent. (See Appendix for Reward Menu.)

3. If there are other children or adolescents in the home, reward them for being responsible.

4. Carefully consider your child's age and experience when giving responsibilities and/or expecting things of your child.

5. When your child does not act responsibly, explain exactly what he/she did wrong, what should have been done and why.

For example: You see your child and some other children throwing rocks at cars. Go to your child and explain that he/she should not be throwing rocks because he/she could destroy others' property or hurt someone.

6. Write a contract with your child.

For example: I, William, will not take things that belong to others for five days in a row. When I accomplish this, I can buy a model.

The contract should be written within the ability level of your child and should focus on only one behavior at a time. (See Appendix for an example of a Behavior Contract.)

7. Make certain that your child sees the relationship between his/her behavior and the consequences which follow (e.g., breaking car windows will result in having to pay for the window to be replaced).

8. Set an example for your child by acting responsibly and showing respect for others at all times.

9. Use a consequence related to your child's inappropriate behavior (e.g., your child will not be allowed to play with those friends with whom he/she was throwing rocks).

10. Know where your child is at all times.

11. Allow your child to participate in activities which will teach responsibility and respect for others (e.g., Boy Scouts, Girl Scouts, 4-H, swimming, tennis, etc.).

12. Do not allow your child unsupervised freedom until your child has demonstrated responsibility when interacting with friends.

13. Get to know your child's friends and their parents and maintain open communications with them.

14. Encourage your child to have friends over to your house in order to provide supervision in activities such as parties, studying, etc.

15. Encourage your child to participate in extra-curricular activities at school (e.g., Chess Club, Math Club, team sports, etc.).

16. Discourage your child from participating in activities where others engage in inappropriate behaviors in order to win, have a good time, etc.

17. Make certain there will be adult supervision when your child visits at a friend's house.

18. Attempt to have an open and honest relationship with your child. Encourage your child to tell the truth and do not use threats (e.g., "You had better tell the truth, or else.") to make your child tell the truth.

19. Separate your child from those children and adolescents who encourage your child to behave inappropriately.

20. Encourage your child to become involved in activities which do not include the children by whom your child is easily influenced (e.g., scouts, swim team, etc.).

21. Maintain trust and confidentiality with your child at all times.

22. Allow your child to pick his/her own friends and play with them as long as your child can be friendly, polite, and cooperative.

23. Talk with your child about individual differences and discuss strengths and weaknesses of individuals your child knows. Stress that your child does not have to do the same things everyone else does.

24. Find a peer to play with your child who would be a good influence (e.g., someone younger, older, same sex, opposite sex, etc.).

25. Make certain your child is well aware of the consequences which follow behaviors constituting vandalism, destruction of property, stealing, drug abuse, etc. (e.g., arrest, detention, trial, incarceration, etc.).

26. Make certain that teachers, baby-sitters, etc., know that your child is easily influenced by others.

27. Increase supervision of your child (e.g., direct supervision by you, another adult, an older adolescent, etc.).

28. Remove your child from others who may be contributing to his/her inappropriate behavior (e.g., take your child to a different swimming pool or skating rink, find other community activities, find new friends, etc.).

29. Make certain your child corrects any inappropriate behaviors (e.g., stolen or destroyed items must be paid for, apologies must be given, etc.).

30. Make certain your child understands that friends cannot ''make'' him/her do something he/she does not want to do.

A Reminder: The kinds of friends with whom your child associates will greatly determine your child's behavior.

1. Establish rules for watching TV (e.g., only one hour of TV a day, homework needs to be completed before TV is watched, daily chores need to be completed before TV is watched, etc.). These rules should be consistent and followed by everyone in the home. Talk about the rules often.

2. Reward your child for following the rules for watching TV. Possible rewards include verbal praise (e.g., "I'm very proud of you for playing outside instead of watching TV." "Thank you for finishing your homework before you watch TV." etc.), a kiss on the cheek, a hug, having a friend over to play, staying up late, watching a favorite show, and playing a game with a parent. (See Appendix for Reward Menu.)

3. If there are other children or adolescents in the home, reward them for following the rules for watching TV.

4. When your child watches too much TV, explain exactly what he/she did wrong, what should have been done and why.

For example: It is time for your child to set the table and he/she is watching TV. Go to your child and say that he/she is watching TV and should be setting the table because it is time to eat dinner.

5. Write a contract with your child.

For example: I, William, will watch two or less hours of TV each day for four days in a row. When I accomplish this, I can have a friend over to spend the night.

The contract should be written within the ability level of your child and should focus on only one behavior at a time. (See Appendix for an example of a Behavior Contract.)

6. Help your child prioritize favorite TV programs in order to watch only one or two favorite programs each day.

7. Attempt to interest your child in activities other than watching TV (e.g., hobbies, extra-curricular activities at school, playing with friends, etc.).

8. Have your child earn time to watch TV (e.g., after completing homework and performing chores, then your child may watch TV).

9. Do not accidentally reinforce your child for watching TV by serving snacks, meals, etc., in front of the TV.

10. Do not watch too much TV. View only the amount you expect your child to watch each day.

11. Allow natural consequences to occur as a result of your child's watching too much TV (e.g., low grades on homework, not receiving an allowance because chores were not performed, etc.).

12. If your child is going to watch TV, encourage viewing educational shows by setting the channel to an educational station or renting an educational video tape.

13. Do not reinforce your child's less desirable TV habits by having every movie and music video channel that cable offers.

14. Identify one, two or three programs a day which you will permit your child to watch; do not allow any additional TV time.

15. List the TV programs your child is allowed to watch and post it by the TV for baby-sitters, relatives, etc., when you may not be home.

16. Turn the TV off after your child watches designated programs.

17. Set aside time each evening when the TV will be turned off for the family to read, talk, etc.

18. Communicate with parents of friends your child visits in order to encourage them to limit your child's television viewing in their homes.

19. Do not provide the TV as a baby-sitter for your child. Provide games, Play Dough, coloring books, etc., for entertainment.

20. Rent movies which are appropriate to your child's age level or educational in nature for your child's TV viewing (e.g., classic Disney productions, documentaries, historical films, etc.).

A Reminder: For some hours of the day or some days of the week, it may be good for the whole family if the TV is turned off.

86 Does not find things

1. Establish a rule for putting things back where they belong so they can be easily found the next time they are needed. This rule should be consistent and followed by everyone in the home. Talk about the rule often.

2. Reward your child for putting things back where they belong. Possible rewards include verbal praise (e.g., "Thank you for putting your toys in the toy box!"), a kiss on the cheek, a hug, having a friend over to play, staying up late, watching a favorite TV show, and playing a game with a parent. (See Appendix for Reward Menu.)

3. If there are other children or adolescents in the home, reward them for putting things back where they belong.

4. Carefully consider your child's age before expecting your child to put things back where they belong. Help your child put away toys, clothes, etc.

5. Teach your child to put things back where they belong by returning things to their places after you use them.

6. When your child forgets to put things back where they belong, explain exactly what he/she did wrong, what should be done and why.

For example: Your child forgot to put a toy back where it belongs. Go to your child and say that he/she forgot to put away the toy, and that it needs to be put back where it belongs so he/she can find it later.

7. Write a contract with your child.

For example: I, William, for five days in a row, will put my toys back where they belong after I'm finished with them. When I accomplish this, I can watch a favorite TV show.

The contract should be written within the ability level of your child and should focus on only one behavior at a time. (See Appendix for an example of a Behavior Contract.)

8. Along with a directive, provide an incentive statement (e.g., "You may watch TV after you put your clothes back where they belong.").

9. Make certain that your child sees the relationship between his/her behavior and the consequences which follow (e.g., not putting away toys will result in not being able to find them and possibly losing them).

10. Allow natural consequences to occur as a result of your child's failing to put things back where they belong (e.g., not being able to find them, the items being damaged and possibly lost, etc.).

11. Make certain there is a designated place for all items in and around the home.

12. Require your child to put his/her coat, gloves, hat, etc., in a designated place upon entering the home.

13. Set aside time each week for your child to straighten his/her room, clothes, toys, etc.

14. Make a list of your child's most frequently used items and/or materials and have your child make sure that each item and/or material is put in its designated place each day.

15. Identify a place for all members of the household to keep frequently used items (e.g., coats, boots, gloves, hats, keys, pens and pencils, purses, etc.).

16. Set aside time each evening when all family members put away things in their proper places and organize their possessions for the next day (e.g., school clothes, books, lunches, etc.).

17. Have your child put away toys, clothes, etc., before getting out new things to play with or wear.

18. Require your child's room to be neat and organized so there will always be a place to put toys, games, clothes, etc.

19. Make certain to be consistent when expecting your child to pick up toys. Do not leave the house with toys in the yard one time and expect the toys to be picked up the next time.

20. When your child has a friend over, have them pick up toys and games 15 minutes before the friend leaves so he/she can help your child.

21. If your child fails to pick up clothes, games, toys, etc., before going to bed, pick up the toys and take them away from your child for a period of time.

22. Do not expect your child to pick up toys and games that friends failed to put away. Encourage your child's friends to pick up toys and games.

23. Communicate with the parents of your child's friends to make certain that your child helps pick up toys when spending time at a friend's house.

24. Tell baby-sitters or others who are involved with your child that he/she is responsible for picking up and putting away his/her own materials.

25. Do not buy additional toys, games, etc., for your child if he/she is not able to take care of what he/she has.

26. Show your child the proper way to take care of things (e.g., shining shoes, hosing off his/her bike, taking care of dolls, etc.). This will teach your child a sense of responsibility with belongings.

27. Have your child pay for things he/she wants (e.g., a baseball mitt, a new doll, a new pair of jeans, etc.). If the child has spent some of his/her own money on the item, he/she may be more willing to take care of it.

28. Provide your child with shelving, containers, organizers, etc., for personal possessions. Label the storage areas and require your child to keep possessions organized.

29. Limit your child's use of those things he/she is not responsible for putting away, returning, etc.

A Reminder: When everything has a "place" your child will be more likely to put things away. It may be worth taking a Saturday to make a "place" for those things your child usually "can't find."

1. Carefully consider your child's age and experience before giving responsibilities (e.g., dusting furniture, washing dishes, drinking from a glass, setting the table, etc.).

2. Directly supervise your child when he/she is engaged in activities which require care (e.g., pouring milk, setting the table, washing the dishes, passing food at the table, etc.).

3. Establish rules (e.g., walk in the house, use both hands when carrying breakables, etc.). These rules should be consistent and followed by everyone in the home. Talk about the rules often and reward your child for following the rules.

4. Reward your child for being careful. Possible rewards include verbal praise (e.g., "Thank you for walking in the house." "I like it when you pass food with both hands." etc.), a kiss on the cheek, a hug, having a friend over to play, staying up late, watching a favorite TV show, and playing a game with a parent. (See Appendix for Reward Menu.)

5. If there are other children or adolescents in the home, reward them for being careful with breakables.

6. Show your child how to care for breakables. Help your child set the table, dust furniture, wash the dishes, etc., in order to model the correct way in which to care for breakables.

7. When your child is careless, explain exactly what he/she is doing wrong, what should be done and why.

For example: Your child is carrying a hot dish from the stove to the table with one hand. Go to your child and say that he/she is using only one hand when carrying a breakable item. Explain that he/she needs to use both hands when carrying a breakable item because it is hot and he/she is less likely to drop it if using both hands.

8. Allow natural consequences to occur due to your child's carelessness (e.g., a car window being broken due to the careless handling of a baseball).

9. Write a contract with your child.

For example: I, William, for three days in a row, will walk and not run while in the house. When I accomplish this I can have a friend over to spend the night.

The contract should be written within the ability level of your child and should focus on only one behavior at a time. (See Appendix for an example of a Behavior Contract.)

10. Make certain that your child sees the relationship between his/her behavior and the consequences which follow (e.g., throwing a ball in the house may result in a piece of furniture being broken).

11. Make certain your child has plenty of room when required to sit near breakables (e.g., at the dinner table, in a crowded room, at the shopping center, etc.).

12. Reduce distractions when your child is around breakables (e.g., turn off the TV during dinner, have your child play outside with friends, etc.).

13. Do not rush your child when he/she is working with breakables (e.g., allow plenty of time to set the table, pass food, wash the dishes, clean, etc.).

14. Require your child to replace damaged items when he/she breaks them because of carelessness.

15. Make certain that items which your child often uses (e.g., toys, bats, balls, etc.) are stored in a place away from breakables in order to prevent accidents.

16. Encourage your child to ask for help when he/she wants something to eat, a play toy, etc., so there will be no need to climb on counters, get into cupboards, etc.

17. Show your child how to hold breakables, hot items, etc., so that your child can learn to handle such items successfully.

18. Allow your child to perform difficult tasks (e.g., pouring water, cleaning the table, etc.) while you are present to supervise.

19. Make certain your child puts glasses of water, hot dishes, and breakables back from the edges of counters, tables, etc.

20. Make certain your child moves things away from arms and elbows when working, eating, cutting, etc.

21. Use plastic containers as often as possible for those things which your child handles.

22. Teach your child to pass things at the dinner table (e.g., the left hand passes to the right hand, pass to the person on the right, etc.).

23. Do not allow any kind of ball playing in the house (e.g., throwing, bouncing, etc.).

24. Require your child to ask for assistance when trying to pour from large containers, move heavy things, handle hot containers, etc.

25. Limit your child's use of those things which your child is careless in using.

26. Make certain your child knows what the consequences will be in your home for carelessness (e.g., loss of privileges, loss of freedom to be left alone, etc.).

27. Make certain that baby-sitters, grandparents, visitors in your home, are aware of your child's tendency to be careless and the importance in maintaining consistency in discipline.

88 Makes excuses

1. Reward your child for accepting responsibility for his/her behavior. Possible rewards include verbal praise (e.g., "Thank you for being honest about tracking in mud on the kitchen floor."), a kiss on the cheek, a hug, having a friend over to play, staying up late, watching a favorite TV show, and playing a game with a parent. (See Appendix for Reward Menu.)

2. If there are other children or adolescents in the home, reward them for accepting responsibility for their own behavior.

3. Carefully consider your child's age before expecting your child to be completely honest about his/her behavior.

4. Set an example for your child by being honest about your behavior. Do not make excuses.

5. When your child makes excuses for a behavior, calmly confront him/her with the facts. Encourage an open and honest line of communication between everyone in your home. Do not make your child fearful of telling the truth even though you will not be happy about the behavior.

6. Make sure your child knows what is expected (e.g., responsibilities, chores, etc.) at all times.

7. Write a contract with your child.

For example: I, William, will be honest about my behavior. I will not make excuses or tell things that are not true for three days in a row. When I accomplish this, I can invite a friend to go to the movies with me.

The contract should be written within the ability level of your child and should focus on only one behavior at a time. (See Appendix for an example of a Behavior Contract.)

8. Make certain that your child sees the relationship between his/her behavior and the consequences which follow (e.g., you will not be able to trust what your child says because he/she makes excuses).

9. Allow natural consequences to occur due to your child's making excuses about his/her behavior (e.g., others not believing everything your child says, loss of privileges, etc.).

10. Do not cause your child to have to make excuses for his/her behavior by giving your child something too difficult to do.

11. When introducing a new responsibility to your child, demonstrate how to perform the task several times before expecting your child to do it on his/her own.

12. Make certain your child has all the materials necessary to successfully perform the responsibility, chore, etc.

13. Explain to your child the difference between "making excuses" about his/her behavior and giving a legitimate reason why he/she behaved in a certain way.

14. Encourage your child to ask for your help whenever it is needed.

15. Supervise your child's responsibilities, chores, etc., in order to be more aware of when your child needs your assistance.

16. Help your child to feel comfortable coming to you for assistance with a problem by listening to him/her and helping with a solution to the problem.

17. Do not become upset or angry when your child does something wrong. Help your child understand what he/she did wrong by talking calmly about the problem. If you get angry with your child, he/she will try to make excuses for his/her behavior.

18. Be consistent with your child. Do not discipline one time for misbehavior and tolerate misbehavior the next time.

19. Do not accept excuses. Your child must understand that, regardless of the reason, it is necessary that he/she takes responsibility for leaving the toy outside last night, for forgetting to let in the dog, etc.

20. Attempt to have an open and honest relationship with your child. Encourage your child to tell the truth and do not use threats to make him/her tell the truth (e.g., ''You had better tell the truth, or else.'').

21. Do not put your child in a situation where he/she feels that making excuses is necessary.

22. Avoid arguing with your child about whether or not he/she is making excuses, simply explain that he/she is not being completely honest about a situation.

23. Make certain your child learns that excuses do not reduce responsibilities (e.g., chores still must be completed, school projects must be done, etc.).

24. Make certain that expectations for your child's chores, responsibilities, etc., are within his/her developmental level and abilities.

25. Make certain that when consequences are delivered for inappropriate behavior, they are not extreme and are directly related to the inappropriate behavior (e.g., things that are destroyed are replaced, work not done during work time has to be made up during recreational time, etc.).

26. Avoid arguing with your child about whether he is telling you the truth. If you do not have proof, it is better to avoid blaming someone who is innocent.

27. Always make certain that you determine the accuracy of your child's claim that something caused him/her to have a problem or failure. In some cases, someone or something may legitimately be causing your child to experience problems or failures.

28. Make certain your child understands that not being honest when confronted will result in more negative consequences than telling the truth. Be certain to be very consistent in this approach.

29. Make certain your child knows what the consequences will be in your home for making excuses for his/her behavior (e.g., loss of privileges, loss of freedom, etc.).

30. Make certain that baby-sitters, grandparents, visitors in your home, etc., are aware of your child's tendency to make excuses for his/her behavior and the importance of maintaining consistency in the discipline of your child.

89 Does not take care of pets

1. Establish rules for taking care of pets (e.g., feed them at 5:00 p.m. each day, make sure they always have enough water to drink, let them out to use the restroom on a regular basis, etc.). These rules should be consistent and followed by everyone in the home. Talk about the rules often.

2. Show your child how to feed, water, and care for pets several times before expecting your child to care for pets alone.

3. Carefully consider your child's age and experience before expecting him/her to care for pets alone.

4. Have a certain time each day when pets are to be fed, watered, etc.

5. Reward your child for caring for pets. Possible rewards include verbal praise (e.g., "Thank you for remembering to feed Missy today!"), a kiss on the cheek, a hug, having a friend over to play, staying up late, watching a favorite TV show, and playing a game with a parent. (See Appendix for Reward Menu.)

6. When your child does not care for pets, explain exactly what he/she is doing wrong, what should be done and why.

For example: When your child forgets to let the dog out, go to your child and say, "William, you forgot to let the dog out. You were supposed to let him out two hours ago. You need to let him out now so he won't have an accident in the house."

7. Write a contract with your child.

For example: I, William, will feed the dog at 5:00 p.m. for five days in a row. When I accomplish this, I can have a friend over to spend the night.

The contract should be written within the ability level of your child and should focus on only one behavior at a time. (See Appendix for an example of a Behavior Contract.)

8. Make certain that your child sees the relationship between his/her behavior and the consequences which follow (e.g., forgetting to feed the dog will result in the dog going hungry).

9. Allow natural consequences to occur due to your child's failure to care for pets (e.g., having to "clean up" after the dog, wash the dog during a favorite TV show, etc.).

10. Allow your child to do something enjoyable after caring for pets (e.g., watching TV, playing a game with a parent, playing with a friend, etc.).

11. Remind your child when it is time to care for pets.

12. Have your child put a star or check mark on a chart beside each chore after completing the chore (e.g., feeds the dog, puts water out for the cat, lets the dog out, etc.). Let your child trade in stars or check marks for rewards.

13. Supervise your child when he/she cares for pets. Provide help when necessary.

14. Encourage your child to ask for help when taking care of pets.

15. Let your children share the responsibility of caring for the pet or pets (e.g., "This week Bobby will feed and water the dog and Susie will walk the dog.").

16. Post a list of "pet responsibilities" so your child can review the list to make sure the pet has everything it needs. (See Appendix for Sample List.)

17. Allow your child to take the pet to school for Show & Tell, take a pet training class, buy a special book about the pet, etc., as a reward for taking care of the pet without reminders for a week, two weeks, etc.

18. Have your child go to the veterinarian with you and your pet in order to take part in helping to care for the pet outside of the home.

19. Help your child take care of the pet by assisting him/her in the care of the pet (e.g., feed and water the pet together, walk the pet together, brush the pet together, etc.). Gradually require your child to take over the total responsibility.

20. Encourage your child to help pick out the animal you select for a pet so he/she is involved from the beginning.

21. Before getting a pet carefully consider your child's age and readiness to accept the responsibility of taking care of the pet.

22. Make certain the responsibility of caring for the pet is appropriate for your child's level of development and ability.

23. Do not force pets on your child. If the child will not care for the pet, it may be better that the pet have another home.

1. Establish rules (e.g., put things away where they belong, return borrowed items in the same or better condition, etc). These rules should be consistent and followed by everyone in the home. Talk about the rules often.

2. Reward your child for following the rules. Possible rewards include verbal praise (e.g., "Thank you for putting your dirty clothes in the hamper!" "I'm so proud of you for finishing your homework before watching TV", etc.), a kiss on the cheek, a hug, having a friend over to play, staying up late, watching a favorite TV show, and playing a game with a parent. (See Appendix for Reward Menu.)

3. If there are other children or adolescents in the home, reward them for following the rules.

4. Carefully consider your child's age and experience before assigning responsibilities to him/her.

5. Show your child how to return things to their proper places, return borrowed items in the same or better condition, complete chores, etc., before expecting your child to perform the responsibilities alone.

6. When your child is not responsible, explain exactly what he/she is doing wrong, what should be done and why.

For example: It is 9:00 p.m. and your child has not started his/her homework. Go to your child and state that he/she has not done any homework and that he/she needs to be doing homework because bedtime is at 9:30 p.m.

7. Write a contract with your child.

For example: I, William, will finish my homework by 8:00 p.m. every weeknight for five nights in a row. When I accomplish this, I can stay up until 11:00 p.m. on Friday night.

The contract should be written within the ability level of your child and should focus on only one behavior at a time. (See Appendix for an example of a Behavior Contract.)

8. Act as a model for your child being responsible at all times.

9. Make certain that your child sees the relationship between his/her behavior and the consequences that follow (e.g., failing to put an object away in its proper place results in its being broken).

10. Allow natural consequences to occur due to your child's failing to be responsible (e.g., forgetting to do homework will result in low grades).

11. Establish a certain time each day for your child to take care of his/her responsibilities (e.g., feeding the dog, completing homework, etc., right after school).

12. Provide your child with a list of responsibilities in order to help him/her remember to take care of responsibilities. (See Appendix for Sample List.)

13. Tell your child when it is time to complete homework, chores, etc.

14. Post a list of your child's responsibilities (e.g., 1. Take out the trash., 2. Feed the dog., 3. Set the table., etc.). Have your child put a check next to each chore completed. Reward your child for completing the chores.

15. Discuss your child's responsibilities at the beginning of each day so your child knows what is expected.

16. Help your child get out the materials necessary to complete responsibilities (e.g., paper for homework, cleaning supplies for cleaning his/her room, etc.).

17. Help your child get started with chores and explain to your child where things belong when he/she is finished using them.

18. Set aside a time each day for the family to put away all materials that have been used throughout the day (e.g., bikes, toys, lawn equipment, dishes, etc.).

19. Make certain there is a designated place for all items in and around the home.

20. Let your child know that materials not put away at the end of the day may be taken away for a period of time due to lack of responsibility.

21. Make a list of your child's frequently used items and/or materials and have your child make sure that each item and/or material is put in its designated place each day.

22. Require your child to put his/her coat, gloves, hat, etc., in a designated place upon entering the home.

23. Teach your child to return things to their places by putting things back where they belong after using them.

24. Make certain that responsibilities given to your child are appropriate for your child's level of development and ability.

25. Provide your child with shelving, containers, organizers, etc., for his/her possessions. Label the storage areas and require your child to keep the possessions together.

26. Assist your child in performing responsibilities. Gradually require your child to independently assume more responsibility as he/she demonstrates success.

27. Make certain your child understands that things that are lost, broken, destroyed, etc., must be replaced by him/her.

28. Do not buy additional toys, games, etc., for your child if he/she is not able to take care of things he/she already has.

29. Limit your child's use of those things he/she is not responsible for putting away, returning, etc.

30. Make certain your child knows what the consequences will be in your home for not being responsible (e.g., loss of privileges, loss of freedom to borrow things, etc.).

31. Make sure your child puts toys away before getting out something else with which to play.

32. Assist your child in putting away his/her things. Gradually reduce the amount of help given to your child as he/she demonstrates success.

33. Set aside time each day when your child is expected to put things away (e.g., 7:00 p.m. each evening).

34. Require your child to put away things even though he/she did not do so at the established time.

35. Tell your child exactly what to put away (e.g., ''You need to put away your bike, skateboard, and tennis racquet before going to bed.'').

36. Make certain your child is paying attention to you when you tell him/her to put away things. Have your child look directly at you to know he/she is listening and have your child repeat the direction to check for understanding.

37. Have your child put away things right after using them instead of later (e.g., put the skateboard away as soon as you get home rather than before bedtime).

91 Is not ready on time

1. Establish rules for getting ready on time (e.g., get out of bed on time, come home on time and clean up for dinner, do not let things such as the TV distract you from getting ready on time, etc.). These rules should be consistent and followed by everyone in the home. Talk about the rules often and reward your child for following the rules.

2. Reward your child for getting ready for things on time. Possible rewards include verbal praise (e.g., ''Thanks for getting ready for school on time!''), a kiss on the cheek, a hug, having a friend over to play, staying up late, watching a favorite TV show, and playing a game with a parent. (See Appendix for Reward Menu.)

3. If there are other children or adolescents in the home, reward them for getting ready on time.

4. Carefully consider your child's age before expecting your child to get ready for things on time by himself/herself.

5. Help your child to get ready for things on time.

6. Set an example for your child by making sure you are ready for things on time. Organize your time and show your child how to follow a routine in order to get ready for things on time.

7. When your child does not get ready for something on time, explain exactly what he/she is doing wrong, what should be done and why.

For example: It is 7:25 a.m. and your child's school bus will arrive in five minutes. Your child is still eating breakfast and has not dressed yet. Go to your child and say ''It is 7:25 and you are not ready for the bus. You need to get dressed and be at the bus stop in five minutes or you will miss the bus.''

8. Make certain that your child sees the relationship between his/her behavior and the consequences which follow (e.g., failing to be ready for school when the bus arrives will result in missing the bus).

9. Write a contract with your child.

For example: I, William, will be dressed and ready for the bus by 7:20 a.m. for four days in a row. When I accomplish this, I can invite a friend to go roller skating on Saturday.

The contract should be written within the ability level of your child and should focus on only one behavior at a time. (See Appendix for an example of a Behavior Contract.)

10. Allow natural consequences to occur due to your child's failing to be ready for things on time (e.g., missing the bus, having to stay home, missing dinner, etc.).

11. In order to help your child get ready for things on time, reduce distractions (e.g., by turning off the radio or TV, not allowing friends to visit, ringing a bell or blowing a whistle when it is time for dinner, etc.).

12. Make sure your child is aware of the times when things will occur (e.g., the time to be ready to meet the bus, the time you are leaving to go shopping, etc.).

13. Establish a routine for getting ready for school (e.g., get up, make bed, eat breakfast, brush teeth, wash face and get dressed).

14. Have breakfast, lunch and dinner at the same time each day in order to help your child organize his/her day.

15. Frequently remind your child of the time he/she needs to be home, ready to go shopping, etc.

16. Use a timer to help your child know how much time he/she has to get ready for an activity (e.g., going shopping, meeting the school bus, eating meals, etc.).

17. Have your child keep a checklist of things to do in order to get ready for school on time and put a star or check mark by each behavior (e.g., eat, brush teeth, dress, etc.) after he/she completes it. Allow your child to trade in stars or check marks for rewards.

18. Help your child prepare for the next day by selecting and laying out clothes, gathering school materials in one place, and reviewing any special activities or events which will occur the next day.

19. Let your child know in advance when changes in his/her schedule will occur (e.g., going shopping after school instead of after dinner, eating an early lunch, etc.).

20. Discuss your child's schedule at the beginning of each day.

21. Do not allow your child to become involved in high interest activities just before it is time to get ready for another activity.

22. Act as a model for your child by being ready for activities on time.

23. Have your child begin getting ready 10 minutes before everyone else so he/she will be ready on time.

24. Use motivators for your child (e.g., "If you get ready for school on time, you can help decide what to have for breakfast." "If you can pick up your toys before dinner, you can choose your seat at the table." "If you are ready to go shopping on time, you may buy something special." "If you are ready for dinner on time, you may have ice cream for dessert." etc.).

25. Establish a regular routine for your child so that he/she knows exactly what is to be done and when it is to be done.

26. Remind your child to keep track of time by asking an adult the time, looking at a watch, etc.

27. Review your child's schedule for the day each morning so he/she knows what is expected.

28. Develop a schedule for your child to follow (e.g., get up at 7:30 a.m., eat breakfast at 8:00 a.m., be ready for the bus at 8:30 a.m., etc.). (See Appendix for Daily Schedule.)

29. Identify what keeps your child from getting ready on time (e.g., failing to get up on time, sharing the bathroom, etc.). Take whatever steps are necessary to remove those obstacles (e.g., get him/her up earlier in the morning, schedule different times for people to use the bathroom to get ready, etc.).

30. Carefully evaluate those things for which your child does not get ready on time. Try to find something that will make your child want to get ready on time for these activities (e.g., a special privilege or chore at school, such as flag raising, for getting there on time; getting to sit in the front seat of the car for being ready on time; etc.).

A Reminder: It is going to be difficult under any circumstances to have your child ready on time for activities to which your child does not look forward or does not enjoy.

1. Establish rules for completing tasks (e.g., take your time, ask for help when necessary, plan ahead in order to complete tasks on time, etc.). These rules should be consistent and followed by everyone in the home. Talk about the rules often.

2. Reward your child for not hurrying just to get things finished. Possible rewards include verbal praise (e.g., ''I am so proud of you for taking your time when you set the table! It looks very nice.''), a kiss on the cheek, a hug, having a friend over to play, staying up late, watching a favorite TV show, and playing a game with a parent. (See Appendix for Reward Menu.)

3. If there are other children or adolescents in the home, reward them for not hurrying just to get finished with things.

4. Carefully consider your child's age and experience before expecting him/her to complete tasks alone.

5. Help your child to complete tasks so he/she will not have to hurry.

6. Encourage your child to ask for help when necessary.

7. Be a good role model by not hurrying just to finish things. Organize your time and finish things without having to hurry in order to do so.

8. When your child is hurrying just to get things finished, explain exactly what he/she is doing wrong, what should have been done and why.

For example: Your child is hurrying through his homework assignments. Tell your child that he/she is hurrying and needs to slow down and carefully read the directions so the assignments will be done correctly.

9. Make certain that your child sees the relationship between his/her behavior and the consequences which follow (e.g., failing to read the directions will result in homework assignments being done incorrectly).

10. Write a contract with your child.

For example: I, William, will carefully read the directions for my homework assignments so I will do the problems correctly. When I accomplish this, I can watch the TV show of my choice.

The contract should be written within the ability level of your child and should focus on only one behavior at a time. (See Appendix for an example of a Behavior Contract.)

11. Allow natural consequences to occur due to your child's hurrying just to get finished (e.g., doing things incorrectly, breaking things, forgetting to do something, etc.).

12. Reduce distractions (e.g., turning the radio or TV off, not allowing friends to visit, etc.) in order to stop your child from hurrying just to finish things.

13. Remind your child when it is time to set the table, feed the dog, perform homework assignments, etc.

14. Provide your child with plenty of time to perform chores so he/she will not need to hurry just to get finished.

15. Require your child to perform a task again if it has been done incorrectly due to his/her hurrying just to get finished.

16. Set a timer and have your child work on a task until the timer goes off. In this situation, hurrying just to get finished will not be to your child's advantage.

17. Limit the number of responsibilities your child has in order that he/she does not have to hurry in order to finish.

18. Let your child play, watch TV, read, etc., when he/she comes home from school so there is a break between school and homework in the evening. Your child may be less likely to rush through work if there is a break between school and homework.

19. Help your child schedule time in order that he/she will not need to hurry to finish.

20. Schedule time each day for your child to work so that he/she can expect to work for 30 minutes, 45 minutes, etc., without distractions/interruptions.

21. Maintain consistency in expecting your child to complete a task in a quality fashion.

22. Help your child begin a task and check it with you before putting away materials so that you can make certain the work was not rushed.

23. Establish a routine for your child to follow in completing chores (e.g., wash out the dog dish, refill food and water, clean up the area around the dog dish, etc.). This will help your child remember what is expected of him/her.

24. Sit or stand in a place where you can see your child while he/she is performing tasks. Make your child aware that you can see the behavior.

25. Make a list of your child's responsibilities and the amount of time you expect him/her to spent on each chore (e.g., dusting room for 10 minutes, cleaning basement for 30 minutes, homework for 30 minutes, etc.).

26. Make certain to check your child's performance on homework, chores, etc., for quality. Working quickly is acceptable if your child performs responsibilities well.

27. Increase supervision of your child while he/she is performing homework, chores, etc. (e.g., by you, another parent, older brother or sister, etc.).

28. Make certain that the responsibilities given to your child are appropriate for your child's level of development and ability.

29. Assist your child in performing responsibilities. Gradually require your child to independently assume more responsibility as he/she demonstrates success.

30. Make certain you are not requiring too much of your child at one time and causing him/her to hurry to get finished.

31. Make certain your child understands that work not done appropriately will be redone, corrected, etc., during recreation time.

32. Along with a directive, provide an incentive statement (e.g., "When you finish your homework correctly, you can watch TV" "You can play outside after your chores are done appropriately." etc.).

93 Does not take care of belongings

1. Establish rules for taking care of belongings (e.g., return belongings to their proper places after you are finished using them, etc.). These rules should be consistent and followed by everyone in the home. Talk about the rules often and reward your child for following the rules.

2. Reward your child for following the rules. Possible rewards include verbal praise (e.g., "Thank you for remembering to put your bike in the garage when you were finished using it!" "I really appreciate it when you put your dirty clothes in the hamper." etc.), a kiss on the cheek, a hug, having a friend over to play, staying up late, watching a favorite TV show, and playing a game with a parent. (See Appendix for Reward Menu.)

3. If there are other children or adolescents in the home, reward them for taking care of their belongings.

4. Carefully consider your child's age and experience before expecting your child to take care of his/her belongings alone.

5. Show your child how to take care of his/her belongings before expecting your child to do so alone.

6. Help your child take care of his/her belongings by reminding him/her to put things in their proper places, assisting him/her in putting belongings in their proper places, etc.

7. Act as a model for taking care of belongings by doing so yourself.

8. When your child does not take care of his/her belongings, explain exactly what he/she did wrong, what should have been done and why.

For example: You are driving into the driveway and your child's bike is blocking the way. Stop the car, get out, go to your child and say, "You forgot to put your bike in the garage. You need to move your bike off the driveway and put it in the garage because it is blocking the driveway."

9. Provide your child with a list of his/her belongings and the proper ways to care for them.

10. Write a contract with your child.

For example: I, William, for three days in a row, will put my bike in the garage when I am not riding it. When I accomplish this, I can have a friend over to spend the night.

The contract should be written within the ability level of your child and should focus on only one behavior at a time. (See Appendix for an example of a Behavior Contract.)

11. Make certain that your child sees the relationship between his/her behavior and the consequences which follow (e.g., failing to put a belonging in its proper place may result in its being broken).

12. Allow natural consequences to occur due to your child's not caring for his/her belongings (e.g., the child's bike being stolen because it was not secured in the garage overnight).

13. Have your child place a star or check mark beside each belonging for which he/she takes proper care and allow your child to trade in the stars or check marks for rewards.

14. Tell your child when he/she needs to care for belongings (e.g., feeding the dog, hanging up a coat, putting away a bike for the evening, etc.).

15. Set aside time each day for everyone in the home to care for belongings.

16. Make sure that your child can reach the places where belongings should be stored when not in use.

17. Limit your child's use of belongings until he/she can care for them properly.

18. Establish a certain time each day for your child to take care of his/her belongings (e.g., putting away clothes or toys right after school, right before bed, etc.).

19. Let your child know that belongings not put in their proper places at the end of the day may be taken away for a period of time due to lack of responsibility.

20. Make a list of your child's frequently used items and have your child make sure that each item is put in its designated place each day.

21. Teach your child to return things to their proper places by putting things back where they belong after you use them.

22. Allow your child to do something enjoyable after caring for belongings (e.g., watch TV, play a game with a parent, play with a friend, etc.).

23. Post a list of your child's responsibilities so he/she can review the list daily. (See Appendix for List of Chores.)

24. Allow your child to take one of his favorite belongings to school as a reward for taking care of responsibilities for a week, two weeks, etc.

25. Along with a directive, provide an incentive statement (e.g., ''You may watch TV after you put your clothes back where they belong.'').

26. Require your child's room to be neat and organized so there will always be a place to put toys, games, clothes, etc.

27. Have your child put away toys, clothes, etc., before being allowed to get out new toys with which to play, different clothes to wear, etc.

28. Communicate with parents of a friend your child visits to make certain that your child helps to pick up toys when he/she is spending time at a friend's house.

29. Do not expect your child to pick up toys and games that friends have left out; encourage the friends to help your child.

30. Tell baby-sitters or others who are involved with your child that your child is responsible for picking up and putting away his/her own materials.

31. Show your child the proper way to take care of things (e.g., shining shoes, hosing off a bike, taking care of dolls, etc.). This will teach your child a sense of responsibility with belongings.

32. Do not buy additional toys, games, etc., for your child if he/she is not able to take care of the things he/she already has.

33. Have your child pay for things he/she wants (e.g., a baseball mitt, a new doll, a new pair of jeans, etc.). If your child has spent some of his/her own money on the item, your child may be willing to care for it.

34. Limit your child's use of those things he/she is not responsible for putting away, returning, etc.

35. Make certain your child understands that things that are lost, broken, destroyed must be replaced by him/her.

36. Make certain that the responsibilities given to your child are appropriate for your child's level of development and ability.

37. Assist your child in performing responsibilities. Gradually require your child to independently assume more responsibility as he/she demonstrates success.

38. If your child fails to pick up clothes, games, toys, etc., before going to bed, pick up the toys and take them away for a period of time.

39. Make certain to be consistent when expecting your child to pick up toys. Do not leave the house with toys in the yard one time and expect the toys to be picked up the next time.

40. Provide your child with shelving, containers, organizers, etc., for personal possessions. Label the storage areas and require your child to keep the possessions organized.

41. Post a list of your child's responsibilities (e.g., put away things in your room, bring in things at night, put away clothes, etc.). Have your child put a check next to each chore that is completed and reward your child for completing the chores.

42. Set aside a time each day for the family to take care of their belongings (e.g., putting away things, shining shoes, doing laundry, organizing rooms, etc.).

43. Discuss your child's responsibilities at the beginning of each day so he/she knows what is expected.

44. Make certain there is a designated place in and around the house for all items.

45. Require your child to put his/her coat, gloves, hat, etc., in a designated place upon entering the home.

94 Pretends to be sick

1. Determine whether your child's physical discomfort is being used as an excuse to avoid doing something or is the result of a medical problem by taking the child to the doctor.

2. If you feel that your child is pretending to be sick in order to get out of school, talk with the school personnel in order to determine why your child does not want to go to school.

3. If your child is having academic difficulties which cause him/her to pretend to be sick in order to avoid going to school, talk with the teacher about your child receiving extra assistance, tutoring, etc. See if there is anything you can do with your child at home in order to help improve skills.

4. Reward your child for participating in activities that he/she does not like (e.g., doing daily chores, going to school, etc.). Possible rewards include verbal praise (e.g., "Thank you so much for cleaning up your room!" "I'm proud of you for going to school today." etc.), a kiss on the cheek, a hug, having a friend over to play, staying up late, watching a favorite TV show, and playing a game with a parent. (See Appendix for Reward Menu.)

5. If there are other children or adolescents in the home, reward them for not pretending to be sick in order to get out of doing things.

6. Encourage your child to tell you when things are wrong so you can help him/her learn to participate in situations even though he/she is feeling scared, anxious, uncertain, etc.

7. Do not pretend to be sick in order to get out of doing things. If you do this, your child will learn to pretend to be sick, also.

8. Involve your child in highly interesting activities at school and in the community in order to help your child learn to participate in activities. These activities may include school clubs, organized sports, 4-H, Girl Scouts/Boy Scouts, etc.

9. Do not accept your child's excuse of being sick in place of meeting his/her responsibilities.

10. Write a contract with your child.

For example: I, William, for three days in a row, will not pretend to be sick in order to get out of doing my chores. When I accomplish this, I can spend two dollars at the store.

The contract should be written within the ability level of your child and should focus on only one behavior at a time. (See Appendix for an example of a Behavior Contract.)

11. Keep a record of your child's physical complaints and when they occur in order to see if there is a pattern. Share this with your child to help him/her better understand why he/she is pretending to be sick in order to get out of doing things.

12. Allow natural consequences to occur due to your child's pretending to be sick in order to get out of doing something (e.g., if your child is "too sick" to go to school, he/she will not be able to play outside with friends after school; etc.). Keep in mind that it is quite normal from time to time for a child or adolescent to pretend to be sick in order to get out of doing something. It can be a problem if it occurs on a frequent basis and is related to something specific (e.g., school, chores, etc.).

13. Notify the school nurse and teachers to make them aware of your child's pattern of pretending to be sick to get out of things.

14. Talk to your child to make certain that he/she knows it is normal to sometimes be frightened about trying new things, but that making excuses about not feeling well is not the way to deal with the problem.

15. Do not push your child to do something that makes him/her feel uncomfortable (e.g., playing football, playing with a certain friend, etc.). Pushing your child to do something he/she does not want to do may cause your child to have a sick feeling.

16. Speak with your child to let him/her know what he/she is doing wrong and why it is important not to "cry wolf" (e.g., people will not believe you when you really are sick or in pain).

17. Make your child aware of the number of times the excuse of being sick is used to get out of doing things he/she does not want to do.

18. Carefully evaluate those things your child is trying to avoid. Try to find something that will make the situation your child is trying to avoid more enjoyable (e.g., some special privileges or chores such as flag raising, passing out papers at school, etc.).

19. Go with your child or have someone else accompany your child to those things he/she may be trying to avoid. Gradually decrease the length of time you or someone else stays with your child.

20. Carefully consider those things your child may be trying to avoid. If something unpleasant is causing your child to pretend to be sick, do all you can to change the situation.

21. Intervene in those activities your child is trying to avoid to reduce demands which may be too much at that time (e.g., assignment may be shortened, the child may not have to read aloud in front of a large group). Demands and expectations may be gradually increased over time.

22. Do not inadvertently reinforce your child by allowing him/her to get out of doing less desirable things in order to do those things that are preferred (e.g., staying home from school to get to watch TV, etc.).

23. When your child does stay at home "sick," make certain that your child is treated as being sick (e.g., must rest in his/her room, not watch TV, finish homework sent from school, stay away from friends, etc.).

24. Reward your child for following through with an activity even though it is not a favorite activity or is something he/she does not feel good about doing.

25. Encourage an open, honest relationship with your child. Let your child know how important it is to tell you things that are bothering him/her.

A Reminder: If your child is experiencing an unpleasant situation, he/she may actually feel sick. Making the experience more pleasant may change the way your child feels.

95 Blames other persons or things

1. Reward your child for accepting responsibility for problems or failures. Possible rewards include verbal praise (e.g., "I'm very proud of you for not blaming your poor grade in math on your teacher."), a kiss on the cheek, a hug, having a friend over to play, staying up late, watching a favorite TV show, and playing a game with a parent. (See Appendix for Reward Menu.)

2. If there are other children or adolescents in the home, reward them for accepting responsibility for their problems or failures.

3. Carefully consider your child's age before expecting him/her to always accept responsibility for problems or failures.

4. When your child blames problems or failures on other persons or things, explain exactly what he/she is doing wrong, what should have been done and why.

For example: Your child brings home an "F" on the math test taken earlier that day and blames the teacher for the low grade. Go to your child and say, "You are blaming your teacher for the low grade you got on your math test. You did not study for the test last night because you were too busy watching TV. You need to stop blaming your teacher and accept responsibility for your low grade on the test."

5. Write a contract with your child.

For example: I, William, for five days in a row, will accept responsibility for my problems or failures when confronted. When I accomplish this, I can have two friends over to spend the night.

The contract should be written within the ability level of your child and should focus on only one behavior at a time. (See Appendix for an example of a Behavior Contract.)

6. Make certain that your child sees the relationship between his/her behavior and the consequences which follow (e.g., blaming problems on persons or materials will cause others to not believe everything he/she says or does).

7. Do not accept your child's excuses in place of meeting his/her responsibilities.

8. Allow natural consequences to occur due to your child's failure to accept responsibility for problems or failures (e.g., others not believing your child, avoiding him/her, etc.).

9. Provide your child with a list of daily chores he/she needs to perform in order to help your child remember which chores to perform and when to perform them. (See Appendix for List of Chores.)

10. Have your child put a star or check mark beside each chore performed and turn in stars or check marks for rewards.

11. Reduce distractions (e.g., turn off the TV, have friends go home, etc.) in order to help your child take care of responsibilities on time.

12. Make sure you show your child how to perform a chore several times before expecting him/her to perform the chore alone. Fear of failure or not knowing how to perform a chore may cause your child to blame other persons or materials.

13. Make sure that you do not blame your problems or failures on other persons or materials. If you do, your child will learn to do the same.

14. Avoid arguing with your child about whether or not he/she is blaming other persons or materials for problems or failures.

15. Encourage your child to ask for help when necessary in order to help him/her be more successful.

16. Tell your child when it is time to perform a chore, do homework, etc.

17. Provide an atmosphere where everyone works together to get things done around the house.

18. Establish a set time or routine when everyone performs chores (e.g., after school, after dinner, etc.).

19. Make sure your child has all the materials needed in order to perform chores successfully.

20. Make sure that the materials your child uses to perform chores are in good condition.

21. Make sure your child has enough time to perform chores.

22. When your child blames others for his/her behavior, calmly confront your child with the facts. Encourage an open and honest line of communication between everyone in your home. Do not make your child fearful of telling the truth even though you will not be happy about the behavior.

23. Supervise your child's responsibilities, chores, etc., in order to be more aware of the times your child needs your assistance.

24. Help your child to feel comfortable coming to you for assistance with a problem by listening and helping with a solution to the problem.

25. Be consistent with your child. Do not discipline for misbehavior one time and ignore misbehavior the next time.

26. Your child must understand that regardless of the reason, it is necessary to take responsibility for leaving the toy outside last night, forgetting to let in the dog, etc.

27. Do not put your child in a situation where your child feels like he/she must blame others for mistakes.

28. Attempt to have an open, honest relationship with your child. Encourage your child to tell the truth and do not use threats to make him/her tell the truth (e.g., ''You had better tell the truth, or else.'').

29. Do not put your child in a situation where he/she feels that it is necessary to make excuses.

30. Avoid arguing with your child about whether or not he/she is making excuses; simply explain that he/she is not being completely honest about a situation.

31. Make certain your child learns that excuses do not reduce responsibilities (e.g., chores still must be completed, school projects must be done, etc.).

32. Make certain that expectations for your child's chores, responsibilities, etc., are within his/her developmental level and abilities.

33. Make certain that consequences delivered for inappropriate behavior are not extreme and are directly related to the inappropriate behavior (e.g., things that are destroyed are not replaced, work not done during work time has to be made up during recreational time, etc.).

34. Avoid arguing with your child about whether or not he is telling you the truth. If you do not have proof, it is better to avoid blaming someone who is innocent.

35. Make certain your child understands that blaming someone or something will not change the consequences for what has occurred.

36. Always make certain that you determine the accuracy of your child's claim that someone or something caused him/her to have a problem or failure. In some cases someone or something may legitimately be causing your child to experience problems or failure.

37. Make certain your child understands that not being honest when confronted will result in more negative consequences than telling the truth. Be certain to be very consistent in this approach.

1. Put all objects that you do not want your child to have in a place where he/she cannot get to them (e.g., a locked medicine cabinet, high cabinets, a locked tool box, etc.).

2. Do not leave objects laying around that you do not want your child to use. Put them away as soon as you are finished using them.

3. Make sure that you know where your child is at all times.

4. Talk with your child about the dangers of using medicine, power tools, matches, etc.

5. Clearly mark those things your child is not allowed to handle. (See Appendix for "Poison" labels and "Do Not Touch" labels.)

6. Use products in your home that have "child-proof" lids and caps. If you have medications which are not in child-proof containers, use empty child-proof containers that have been relabeled.

7. Make sure your child knows exactly what is to be used and what is not to be used.

8. Establish rules (e.g., ask before touching, do not get into things that do not belong to you, etc.). These rules should be consistent and followed by everyone in the home. Talk about the rules often and reward your child for following the rules.

9. Reward your child for staying away from those things which are not supposed to be used. Possible rewards include verbal praise (e.g., "Thank you for leaving the medicine alone."), a kiss on the cheek, a hug, having a friend over to play, staying up late, watching a favorite TV show, and playing a game with a parent. (See Appendix for Reward Menu.)

10. If there are other children or adolescents in the home, reward them for following the rules.

11. Carefully consider your child's age before expecting him/her to stay away from things that are not supposed to be used.

12. When your child gets into things that he/she should not, explain exactly what he/she is doing wrong, what should be done and why.

For example: You find your child playing with some tools. Go to him/her and say, "You are playing with these tools and you did not ask permission to use them. You are supposed to ask permission first, so I can show you how to use them properly."

13. Write a contract with your child.

For example: I, William, for five days in a row, will remember to ask permission to use the tools. When I accomplish this, I can go roller skating.

The contract should be written within the ability level of your child and should focus on only one behavior at a time. (See Appendix for an example of a Behavior Contract.)

14. Make certain that your child sees the relationship between his/her behavior and the consequences which follow (e.g., getting poisoned, burned, hurt, etc.).

15. Require your child to always ask before using things that do not belong to him/her.

16. Give your child safe tools, empty medicine bottles, and empty makeup containers with which to play.

17. Establish a cabinet for your child to keep all "safe" items with which he/she is allowed to play. Mark the cabinets in which you do not want your child to play so he/she knows which cabinets are allowed to be used. (See Appendix for "Do Not Touch" labels.)

18. Make certain that others who are involved with your child are aware that your child has a tendency to get into places where he/she does not belong.

19. Increase supervision of your child (e.g., by you, another adult, older adolescent, etc.).

20. Remove any medicines, tools, cleaning products, matches, lawn and garden chemicals, etc., that are not absolutely necessary to keep around the house.

21. Change the location of things your child should not use in order to reduce the likelihood that your child will find them.

22. Lock all tools and equipment into secure storage containers.

23. Communicate with baby-sitters, other adults, and older brothers and sisters about your child's tendency to get into things.

24. Teach your child the meaning of the poison symbol on containers in the home.

25. Place large poison symbols on containers of potentially harmful substances which are kept in your home (e.g., medicine, detergent, lawn and garden chemicals, etc.). (See Appendix for "Poison" labels.)

A Reminder: Guns or knives are dangerous for adults to handle. They are lethal in the hands of children.

97 Is afraid to try something new

1. Do not force your child to attempt something that is new.

2. Encourage your child to talk about his/her fears with you.

3. Do not "make fun" when your child cries or avoids something new.

4. Talk with your family doctor, a school official, a social worker, a mental health worker, etc., if your child is afraid of attempting everything that is new or different.

5. Attempt things together that are new to your child.

6. As a family, attempt things that are new to your child.

7. Reward your child for attempting something new. Possible rewards include verbal praise (e.g., "I'm very proud of you for riding the bus today!"), a kiss on the cheek, a hug, having a friend over to play, staying up late, watching a favorite TV show, and playing a game with a parent. (See Appendix for Reward Menu.)

8. If there are other children or adolescents in the home, reward them for attempting something new.

9. Have your child try something new with peers with whom he/she feels comfortable (e.g., swim lessons, dancing, baseball, etc.).

10. Do not force your child to do something he/she feels very strongly about not doing, but do not let it become an excuse for getting out of things.

11. If your child begins to use "afraid of doing it" as an excuse, take your child to the activity, see him/her into the location, leave and come back when the activity is over. Make certain the person with whom you are leaving your child understands the situation.

12. Allow your child to attempt something new in private before doing so in front of others.

13. Provide your child with a choice (e.g., "You can go to summer camp or take swim lessons. You may decide which you want to do.") Make certain your child understands he/she will do one or the other.

14. Make certain that your child feels comfortable with the instructor, other children in the activity, and the activity itself.

15. Make certain that what you are encouraging your child to attempt is appropriate for your child's level of development and ability.

16. Accompany your child in attempting new things. Gradually require your child to attempt things alone as he/she feels comfortable with them.

17. Present learning new activities in the most attractive manner possible (e.g., the family going together to learn to swim, everyone riding a bike at the same time, etc.).

18. Do not convey your own personal fears to your child (e.g., fear of water, heights, skating, skiing, etc.).

19. Be personally available when your child is attempting something new (e.g., get in the pool with your child during first swim lessons).

20. Provide your child with optional courses of action in order to prevent total refusal to attempt something new (e.g., if your child is afraid to have you teach him/her to swim, your child can get instructions at a pool; if your child is afraid of lessons at a pool, you can teach him/her to swim).

21. Reduce the emphasis on competitiveness in the family or neighborhood. Fear of failure may cause your child to refuse to attempt something new.

22. Allow your child many opportunities to attempt something new (e.g., learning to ride a bike, learning to swim, etc.). Nothing is so important that it has to be learned or mastered the first time.

A Reminder: Most of us are a little uncomfortable at some time in our lives when trying "new" things. Having someone there to help us get started can make a big difference until we get over our fear.

1. Establish rules for using things (e.g., do not take out more food than you can eat, use things sparingly, etc.). These rules should be consistent and followed by everyone in the home. Talk about the rules often and reward your child for following the rules.

2. Reward your child for not being wasteful. Possible rewards include verbal praise (e.g., ''Thank you for not wasting the glue!''), a kiss on the cheek, a hug, having a friend over to play, staying up late, watching a favorite TV show, and playing a game with a parent. (See Appendix for Reward Menu.)

3. If there are other children or adolescents in the home, reward them for not being wasteful.

4. Teach your child to not be wasteful (e.g., when eating, show your child how to take small helpings; when washing dishes, show your child the amount of detergent to use; etc.).

5. Make sure that you are not wasteful. If you are wasteful, your child will learn to be wasteful.

6. Carefully consider your child's age and experience when allowing your child to use things (e.g., glue, tape, paper, etc.) and to serve himself/herself.

7. When your child is wasteful, explain exactly what he/she is doing wrong, what should be done and why.

For example: You see your child using too much shampoo. Tell your child that he/she is using too much shampoo. Show your child the amount to use and explain that a small amount will get hair clean.

8. Have your child earn things that he/she wastes in order to teach conservation.

9. Allow your child to earn money by working around the house and then have your child buy personal items.

10. Do not allow your child to use things that are wasted.

11. Supervise and direct your child when he/she is using something that can be wasted.

12. Write a contract with your child.

For example: I, William, will not waste shampoo for five days in a row. When I accomplish this, I can earn $1.

The contract should be written within the ability level of your child and should focus on only one behavior at a time. (See Appendix for an example of a Behavior Contract.)

13. Make certain that your child sees the relationship between his/her behavior and the consequences which follow (e.g., running out of something, having to go without something for awhile, people not wanting to let him/her borrow things, etc.).

14. Allow natural consequences to occur as a result of your child's wastefulness (e.g., having to go without something for several days or weeks, not being able to ''borrow'' things, etc.).

15. If your child has any form of income, require your child to buy things he/she needs (e.g., food, soap, toothpaste, shampoo, etc.) in order to teach your child not to be wasteful.

16. Limit your child's use of those things that are wasted.

17. If your child is wasteful, do not buy additional toys, games, etc.

18. Do not allow your child to have more of anything than what is needed (e.g., instead of an entire tablet of paper, give your child one piece at a time).

19. Show your child exactly how much milk, shampoo, sugar, ice cream, etc., he/she is allowed to have or use at one time.

20. Make certain your child knows what the consequences will be in your home for being wasteful (e.g., not allowed to get new things, loss of privileges, etc.).

21. Make certain that baby-sitters, grandparents, visitors in your home, etc., are aware of your child's tendency to be wasteful and the importance of maintaining consistency in the discipline of your child.

22. Require that your child buy those things which are wasted in order to teach the importance of conserving rather than wasting.

1. Establish rules for following directions (e.g., listen, do not argue, ask questions if you do not understand, follow the directions, etc.). These rules should be consistent and followed by everyone in the home. Talk about the rules often and reward your child for following the rules.

2. Reward your child for not arguing when told to do something. Possible rewards include verbal praise (e.g., "Thank you for doing the dishes without arguing."), a kiss on the cheek, a hug, having a friend over to play, staying up late, watching a favorite TV show, and playing a game with a parent. (See Appendix for Reward Menu.)

3. If there are other children or adolescents in the home, reward them for not arguing.

4. Do not argue with your child.

5. Do not argue with others. If you do so, your child will learn to argue.

6. Treat your child with respect. Talk in an objective manner at all times.

7. Avoid confrontations with your child which may lead to arguing by giving options (e.g., say, "You can either set the table or wash the dishes tonight. Which do you want to do?").

8. Develop a routine schedule of activities and chores for your child in order that he/she knows what to expect at all times.

9. When your child argues, explain exactly what he/she is doing wrong, what should be done and why.

For example: You ask your child to take out the trash and he/she begins to argue. Stop your child and say, "You are arguing with me. I asked you to take out the trash and that is what you need to do."

10. Avoid arguing with your child by discussing in advance the reason(s) he/she must be home at a certain time, why he/she cannot go out on a school night, etc.

11. Write a contract with your child.

For example: I, William, for three days in a row, will not argue when given a direction. When I accomplish this, I can go to the zoo.

The contract should be written within the ability level of your child and should focus on only one behavior at a time. (See Appendix for an example of a Behavior Contract.)

12. Make certain that your child sees the relationship between his/her behavior and the consequences which follow (e.g., others avoiding your child, hurting someone's feelings, etc.).

13. Have your child keep track of the number of times he/she does not argue when given a direction by placing a sticker, star, etc., on a piece of paper.

14. Be flexible in helping your child be able to do those things he/she wants to do (e.g., if you do not think it would be appropriate for your child to spend the night at a friend's house, allow the friend to spend the night at your house).

15. Make certain your child understands his/her responsibilities and when to take care of them.

16. Carefully consider your child's age and experience before asking your child to do something that is too difficult and may result in arguing.

17. Along with a directive, provide an incentive statement (e.g., "When you finish the dishes, you may watch TV." "You may play outside after you finish your homework." etc.).

18. When your child argues in public (e.g., at the grocery store, in the mall, playing with friends, etc.) remove him/her from the situation until he/she can demonstrate self-control and refrain from arguing.

19. Do not give your child more than two or three steps to follow in one direction. Directions that involve several steps can be confusing and cause your child to argue. An example of a two-step direction is: "Please turn off the radio and go to bed."

20. Deliver directions in a supportive rather than a threatening manner (e.g., "Please take out the trash." rather than "You had better take out the trash or else!").

21. Make certain that your child understands that total fairness is impossible. Sometimes we have to do more than others or do things we do not want to do simply because they have to be done.

22. Encourage your child to ask permission and/or discuss things he/she wants to do well in advance in order to avoid misunderstandings and increase the likelihood of finding solutions to disagreements without arguing.

23. Encourage your child to express feelings and teach him/her how to talk about feelings in a controlled manner.

24. Be consistent; do not give in to your child's arguing one time and expect your child not to argue the next time.

25. Model appropriate ways to question someone's decision.

26. Let your child know that "questioning" should be done in private (at home) and not in public places (e.g., at the mall, skating rink, grocery store, etc.).

27. Separate your child from those children and adolescents who encourage arguing, talking back, etc.

28. Tape record your child to let him/her hear talking back, arguing, etc.

29. Intervene early when your child is arguing with someone else. Do not allow your child to return to the situation unless he/she can behave appropriately.

30. Make certain that the people in the homes your child visits are aware of the behavioral expectations that you have for your child (e.g., picking up, not arguing, being friendly, etc.).

31. Make certain that your child does not get out of doing things or get his/her way simply because of being persistent in arguing (e.g., arguing about who will take out the trash will not get him/her out of taking out the trash, etc.).

32. Do not surprise your child with requests, chores, etc. Be consistent in expectations so your child knows what his/her responsibilities are and has no reason to argue (e.g., trash is taken out each evening, he/she washes the dishes on Tuesdays and Thursdays, etc.).

33. Make certain that all adults who supervise your child (e.g., parents, baby-sitters, grandparents, etc.) are consistent in not accepting arguing. If one person allows the child to argue to get his/her way or to get out of doing things, your child will continue to argue.

34. Make certain your child gets attention from you, from others, in the presence of others, etc., for behaving appropriately and not arguing. Include your child in conversations, activities, etc., when others are present in order to satisfy your child's need for attention.

1. Establish rules for interacting with others (e.g., be cooperative, talk in an acceptable manner, etc.). These rules should be consistent and followed by everyone in the home. Talk about the rules often and reward your child for following the rules.

2. Reward your child for interacting with others in an acceptable manner. Possible rewards include verbal praise (e.g., "You were very nice when the Johnstons were here." "I appreciate it when you talk with me in a nice tone of voice." etc.), a kiss on the cheek, a hug, having a friend over to play, staying up late, watching a favorite TV show, and playing a game with a parent. (See Appendix for Reward Menu.)

3. If there are other children or adolescents in the home, reward them for interacting with others in an acceptable manner.

4. Treat your child with respect when interacting with him/her.

5. When interacting with others, show them respect. Your child will learn how to interact with others by observing you.

6. When your child is rude to someone, explain exactly what he/she is doing wrong, what he/she is supposed to be doing and why.

For example: The baby-sitter reports that your child made several rude comments toward her. Talk with your child as soon as possible about the rude comments and help him/her understand that he/she is not to make rude comments because it is not nice and others will not want to be around him/her.

7. Immediately remove your child from the situation when he/she begins to make rude comments or gestures. Do not allow your child to return unless he/she can demonstrate acceptable behavior.

8. Make certain that your child sees the relationship between his/her behavior and the consequences which follow (e.g., others being rude in return, hurting someone's feelings, being avoided by others, getting in trouble with the law, etc.).

9. Write a contract with your child.

For example: I, William, will interact with others in an acceptable manner for two hours. When I accomplish this I can earn the money to buy a model.

The contract should be written within the ability level of your child and should focus on only one behavior at a time. (See Appendix for an example of a Behavior Contract.)

10. Teach your child acceptable ways in which to interact with others (e.g., making conversation, using appropriate language, etc.).

11. If your child has difficulty playing nicely with others, do not allow him/her to play unless he/she plays in a friendly manner.

12. Make sure that others are friendly and cooperative when interacting with your child.

13. Teach your child acceptable ways in which to show displeasure, anger, frustration, etc.

14. Try to prevent competition of any form from occurring in the home.

15. Do not appear shocked or surprised when your child makes rude comments or gestures. Deal with his/her behavior in a calm and deliberate manner.

16. Be consistent when dealing with your child's rude comments or gestures.

17. Encourage your child to interact with children or adolescents who behave appropriately.

18. Make certain that baby-sitters, guests in your home, etc., understand that your child should not be allowed to talk to them in a disrespectful manner, make rude comments or gestures, etc. Encourage them to report misbehavior to you if your child behaves inappropriately.

19. Make certain that guests in your home are aware of how you deal with your child's rude comments or gestures in order that they will do the same.

20. Talk with your child about peers, guests, baby-sitters, etc., before they arrive in order to help your child prepare for their arrival and feel more comfortable when others are in your home. If your child feels comfortable with peers, guests, baby-sitters, etc., he/she may be less likely to make rude comments, gestures, etc.

21. Supervise your child when he/she is interacting with others.

22. Make certain your child knows exactly what it is he/she says that is rude.

23. Children often make rude comments in order to get the attention of others. Make certain that your child gets your attention when he/she is behaving appropriately.

24. Do not laugh at or ignore your child when he/she is insensitive to others' feelings.

25. Remind your child before guests or baby-sitters arrive, he/she visits in others' homes, etc., that he/she should be careful not to make rude comments to others.

26. Talk to your children in the manner that you want them to talk to you and others. Treat them with respect and do not "talk down" to them.

27. Separate your child from those children and adolescents who encourage your child to make rude comments, gestures, etc.

28. If your child does make rude comments or gestures toward parents, guests, baby-sitters, etc., deal with the situation immediately by sending your child to his/her room, removing him/her from the situation to talk about behavior and self-control, etc.

1. Establish rules for behaving when with a baby-sitter (e.g., follow the baby-sitter's instructions, go to bed on time, stay in the yard, abide by the household rules, etc.). These rules should be consistent and followed by everyone in the home. Talk about the rules often and reward your child for following the rules.

2. Reward your child for behaving appropriately when with a baby-sitter. Possible rewards include verbal praise (e.g., ''Thank you for being good for the baby-sitter!'' ''I appreciate your going to bed on time when the baby-sitter was here!'' etc.), a kiss on the cheek, a hug, having a friend over to play, staying up late, watching a favorite TV show, and playing a game with a parent. (See Appendix for Reward Menu.)

3. If there are other children or adolescents in the home, reward them for behaving appropriately when with a baby-sitter.

4. Carefully consider your child's age and experience before expecting appropriate behavior when your child is with a baby-sitter.

5. Talk with your child about how you expect him/her to act before leaving him/her with a baby-sitter.

6. Make sure your child knows when you are leaving, where you will be, and when you will be home, in order to help him/her feel more comfortable about your leaving.

7. Encourage your child to tell you about things that happen when staying with a baby-sitter (e.g., ask him/her if the baby-sitter is nice, how he/she is disciplined, etc.).

8. Allow your child take part in the decision of selecting a baby-sitter. Ask your child who he/she prefers and why.

9. Give the baby sitter information (e.g., where you will be, when you will be home, phone numbers of people to contact in case of an emergency, a list of household rules, etc.) and inform the baby-sitter of the action to take if your child does not behave appropriately.

10. Make certain that your child understands that rules and consequences for inappropriate behavior will be in effect when he/she is with a baby-sitter.

11. Inform the baby-sitter of all of your child's privileges.

12. Make sure the baby-sitter understands the importance of maintaining consistency in the discipline of your child.

13. Write a contract with your child.

For example: I, William, will do what the baby-sitter asks me to do when she is here. When I accomplish this, I can have a friend spend the night.

The contract should be written within the ability level of your child and should focus on only one behavior at a time. (See Appendix for an example of a Behavior Contract.)

14. Make certain that your child sees the relationship between his/her behavior and the consequences which follow (e.g., losing privileges).

15. Allow natural consequences to occur due to your child's inappropriate behavior when with a baby-sitter (e.g., refusing to go to bed on time will result in having to go to bed earlier the next night).

16. Ask the baby-sitter to arrive 10 minutes early so that you can introduce him/her to your child, tell the baby-sitter about things your child enjoys doing, etc.

17. Have your child perform a ''special'' job when staying with a baby-sitter (e.g., helping get a younger brother or sister in bed, keeping the house ''picked up,'' answering the baby-sitter's questions, etc.).

18. Make sure your child understands that the baby-sitter is in charge at all times.

19. Make every attempt to find a baby-sitter who has the skills necessary to manage your child's behavior.

20. If your child is earning a reward for behaving appropriately, has a behavior contract, etc., make sure the baby-sitter is aware of it.

21. Provide as much structure as possible when your child is with a baby-sitter (e.g., your child should have the same meal times, bath time, bed time, etc., as when there is not a baby-sitter in the home).

22. Tell the baby-sitter about any games, friends, etc., that are likely to cause your child to have difficulty behaving appropriately.

23. Do not allow your child's friends to visit when there is a baby-sitter in the home.

24. Require your child to stay in the house, yard, etc., when there is a baby-sitter in the house.

25. Have plenty of activities for your child (e.g., coloring, watching TV or a video, playing games, reading, etc.) when staying with a baby-sitter.

26. Call at least one time while you are away in order to check on things and to talk with the baby-sitter and your child concerning his/her behavior.

27. Make sure the baby-sitter does not allow your child to engage in activities that are overly exciting (e.g., running, jumping, watching certain TV programs, etc.).

28. Provide a list for your baby-sitter of your child's responsibilities (e.g., washing face, brushing teeth, clearing the dinner table, etc.).

29. Provide a list of rules for your baby-sitter to follow concerning your child (e.g., no talking on the phone, stay out of certain rooms, etc.) and list the consequences to follow inappropriate behavior.

30. Interview your baby-sitters to find out the kinds of experiences they have had with children, if their parents will be home while they are baby-sitting if they are young, etc. Have your child be a part of the interview process.

31. Provide the baby-sitter with a list of your child's responsibilities (e.g., lunch time, nap time, when the TV must be turned off, etc.).

32. Tell the baby-sitter in front of your children that you will expect a full report when you get home.

33. If you anticipate inappropriate behavior on the part of your child, call home every hour and a half, two hours, etc., to talk to your child.

34. Schedule activities for the evening for the baby-sitter to supervise (e.g., renting movies, ordering pizza, going out to a fast food restaurant, going skating, etc.).

Note: If your child has a tendency to behave inappropriately, make certain the baby-sitter you hire is at least a young adult, is responsible and has recommendations.

102 Is insensitive to others' feelings

1. Establish rules (e.g., be friendly, make nice comments to others, etc.). These rules should be consistent and followed by everyone in the home. Talk about the rules often and reward your child for being sensitive to others' feelings.

2. Reward your child for being sensitive to others' feelings. Possible rewards include verbal praise (e.g., "Thank you for making only nice comments when your friends were here visiting."), a kiss on the cheek, a hug, having a friend over to play, staying up late, watching a favorite TV show, and playing a game with a parent. (See Appendix for Reward Menu.)

3. If there are other children or adolescents in the home, reward them for being sensitive to others' feelings.

4. Show your child the appropriate way to interact with others. Teach your child appropriate things to say, acceptable things to discuss, etc.

5. Make sure you are sensitive to others' feelings. Do not tease others or say embarrassing things, or your child will learn to do the same.

6. Do not tease, say embarrassing things, etc., when interacting with your child.

7. When your child is insensitive to others' feelings, explain exactly what he/she did wrong, what should have been done and why.

For example: You overhear your child teasing a neighbor's child. Go to your child and say, "You are teasing. You need to stop teasing because you are hurting John's feelings."

8. Write a contract with your child.

For example: I, William, will not tease others for one day. When I accomplish this I can go on a walk with my mother.

The contract should be written within the ability level of your child and should focus on only one behavior at a time. (See Appendix for an example of a Behavior Contract.)

9. Remove the child from the situation until he/she can be sensitive to others' feelings.

10. Teach your child the difference between friendly teasing, where <u>everyone</u>, including the other person, laughs, and teasing that hurts others' feelings.

11. Make certain that your child sees the relationship between his/her behavior and the consequences which follow (e.g., hurting others' feelings, making others mad, being avoided by others, etc.).

12. Teach your child acceptable ways to communicate displeasure, anger, frustration, etc.

13. Make certain your child knows exactly what it is that he/she says or does that embarrasses others and/or hurts their feelings.

14. Sometimes children are unkind in order to get the attention of others. Make certain that your child gets your attention when behaving appropriately.

15. Find a peer with whom your child can play and learn appropriate interaction skills.

16. Do not allow your child to interact with those individuals who he/she embarrasses or whose feelings your child hurts.

17. Reduce any emphasis on competition. Competitiveness or repeated failures may result in anger and frustration which may take the form of teasing, saying things that are embarrassing, etc.

18. Make certain your child knows appropriate conversational things to say to others or in the presence of others.

19. Do not laugh at or ignore your child when he/she is insensitive to others' feelings.

20. Remind your child before guests arrive or visiting with others that he/she should be careful not to embarrass others or say things to hurt their feelings.

21. Tape record your child teasing others and have your child listen to the tape.

22. Supervise your child when interacting with others to make sure your child is sensitive to their feelings.

23. Explain to your child how people feel when they are teased (e.g., their feelings are hurt, they feel bad about themselves, etc.).

24. Have your child put himself/herself in someone else's place (e.g., "How would you feel if someone teased you about being in a lower reading group?" etc.).

25. Talk to your child and explain that everyone is different, some people learn at a slower pace, some kids have trouble walking and running, some children talk differently, etc.

26. Separate your child from those children and adolescents who encourage your child to tease others.

27. After your child teases others or hurts others' feelings, discuss alternative ways in which he/she could have acted.

28. Encourage your child to express feelings to you in a private setting.

29. Answer your child's questions concerning other people (e.g., when your child makes a comment about someone in a wheelchair, take your child aside and explain the handicap). Explaining differences to your child may make him/her willing to accept the differences.

30. Limit your child's opportunities to interact with those persons he/she teases.

31. Increase supervision of your child in those situations in which he/she would be likely to tease others.

103 Talks back

1. Talk to your children in the manner in which you want them to talk to you. Treat them with respect and do not "talk down" to them.

2. Establish rules (e.g., listen calmly to what others have to say, state your opinion in a kind manner, make appropriate comments, accept directions from authority figures, etc.). These rules should be consistent and followed by everyone in the home. Talk about the rules often.

3. Reward your child for following the rules. Possible rewards include verbal praise (e.g., "I like it when you talk nicely to me." "Thank you for listening to my side of the story." etc.), a kiss on the cheek, a hug, having a friend over to play, staying up late, watching a favorite TV show, and playing a game with a parent. (See Appendix for Reward Menu.)

4. If there are other children or adolescents in the home, reward them for following the rules.

5. When your child talks back, explain exactly what he/she is doing wrong, what should have been done and why.

For example: You tell your child to set the table for dinner and your child says, "Set it yourself!" in return. Go to your child and explain that he/she is talking to you in an unkind manner and that he/she needs to be setting the table because dinner will be ready in five minutes.

6. Write a contract with your child.

For example: I, William, for five days in a row, will not talk back to my parents when they tell me it is time to go to bed. When I accomplish this, I can stay up until 11:00 on a Friday night.

The contract should be written within the ability level of your child and should focus on only one behavior at a time. (See Appendix for an example of a Behavior Contract.)

7. Before giving your child a direction, make certain that he/she is capable of doing what you are asking to be done.

8. Do not argue with your child. Arguing with your child or with others tells your child that arguing and talking back is okay.

9. Allow natural consequences to occur as a result of your child talking back (e.g., not getting to participate in the activity, having to go to his/her room, losing special privileges, etc.).

10. Model appropriate ways to question someone's decision.

11. Let your child know that "questioning" should be done in private (at home) and not in public places (e.g., at the mall, skating rink, grocery store, etc.).

12. Be consistent with your child when he/she talks back. Decide on an appropriate consequence for talking back (e.g., go to his/her room for five minutes) and use it every time your child talks back.

13. Separate your child from those children and adolescents who encourage your child to talk back.

14. After giving your child a direction, let your child know that there will not be a discussion (e.g., by walking away, starting a new task, etc.). This will show your child that there will not be any discussion. If your child does not follow the direction, deliver consequences in a consistent manner.

15. When giving your child a chore to do, explain what time it needs to be done, how long your child has to do it, and how long you think it will take.

16. Let your child know that directions will only be given once and that you will not remind him/her to follow the directions.

17. Tape record your child to let him/her know how it sounds when talking back, having the last word, etc.

18. Intervene early when your child is arguing with someone else. Do not allow your child to return to the situation unless he/she can behave appropriately.

19. Make certain that the people in the homes your child visits are aware of the behavioral expectations that you have for your child (e.g., picking up, not arguing, being friendly, etc.).

20. Make certain that baby-sitters and guests in your home understand that your child should not be allowed to talk back. Encourage them to report to you if your child has behaved inappropriately.

21. Make certain that guests in your home are aware of how you deal with your child's talking back.

22. Make certain that your child knows exactly what was said that is rude.

23. Make certain that your child knows exactly what is considered to be talking back, having the last word, etc.

24. Children often talk back, have the last word, etc., in order to get the attention of others. Make certain that your child gets your attention when behaving appropriately.

25. Remind your child before guests, baby-sitters, etc., arrive or before visiting others' homes that he/she should be careful not to talk back.

26. If your child does make rude comments or gestures toward parents, guests, baby-sitters, etc., deal with the situation immediately by sending your child to his/her room, removing your child to talk about the behavior and self-control, etc.

27. Separate your child from those children and adolescents who encourage your child to make rude comments, gestures, etc.

28. Along with a request or directive, provide an incentive statement (e.g., ''Since you always do a good job of setting the table, would you please set it for dinner tonight.'' ''Would you please use your organizational skills to clean out the kitchen cupboards and reorganize them for me?'' etc.).

29. Refrain from communicating with your child in such a way as to stimulate talking back (e.g., ''Your room is always such a mess. When are you going to get in there and clean it up?'' ''Since you're never going to take the trash out, I guess I'm going to have to take it out again tonight.'' etc.)

30. When your child talks back in public (e.g., at the grocery store, in the mall, playing with friends, etc.) remove your child from the situation until he/she can demonstrate self-control and refrain from talking back.

31. Do not surprise your child with requests, chores, etc. Be consistent in expectations so your child knows what his/her responsibilities are and has no reason to talk back (e.g., trash is taken out each evening, he/she washes the dishes on Tuesdays and Thursdays, etc.).

32. Refrain from correcting your child in front of peers as much as possible. Your child is more likely to talk back if told to do something, corrected, etc., in front of friends. Speak with your child in private to scold or correct him/her.

104 Behaves inappropriately when others use the telephone

1. Establish rules for using the telephone (e.g., do not interrupt, play quietly, wait quietly until it is your turn to speak, interrupt only in an emergency, etc.). These rules should be consistent and followed by everyone in the home. Talk about the rules often and reward your child for following the rules.

2. Reward your child for behaving appropriately when someone is using the telephone. Possible rewards include verbal praise (e.g., "I really appreciated how you played quietly while I was on the telephone." "Thank you for waiting your turn to talk." etc.), a kiss on the cheek, a hug, having a friend over to play, staying up late, watching a favorite TV show, and playing a game with a parent. (See Appendix for Reward Menu.)

3. If there are other children or adolescents in the home, reward them for behaving appropriately when someone is using the telephone.

4. Carefully consider your child's age and experience before expecting your child to behave appropriately when someone is using the telephone.

5. Do not use the telephone for long periods of time if your child needs your attention and direct supervision.

6. Do not talk loudly and interrupt your child while he/she is using the telephone.

7. Do not continue talking while your child is behaving inappropriately. End the conversation as soon as possible and deal with your child concerning his/her unacceptable behavior.

8. Tell your child that you will be using the telephone and ask if he/she needs to talk with you or ask any questions before you use the telephone.

9. Give your child individual time and attention when you are finished using the phone.

10. Use a signal which indicates that you are using the telephone (e.g., a sign) in order to let your child know that he/she is to play quietly and not interrupt you.

11. Have regular activities prepared to occupy your child (e.g., coloring, watching TV, eating a snack, playing outside, etc.) while you are using the telephone.

12. When your child behaves inappropriately while someone is using the telephone, explain exactly what he/she is doing wrong, what should have been done and why.

For example: Your child turns up the TV while you are talking on the phone. Go to your child and say, "I am talking on the telephone and cannot hear because the TV is too loud. You need to turn down the TV so I can hear."

13. Allow natural consequences to occur due to your child's behaving inappropriately when someone is talking on the telephone (e.g., having to turn off the TV, not being able to play with friends, losing telephone privileges, etc.).

14. Make certain that your child sees the relationship between his/her behavior and the consequences which follow (e.g., losing telephone privileges, having to turn off the TV, etc.).

15. Write a contract with your child.

For example: I, William, for three days in a row, will not interrupt others when they are using the telephone. When I accomplish this, I can talk to my best friend for 15 minutes on the telephone.

The contract should be written within the ability level of your child and should focus on only one behavior at a time. (See Appendix for an example of a Behavior Contract.)

16. Make your child aware of the number of times he/she behaves inappropriately when someone is using the telephone by placing a star on a chart.

17. Make certain that your child is not being made to wait too long while you use the telephone.

18. Have your child leave a signal for you (e.g., a piece of paper on the table) to let you know that he/she needs to talk with you as soon as possible.

19. Stand or sit in a place where you can see your child and he/she can see you to let your child know that you are aware of the behavior.

20. Remove objects from the phone area that make noise.

21. Allow your child to call and talk with someone on the telephone to understand why he/she needs to be quiet and not interrupt when someone else is using the phone. Discuss how hard it is to listen and talk to someone on the telephone while you are being interrupted.

22. Be consistent when expecting your child to behave appropriately when someone is using the telephone. Do not allow your child to interrupt someone one time and expect appropriate behavior the next time.

23. Post a list of phone rules so your child can review the list daily (e.g., talk quietly when someone is using the phone, only interrupt when there is an emergency, etc.). (See Appendix for Posted Rules.)

24. Provide your child with a pad of paper and a pencil in order to have some form of communication if he/she needs to talk with you while you are on the phone.

25. Limit your "visiting" phone calls to a time when your children are playing outside, napping, etc.

26. Do not interrupt your child while he/she is talking on the telephone.

27. Before beginning a telephone conversation that will be time-consuming, ask your child if he/she needs to talk with you or has any questions.

28. Give your child opportunities to use the telephone to talk with family or friends to satisfy the need to have use of the telephone.

29. Do not spend extended periods of time using the telephone. Your child will be less likely to behave inappropriately if your telephone conversations are of short duration.

A Reminder: Children enjoy using the telephone and may be jealous of others' opportunities to use the telephone. Try to find occasions when your child gets to use the telephone alone, during part of your conversation, etc.

105 Is critical of others

1. Attempt to be as positive as possible with your child and others. If you are overly critical of others, your child will learn to be overly critical.

2. Establish rules for interacting with others (e.g., be friendly, talk nicely, share, play cooperatively, etc.). These rules should be consistent and followed by everyone in the home. Talk about the rules often and reward your child for following the rules.

3. Reward your child for being friendly toward others and not criticizing them. Possible rewards include verbal praise (e.g., "It was nice of you to let your little brother play with you and your friends today!"), a kiss on the cheek, a hug, having a friend over to play, staying up late, watching a favorite TV show, and playing a game with a parent. (See Appendix for Reward Menu.)

4. If there are other children or adolescents in the home, reward them for not being critical of others.

5. Teach your child how to interact with others without being critical.

6. When your child is being overly critical of someone, explain exactly what he/she is doing wrong, what should be done and why.

For example: You overhear your child calling a friend "dumb." Go to your child and say "William, you just told Steve that he is dumb. You need to be patient and friendly or Steve will not want to play with you anymore."

7. Write a contract with your child.

For example: I, William, will not call someone "dumb" for one week. When I accomplish this, I can go roller skating on Saturday.

The contract should be written within the ability level of your child and should focus on only one behavior at a time. (See Appendix for an example of a Behavior Contract.)

8. Allow natural consequences to occur as a result of your child being overly critical of others.

9. Make certain that your child sees the relationship between his/her behavior and the consequences which follow (e.g., hurting others' feelings, losing friends, etc.).

10. Tape record your child being critical of others and let him/her listen to the tape.

11. Explain to your child how others might feel about being called "dumb" or "stupid," having fun made of them, etc.

12. Have your child put himself/herself in someone else's place (e.g., "How would you feel if someone called you dumb or stupid?").

13. Talk to your child and explain that everyone is different (e.g., some people learn at a slower pace than others, some kids have trouble walking and running, some children talk differently, etc.).

14. Answer your child's questions concerning other people (e.g., when your child makes a comment about someone in a wheelchair, take your child aside and explain some possible reasons for the person being in the wheelchair). Explaining differences to your child may make him/her willing to accept individual differences.

15. Encourage you child to associate with people of different backgrounds, colors, handicaps, etc. This will help your child to become more accepting of individual differences.

16. Encourage your child to express feelings to you in a private setting.

17. Be consistent. Try to deal with your child's behavior in a manner that is as fair as possible.

18. Discuss alternative ways in which your child could have acted after teasing and/or hurting others' feelings.

19. Encourage your child to have friends over to your house in order to provide supervision in activities so you can make certain your child is not being overly critical of others.

20. Separate your child from those children and adolescents who encourage your child to be critical of others.

21. Immediately remove your child from the situation when he/she begins to be critical of others. Do not allow your child to return unless he/she can demonstrate acceptable behavior.

22. Teach your child to respect others and their belongings by respecting your child's belongings.

23. Increase supervision of your child (e.g., direct supervision by you, another adult, older adolescents, etc.).

106 Mistreats younger brothers and sisters

1. Establish rules (e.g., play cooperatively, share toys, do not fight, etc.). These rules should be consistent and followed by everyone in the home. Talk about the rules often and reward your child for following the rules.

2. Reward your child for treating younger brothers and/or sisters nicely. Possible rewards include verbal praise (e.g., "Thank you for helping your brother pick up his toys!" "I really appreciate it when you play cooperatively with your sister." etc.), a kiss on the cheek, a hug, having a friend over to play, staying up late, watching a favorite TV show, and playing a game with a parent. (See Appendix for Reward Menu.)

3. Reward all of your children for treating their brothers and/or sisters nicely.

4. Carefully consider your child's age before expecting him/her to play cooperatively, share toys, and not fight with brothers and/or sisters.

5. Show your child how to play cooperatively, share toys, and settle conflicts without fighting.

6. Treat your children with respect. If you mistreat them, they will learn to mistreat others.

7. When your child mistreats a younger brother and/or sister, explain exactly what he/she did wrong, what should have been done and why.

For example: You overhear your child calling his/her younger brother names. Go to your child and say, "William, you are calling your brother names. When you are upset you need to talk about your feelings without calling someone names. When you call someone names, it hurts their feelings and they won't want to be friends with you."

8. Teach your child alternative ways to deal with anger and frustration rather than mistreating younger brothers and/or sisters (e.g., move away from the situation, talk with a parent, etc.).

9. Immediately remove your child from younger brothers and/or sisters until he/she can treat them nicely.

10. Write a contract with your child.

For example: I, William, for four days in a row, will not call Kim names when I get mad at her. When I accomplish this, I can camp out 1 night in the yard with Dad.

The contract should be written within the ability level of your child and should focus on only one behavior at a time. (See Appendix for an example of a Behavior Contract.)

11. Make certain that your child sees the relationship between his/her behavior and the consequences which follow (e.g., loss of privileges).

12. Reduce the emphasis on competitiveness. Competition may cause your child to mistreat younger brothers and/or sisters.

13. Supervise your children's interactions at all times in order to correct your child and model appropriate interaction skills.

14. Limit your child's interaction with younger brothers and/or sisters when you are unable to supervise them.

15. Do not leave your child unsupervised at any time.

16. Spend individual time with all of your children. Do not give more attention to the younger one(s) than to the older ones. Do not make your children compete for your attention, time, and/or praise.

17. Speak with your child about the limitations and "immature" behaviors of younger brothers and/or sisters in order to help your child become more tolerant.

18. Do not require your child to take a parental role with younger brothers and/or sisters. Your child should not be expected to feed, dress, bath, supervise, etc., younger brothers and/or sisters on a frequent basis.

19. Allow your child some time for activities without having a younger brother and/or sister around to interfere.

20. Do not assume that your child is being treated nicely by a younger brother and/or sister. The younger brother or sister may be stimulating inappropriate behavior on the part of the older brother or sister.

21. Give your child certain "important" responsibilities involving younger brothers and/or sisters (e.g., baby-sitting for 15 minutes, helping with giving baths, etc.). Reward your child for helping (e.g., give your child a dollar, spend time alone with him/her, etc.)

22. Make certain that your child is allowed to play with friends without a little brother or sister around.

23. Specify a certain chair or corner where your child can go when he/she begins to mistreat younger brothers and/or sisters. Make certain that baby-sitters, guests, etc., are aware of the consequences for mistreating brothers and/or sisters.

24. Be consistent. Try to deal with your child and behavior in a manner that is as consistent as possible (e.g., by reacting in the same manner each time, using the same consequences, etc.).

25. Make certain your child knows the "responsibilities" of being an older brother or sister (e.g., setting a good example, helping Mom and Dad, etc.).

26. Have a special closet for your child to put toys, games, clothes, etc., that he/she does not want brothers and/or sisters to have.

27. Have your child spend short periods of time with younger brothers and/or sisters in order to be more patient with them.

28. Remind your child of how it felt when he/she was learning something new and help your child see how younger brothers and/or sisters feel.

29. Show your child how to be patient with younger brothers and/or sisters by being patient yourself (e.g., talk in a calm voice, avoid demonstrating frustration or anger, etc.).

30. Give your child suggestions of things to do when angry (e.g., counting to 10, saying the alphabet, walking away from the situation and then returning, etc.) in order to avoid being mean or angry with younger brothers and/or sisters.

31. Make certain the younger brother or sister has enough personal possessions so he/she does not need to play with the older brother or sister's things.

32. Make certain your child is not allowed time alone with a younger brother or sister when he/she is upset or angry.

107 Has trouble getting along with friends

1. Establish rules for getting along with friends (e.g., play cooperatively, share, talk in an acceptable manner, do not fight, etc.). These rules should be consistent and followed by everyone in the home. Talk about the rules often and reward your child for following the rules.

2. Reward your child for getting along with friends. Possible rewards include verbal praise (e.g., "I'm so proud of you for playing fairly with your friends!"), a kiss on the cheek, a hug, having a friend over to play, staying up late, watching a favorite TV show, and playing a game with a parent. (See Appendix for Reward Menu.)

3. If there are other children or adolescents in the home, reward them for getting along with their friends.

4. Carefully consider your child's age and experience in playing with others before expecting your child to play cooperatively and share.

5. Show your child how to play cooperatively, share, talk in an acceptable manner, and refrain from fighting with others.

6. Make sure that you get along with others. Your child learns how to interact with others by watching your interactions.

7. When your child does not get along with a friend, explain exactly what he/she is doing wrong, what should have been done and why.

For example: You see your child playing uncooperatively with a friend. Go to your child and say, "William, you are not sharing. You need to share the toys so others will want to play with you."

8. Write a contract with your child.

For example: I, William, will share my toys with my friends. When I do, I can watch a favorite TV show.

The contract should be written within the ability level of your child and should focus on only one behavior at a time. (See Appendix for an example of a Behavior Contract.)

9. Make certain that your child sees the relationship between his/her behavior and the consequences which follow (e.g., calling names will cause friends to not want to play).

10. Have your child watch an older brother and/or sister play nicely with their friends. This will help your child learn to treat friends nicely.

11. Immediately remove your child from interacting with friends when he/she has trouble getting along with them.

12. Do not allow your child to play with those children with whom he/she has trouble getting along.

13. Do not emphasize competition. Competitive activities may cause your child to have trouble getting along with friends.

14. Supervise your child's interactions with friends in order to stop inappropriate behavior and encourage appropriate behavior.

15. Do not allow your child to play stimulating activities which cause him/her to have trouble getting along with friends.

16. When your child has had trouble getting along with friends, sit down and talk about the alternative things he/she could have done in order to help your child understand how to get along better with friends.

17. Talk with your child about appropriate ways to deal with anger and frustration (e.g., compromising, walking away from the situation, talking about the problem with an adult, etc.).

18. Do not make your child play with a certain child or group of children. Allow your child to pick his/her own friends.

19. Encourage your child to play with children or adolescents who get along well with others.

20. Treat your child with respect. Talk in an objective manner at all times using a calm, quiet voice without losing your temper.

21. Be consistent. Try to deal with your child and his/her behavior in a manner that is as consistent as possible (e.g., react in the same manner each time, use the same consequences, etc.).

22. Provide your child with a quiet place to go when he/she becomes upset or angry with a friend or friends.

23. Help your child choose activities to play when friends are visiting that do not cause him/her to become angry, frustrated, anxious, etc.

24. Intervene early when your child begins to argue, threaten, etc., in order to prevent your child from fighting.

25. Arrange for your child to be involved in many activities with other children in order to help him/her learn the skills necessary to interact appropriately with others.

26. Make sure your child understands that the privilege of having a friend over or going to a friend's house will be taken away if he/she is not nice to friends.

27. Do not laugh at your child or ignore your child when he/she is insensitive to others' feelings.

28. Get to know your child's friends and their parents and maintain open communication with them.

29. Encourage your child to participate in supervised extracurricular activities at school (e.g., Chess Club, Math Club, team sports, etc.) in order to help him/her learn appropriate interaction skills.

30. Allow your child to participate in activities that will teach responsibility and respect for others (e.g., Boy Scouts, Girl Scouts, 4-H, swimming, tennis, etc.).

31. Give your child suggestions of things to do (e.g., count to 10, say the alphabet, walk away from the situation and then return, etc.) in order to avoid getting upset and fighting.

32. Remind your child before going to school or out to play that he/she is not to argue or fight.

33. Ask your child's teacher to have your child participate in group activities, act as a peer tutor, etc., in order to help your child learn interaction skills with others.

34. Talk to the school counselor about getting your child in a group to discuss and deal with angry feelings.

35. Children often are unkind in order to get the attention of others. Make certain that your child gets your attention when behaving appropriately.

36. If your child has difficulty playing nicely with others, do not allow play time unless he/she can do so in a friendly manner.

37. Do not appear shocked or surprised when your child gets in trouble in the neighborhood or at school. Deal with the behavior in a calm and deliberate manner.

38. Separate your child from those children or adolescents who encourage your child to argue and fight.

39. Allow your child to pick his/her own friends and play with them as long as he/she can be friendly, polite and cooperative.

40. Point out to your child how it feels to be teased and/or have people make fun of him/her. Help your child understand that this is how others feel when teased and/or made fun of.

41. Discuss alternative ways in which your child could have acted, after fighting with others.

42. Allow natural consequences to occur due to your child's inappropriate behavior (e.g., fighting with friends results in not being able to have them over, visit in their homes, play with them outside of the home, etc.).

43. Inform the parents of your child's friends of the tendency of your child to have trouble getting along with friends in order that they may increase supervision when your child is at their houses.

108 Fights at school and/or in the neighborhood

1. Establish rules for getting along with others (e.g., play cooperatively, talk in an acceptable manner, do not fight, etc.). These rules should be consistent and followed by everyone in the home. Talk about the rules often and reward your child for following the rules.

2. Reward your child for not fighting at school and/or in the neighborhood. Possible rewards include verbal praise (e.g., "I'm so proud of you for walking away from a possible fight on the playground!"), a kiss on the cheek, a hug, having a friend over to play, staying up late, watching a favorite TV show, and playing a game with a parent. (See Appendix for Reward Menu.)

3. If there are other children or adolescents in the home, reward them for getting along with others at school and/or in the neighborhood.

4. Show your child how to avoid fighting with others (e.g., play cooperatively, share, talk in an acceptable manner, do not threaten others, etc.).

5. Make sure that you do not fight with others. Your child learns how to interact with others by watching your interactions.

6. When your child fights, explain exactly what he/she is doing wrong, what should have been done and why.

For example: You receive a phone call about your child fighting at school. When your child comes home from school, sit down with him/her and say, "William, you were fighting today at school. The next time you get into a conflict with another child, you need to walk away from the situation. If you resort to fighting, you will be suspended from school."

7. Write a contract with your child.

For example: I, William, will not fight at school for one week. When I accomplish this I can stay up late on Saturday night.

The contract should be written within the ability level of your child and should focus on only one behavior at a time. (See Appendix for an example of a Behavior Contract.)

8. Make certain that your child sees the relationship between his/her behavior and the consequences which follow (e.g., losing friends, having to stay in from recess, being suspended from school, etc.).

9. Have your child watch an older brother and/or sister handle conflicts with others. This will help your child learn how to solve conflicts without resorting to fighting.

10. Immediately remove your child from interacting with others when beginning to fight.

11. Do not allow your child to play with those children with whom he/she fights.

12. Do not emphasize competition. Competitive activities may cause your child to fight.

13. Supervise or make sure your child is supervised when interacting with others.

14. Do not allow your child to play stimulating activities which cause fighting.

15. When your child fights, sit down and discuss the alternative things that could have been done to avoid fighting.

16. Talk with your child about appropriate ways to deal with anger and frustration (e.g., compromise, walk away from the situation, talk with an adult about the problem, etc.).

17. Do not make your child play with a certain child or group of children. Allow your child to pick his/her own friends.

18. Encourage your child to interact with those children with whom he/she can demonstrate appropriate behavior.

19. Intervene early when your child begins to argue, threaten, etc., in order to prevent fighting.

20. Arrange for your child to be involved in many activities with other children in order to help him/her learn the skills necessary to interact appropriately with others.

21. Make sure your child understands that the privilege of having a friend over or going to a friend's house will be taken away if fighting begins.

22. Make sure your child understands the natural consequences of fighting (e.g., others being hurt, getting hurt himself/herself, etc.).

23. Be consistent. Try to deal with your child and the behavior in a manner that is as fair as possible (e.g., react in the same manner, use the same consequences, etc.).

24. Give your child suggestions of things to do (e.g., count to 10, say the alphabet, walk away from the situation and then return, etc.) in order to avoid getting upset and fighting.

25. Ask your child's teacher to allow your child to participate in group activities, act as a peer tutor, etc., in order to help him/her learn interaction skills with others.

26. Talk to the school counselor about getting your child in a group to discuss and deal with angry feelings.

27. Children often are unkind in order to get the attention of others. Make certain that your child gets your attention when behaving appropriately.

28. If your child has difficulty playing nicely with others, do not allow play time unless he/she can do so in a friendly manner.

29. Do not appear shocked or surprised when your child gets in trouble in the neighborhood or at school. Deal with the behavior in a calm and deliberate manner.

30. Remind your child before going to school or out to play that he/she is not to argue or fight.

31. Separate your child from those children or adolescents who encourage your child to argue and fight.

32. Get to know your child's friends and their parents and maintain open communication with them.

33. Encourage your child to participate in supervised extracurricular activities at school (e.g., Chess Club, Math Club, team sports, etc.) in order to help him/her learn appropriate interaction skills.

34. Allow your child to pick his/her own friends and play with them as long as he/she can be friendly, polite and cooperative.

35. Point out to your child how it feels to be teased and/or have people make fun of him/her. Help your child understand that this is how others feel when teased and/or made fun of.

36. Discuss alternative ways in which your child could have acted, after fighting with others.

37. Carefully consider your child's age and experience in playing with others before expecting him/her to play cooperatively and share.

38. Encourage your child to play with children or adolescents who get along well with others.

39. Treat your child with respect. Always talk in an objective manner using a calm, quiet voice without losing your temper.

40. Provide your child with a quiet place to go when he/she becomes upset or angry with a friend or friends.

41. Make certain that your child is allowed to play with friends without a little brother or sister present.

42. Do not laugh at or ignore your child when fighting with other children.

43. Allow natural consequences to occur due to your child's inappropriate behavior (e.g., fighting with friends results in not being able to have them over, visit in their homes, play with them outside of the home, etc.).

44. Inform the parents of your child's friends of the tendency of your child to have trouble getting along with friends in order that they may increase supervision when your child is at their houses.

109 Is overly competitive

1. Establish rules for playing games (e.g., share materials, take turns, follow game rules, problem-solve, talk nicely, etc.). These rules should be consistent and followed by everyone in the home. Talk about the rules often.

2. Reward your child for following the rules. Possible rewards include verbal praise (e.g., "Thank you for waiting your turn to play the game."), a kiss on the cheek, a hug, having a friend over to play, staying up late, watching a favorite TV show, and playing a game with a parent. (See Appendix for Reward Menu.)

3. If there are other children or adolescents in the home, reward them for sharing materials, taking turns, following game rules, problem-solving, talking nicely, etc.

4. When your child is overly competitive, explain exactly what he/she is doing wrong, what should have been done and why.

For example: Your child is arguing about the rules of a game. Explain the rules of the game and say, "If you are going to play, you need to stop arguing about the rules."

5. Make sure you share materials, take turns, follow game rules, problem-solve, and talk nicely when engaged in competitive games.

6. Limit your child's participation in competitive activities.

7. Teach your child appropriate ways in which to deal with anger, frustration, over-competitiveness, etc.

8. Write a contract with your child.

For example: I, William, will follow the rules of the game. When I accomplish this, I can stay up late on a Saturday night.

The contract should be written within the ability level of your child and should focus on only one behavior at a time. (See Appendix for an example of a Behavior Contract.)

9. Immediately remove your child from an activity until he/she can play by the rules, refrain from arguing, take turns, stop crying, etc.

10. Make certain that your child sees the relationship between his/her behavior and the consequences which follow (e.g., others not wanting to play, being removed from the activity, etc.).

11. Reduce the emphasis on competition and "winning." Emphasize working together, having fun, making new friends, etc.

12. Supervise your child closely when engaged in competitive activities in order to provide alternative ways in which to behave.

13. Before beginning a game or competitive activity, make sure your child knows the rules, is familiar with the game, and will be compatible with the other individuals who will be playing.

14. Allow natural consequences to occur as a result of your child's overcompetitiveness (e.g., others may not want to interact, competition over grades may result in loss of friends, always having to tell the biggest tale or brag about ownership may limit the number of friends, etc.).

15. Be a model for participating for enjoyment rather than always needing to "win" or "beat" someone else.

16. Encourage your child to engage in less competitive activities (e.g., reading, clubs, scouting, student council, etc.).

17. Encourage your child to participate in activities, sports, etc., for self-improvement rather than to "win" or "beat" someone else (e.g., try to improve personal batting average or defensive skills rather than being disappointed if his/her team does not win).

18. Encourage your child to participate in more individualized sports (e.g., aerobics, swimming, track and field, golf, etc.).

19. Help your child to have self-confidence and satisfaction in self-worth and successes by pointing out strengths, emphasizing positive aspects, etc.

20. Reduce the emphasis on competition among brothers and sisters in your family. Competitiveness learned in the home will be demonstrated at school and elsewhere.

21. Encourage your child to refrain from "one-upmanship" with friends (e.g., when friends talk about a new possession, it may be more desirable to say "You're lucky." or "That's great." rather than "That's nothing, my dad's going to buy me a....").

22. Encourage your child to play and interact with friends who are not highly competitive.

23. Use natural consequences which will demonstrate to your child that when being overly competitive to the extent of making participation unpleasant, participation will need to be discontinued for awhile (e.g., becoming angry and abusive during a game will result in sitting out the rest of the game, arguing with officials will result in being thrown out of a game, etc.).

110 Teases and makes fun of others

1. Establish rules (e.g., be friendly, polite, cooperative, etc.). These rules should be consistent and followed by everyone in the home. Talk about the rules often.

2. Reward your child for being friendly, polite, and cooperative toward others. Possible rewards include verbal praise (e.g., ''I'm proud of you for not teasing your friend.'' ''You are a good friend! You don't make fun of others.'' etc.), a kiss on the cheek, a hug, having a friend over to play, staying up late, watching a favorite TV show, and playing a game with a parent. (See Appendix for Reward Menu.)

3. If there are other children or adolescents in the home, reward them for being friendly, polite, and cooperative toward others.

4. Do not allow others to tease and/or make fun of your child.

5. Make sure that you do not tease and/or make fun of others and/or your child. If you do, your child will learn to tease and/or make fun of others.

6. Make sure your child understands when it is acceptable to tease and/or make fun of others (e.g., when it is in a friendly manner, when the other person teases and/or makes fun of you in return, etc.).

7. When your child teases and/or makes fun of others, explain exactly what he/she is doing wrong, what should be done and why.

For example: You overhear your child teasing another child. Go to your child and say, ''William, you are teasing Kim. You need to stop teasing because Kim does not think it is funny and she will not want to play with you.''

8. Write a contract with your child.

For example: I, William, will not make fun of others for four days in a row. When I accomplish this, I can have a friend spend the night.

The contract should be written within the ability level of your child and should focus on only one behavior at a time. (See Appendix for an example of a Behavior Contract.)

9. Make certain that your child sees the relationship between his/her behavior and the consequences which follow (e.g., hurting others' feelings, others not wanting to play, exclusion from activities, etc.).

10. Talk with your child about appropriate ways to deal with anger, frustration, disappointment, etc.

11. Make sure your child understands the difference between friendly teasing and hurting others' feelings.

12. Immediately remove your child from interacting with others when teasing and/or making fun of others begins.

13. Discuss alternative ways in which your child could have acted, after teasing and/or hurting others' feelings.

14. Reduce the emphasis on competition. Competitive activities may cause your child to tease and/or make fun of others.

15. Provide your child with opportunities to play with others who do not tease and/or make fun in order to learn to be friendly, polite, and cooperative.

16. Do not allow your child to play with those individuals whom he/she teases and/or makes fun.

17. Do not make your child play with children whom he/she does not like or enjoy playing.

18. Allow your child to pick his/her own friends and play with them as long as your child can be friendly, polite and cooperative.

19. Point out to your child how it feels to be teased and/or have someone make fun of him/her. Help your child understand that this is how others feel when they are teased and/or made fun of.

20. Do not reinforce your child's inappropriate behavior by laughing when your child is silly, rude, etc.

21. Supervise your child at all times in order to prevent teasing and/or making fun of others. Reduce the supervision as your child is able to be friendly, polite, and cooperative with others.

22. Tape record your child teasing and making fun of others and let your child listen to the tape.

23. Talk with your child about individual differences and discuss strengths and weaknesses of individuals your child knows.

24. Talk to your child and explain to him/ her that everyone is different, some people learn at a slower pace, some kids have trouble walking and running, some children talk differently, etc.

25. Separate your child from those children and adolescents who encourage your child to tease others.

26. Discuss alternative ways in which your child could have acted after teasing and/or hurting others' feelings.

27. Answer your child's questions concerning other people (e.g., when your child makes a comment about someone in a wheelchair, take your child aside and explain about the handicap). Explaining differences to your child may make him/her willing to accept differences.

28. Encourage your child to express feelings to you in a private setting.

29. Limit your child's opportunities to interact with those persons he/she teases.

30. Teach your child the difference between friendly teasing, where <u>everyone</u>, including the other person, laughs, and teasing that hurts others' feelings.

31. Remove your child from the situation until he/she can be sensitive to others' feelings.

32. Make certain your child knows exactly what it is that is said or done to embarrass others and/or hurts their feelings.

33. Sometimes children are unkind in order to get the attention of others. Make certain that your child gets your attention when behaving appropriately.

34. Make certain your child knows appropriate conversational things to say to others or in the presence of others.

35. Remind your child before guests arrive or visiting with others that he/she should be careful not to embarrass others or say things to hurt their feelings.

111 Is shy

1. Encourage your child to interact with others.

2. Teach your child conversational questions (e.g., "Hi! How are you?" "What have you been doing?" "What are some of your hobbies?" "Would you like to play a game?" etc.).

3. Do not force your child to interact with others.

4. Reward your child for interacting with peers, guests, baby-sitters, etc. Possible rewards include verbal praise (e.g., "I'm very proud of you for talking with our guests!"), a kiss on the cheek, a hug, having a friend over to play, staying up late, watching a favorite TV show, and playing a game with a parent. (See Appendix for Reward Menu.)

5. If there are other children or adolescents in the home, reward them for interacting with peers, guests, baby-sitters, etc.

6. Allow your child time to get used to being around peers, guests, baby-sitters, etc., before expecting him/her to interact with them.

7. Talk with your child about peers, guests, baby-sitters, etc., before they arrive in order to help your child prepare for their arrival and to help him/her feel more comfortable when they are in your home.

8. Make certain that your child sees the relationship between his/her behavior and the consequences which follow (e.g., having no one with whom to play, not making new friends, etc.).

9. Ask your child's teacher to have your child meet new children, participate in group activities, act as a peer tutor, etc., in order to help him/her feel more comfortable when interacting with others.

10. Provide your child with frequent opportunities to meet new people.

11. Be a model for your child by introducing yourself, conversing with others, meeting new people, shaking hands, etc.

12. Arrange for your child to help others learn a new skill, share abilities with peers, etc., in order to help him/her feel more comfortable when interacting with others.

13. Provide your child with opportunities to join clubs, participate in sports, volunteer to help others, etc., in order to help him/her feel more comfortable when interacting with others.

14. Ask your child why he/she does not want to interact with peers, guests, baby-sitters, etc.

15. If your child does not feel comfortable enough to interact with a certain baby-sitter, find another baby-sitter with whom your child feels more comfortable.

16. Do not leave your child with someone with whom he/she does not feel comfortable.

17. Have a calendar of family activities and indicate on the calendar when guests will visit, doctors' appointments, etc.

18. Sit down and explain changes, new activities, etc., a few days before they happen if possible.

19. Do not "push" your child too hard when encouraging interaction with others. Your child may become frightened.

20. Participate in new situations with your child (e.g., go with your child on the first day of school, teach your child how to ride a bike, be near when he/she is learning to swim, etc.).

21. Allow enough time for your child to prepare for a new activity (e.g., talking about the first day of school several months in advance, going to visit the school several weeks before it starts, etc.).

22. Encourage your child to participate in new activities or meet new people when with a peer with whom your child feels comfortable (e.g., going to a birthday party with a friend, having a friend over when a new baby-sitter comes, etc.).

23. Make those who are in contact with your child aware of your child's shyness in order that they may help your child feel comfortable in new situations.

24. Because your child is shy, do not inadvertently reinforce the shyness by letting your child get out of doing things because he/she is afraid.

25. Encourage your child to attempt new things and to play with children who are outgoing.

26. Discuss your child's schedule at the beginning of each day in order to prepare for the day and avoid unpleasant surprises.

27. Encourage your child to have friends to your house to play in order to feel comfortable playing with others. Gradually require your child to play at others' homes as he/she feels more comfortable with new friends, other children's parents, etc.

28. Make certain your child is old enough to be expected to greet new situations, peers, baby-sitters, adults, etc., without demonstrating some shyness or fear of a new situation.

29. Get to know your child's friends and their parents and maintain open communication with them.

30. Do not make meeting someone new threatening for your child (i.e., a "big deal"). Introduce your child to the new situation and encourage your child to be a part of conversations, games, etc. If you do not encourage your child to participate in the new situation, he/she may find it easier to ignore the situation.

31. Do not "make fun" of your child when he/she acts shy or avoids new situations.

32. Encourage your child to play with children who are younger and with whom he/she would be less likely to be shy.

33. Participate in new situations with your child. Gradually require your child to attempt new things as he/she becomes comfortable with new situations.

34. Teach your child how to meet new people by discussing how to shake hands, answer conversational questions as well as ask conversational questions (e.g., "I'm fine. How are you?") etc.

1. Establish rules for interacting with others (e.g., mind your own business, be friendly, play cooperatively, etc.). These rules should be consistent and followed by everyone in the home. Talk about the rules often.

2. Reward your child for interacting with others in an appropriate manner. Possible rewards include verbal praise (e.g., "I'm proud of you for not tattling on others. You're doing great at minding your own business."), a kiss on the cheek, a hug, having a friend over to play, staying up late, watching a favorite TV show, and playing a game with a parent. (See Appendix for Reward Menu.)

3. If there are other children or adolescents in the home, reward them for interacting appropriately with others.

4. Carefully consider your child's age and experience in interacting with others before expecting your child to always be friendly, cooperative, and mind his/her own business.

5. Do not allow your child to play with specific children if it results in tattling.

6. Teach your child how to deal with others' inappropriate behavior without resorting to tattling on them (e.g., ignore them, walk away from the situation, talk with them about their behavior, etc.).

7. Supervise your child's activities as closely as possible in order to reduce the need to tattle on others.

8. When your child tattles, explain exactly what he/she is doing wrong, what should be done and why.

For example: Your child comes to you and tattles on an older sister. When your child is through tattling say, "William, you are tattling. You need to mind your own business because others will not want to play with you if you tattle on them."

9. Make certain that your child sees the relationship between his/her behavior and the consequences which follow (e.g., others avoiding your child, teasing, making fun, etc.).

10. Write a contract with your child.

For example: I, William, will not tattle on Kim for four days in a row. When I accomplish this I can ask a friend to go roller skating with me on Saturday.

The contract should be written within the ability level of your child and should focus on only one behavior at a time. (See Appendix for an example of a Behavior Contract.)

11. Make sure your child knows which information is important to report (e.g., emergencies, injuries, fighting, etc.).

12. Make sure your child knows which information is not appropriate to report (e.g., others calling names, not playing fairly, etc.).

13. Do not overreact when your child tattles. Deal only with those behaviors you observe, not the ones that are reported to you in a "tattling manner."

14. Refuse to listen to your child tattle by immediately stopping your child when tattling begins.

15. Reduce the opportunity for your child to be in competitive activities that cause tattling.

16. Immediately remove your child from interacting with others when tattling begins.

17. Allow natural consequences to occur when your child tattles (e.g., friends not wanting to play, people not inviting your child to do things, etc.).

18. When your child comes to you to tattle, stop and ask, "Is this something that is so important that you need to come to me?" "Is someone hurt, or is this something you can solve without me?", etc.

19. Make certain that visitors in your home, baby-sitters, teachers, etc., are aware of your child's tendency to tattle so they will know not to respond to the tattling unless it is necessary (as in Intervention 18).

20. Be consistent in dealing with your child's tattling. Do not allow tattling one time and expect appropriate behavior the next time.

21. Make a list of the number of times a day your child tattles. Make your child aware of the number of times a day he/she comes to you or another adult to tattle.

22. If your child has difficulty playing nicely with others, do not allow play time.

23. Make sure that others are friendly and cooperative when interacting with your child.

24. Encourage your child to play with peers who do not tattle.

25. Do not reinforce your child's tattling by checking on the situation every time your child comes to you to tattle.

26. Remind your child before having a friend over, going to a friend's house, etc., about which situations are important enough to involve an adult and which situations are considered tattling.

27. Have your child repeat to you the rules for playing with others; say, "Now tell me what I said."

28. If you are leaving your child somewhere to play, remind your child in front of the adult who is in charge that there will be no tattling and to only report things that need adult attention.

29. Provide increased supervision of your child with friends, playmates, etc., in order to prevent the opportunity/need to tattle (e.g., look in on your child's activities frequently).

30. Increase supervision of your child in situations where tattling is likely to occur.

31. When your child has friends over to play, encourage your child to select a few toys, games, etc., with which he/she wants to play while friends are there. By offering just a few games, toys, etc., you reduce the chance of fighting and tattling over selecting a toy, what to play next, etc.

32. Do not make your child play with a certain child or group of children. Allow your child to pick his/her own friends.

33. Determine the thing about which your child most frequently tattles (e.g., not playing a certain game fairly, someone calling names, someone playing with a certain toy, etc.) and remove whatever it is from your child's situation (e.g., take the game away, do not invite the child who calls names over again, remove the toy that always causes problems, etc.).

34. Determine if there is legitimate reason for your child to report the behavior of others (another child may be playing too roughly, breaking toys, etc.).

35. Make certain that your child is aware that unnecessary tattling will result in friends being sent home, termination of activities, etc.

36. Talk to your child about ways of handling situations successfully without tattling (e.g., walk away from a situation, change to another activity, ask for help, etc.).

37. Make certain that there are enough play items for your child and friends, that sharing is not a problem, etc.

113 Forcibly takes things from others

1. Establish rules (e.g., be friendly, ask permission to borrow things, share, etc.). These rules should be consistent and followed by everyone in the home. Talk about the rules often and reward your child for following the rules.

2. Reward your child for not taking things from others in a forceful manner. Possible rewards include verbal praise (e.g., "Thank you for asking your brother's permission to use his bike."), a kiss on the cheek, a hug, having a friend over to play, staying up late, watching a favorite TV show, and playing a game with a parent. (See Appendix for Reward Menu.)

3. If there are other children or adolescents in the home, reward them for not taking things from others in a forceful manner.

4. Show your child how to ask permission to use something and how to react if he/she is told "no."

5. When your child forcefully takes things from others, explain exactly what he/she did wrong, what should have been done and why.

For example: You see your child forcefully taking a toy away from a peer. Go to your child and say, "William, you grabbed the toy from Kim. You need to ask permission to use things before taking them. If you don't, others will not want to play with you."

6. Write a contract with your child.

For example: I, William, will not take things from others in a forceful manner, for four days in a row. When I accomplish this, I can spend $1 at the store.

The contract should be written within the ability level of your child and should focus on only one behavior at a time. (See Appendix for an example of a Behavior Contract.)

7. Immediately remove your child from interacting with others when he/she begins to take things in a forceful manner.

8. Supervise your child at all times in order to prevent your child from taking things from others in a forceful manner.

9. Make certain that your child sees the relationship between his/her behavior and the consequences which follow (e.g., others avoiding your child, being removed from an activity, hurting someone, breaking something, etc.).

10. Make certain that your child returns, as soon as possible, those things which have been taken from others in a forceful manner.

11. Do not allow others to take things from your child in a forceful manner.

12. Identify those things your child takes from others in a forceful manner and allow your child to earn them for not taking things from others in a forceful manner.

13. Teach your child to handle anger, frustration, disappointment, etc., by walking away from the situation, talking with an adult, etc.

14. Do not take things from others in a forceful manner. Your child will learn to forcefully take things from others if you do so.

15. Teach your child to ask for things in a positive manner. Teach key words and phrases (e.g., "May I please use your bike?" "May I borrow your skateboard?" "Do you mind if I play with your doll?" etc.).

16. Set an example for your child by asking for things in a positive manner. Use key words and phrases (e.g., "May I please use your pencil?" "May I use your brush?" etc.).

17. Do not allow your child to play with other children if your child has trouble getting along.

18. Intervene early when your child begins to take things forcefully in order to prevent him/her from fighting.

19. Give your child suggestions of things to do (e.g., count to 10, say the alphabet, walk away from the situation and then return, etc.) in order to avoid taking things away forcefully, getting upset, etc.

20. Be consistent. Try to deal with your child and his/her behavior in a manner that is as fair as possible by reacting in the same manner, using the same consequences, etc.

21. Carefully consider your child's age and experience in playing with others before expecting him/her to play cooperatively.

22. Show your child how to play cooperatively, share, talk in an acceptable manner, and refrain from fighting with others.

23. Make sure that you get along with others. Your child learns how to interact with others by watching how you interact.

24. Do not allow your child to play stimulating activities which cause him/her to have trouble getting along with friends.

25. Do not make your child play with a certain child or group of children. Allow your child to pick his/her own friends.

26. Encourage your child to play with children or adolescents who get along well with others.

27. Provide your child with a quiet place to go if upset or angry with a friend or friends.

28. Help your child choose activities, toys, games, etc., to play when friends are over that do not cause him/her to become angry, frustrated, etc.

29. Arrange for your child to be involved in many activities with other children in order to learn the skills necessary to interact appropriately with them.

30. Make sure your child understands that the privilege of having a friend over or going to a friend's house will be taken away if he/she is not nice to friends.

31. Teach your child the concept of borrowing by "loaning" those things he/she has been taking from others and then requiring the return of those things. Repeat this process so your child is comfortable asking for things, returning them, etc.

32. Get to know your child's friends and their parents and maintain open communication with them.

33. Make certain that your child does not get away with taking things from others by having him/her return what was taken forcefully.

34. Make certain your child understands that things broken, destroyed, etc., when taking things forcefully, will be replaced by him/her.

35. Remind your child before going to a friend's house, having a friend over, etc., about sharing and not taking things forcefully from others.

36. Do not expect your child to share everything with others. Your child should have some belongings that do not have to be shared with others.

37. Identify those things your child has been taking from others and provide those items as reinforcers for appropriate behavior.

38. Make certain your child understands that he/she can earn those things that are wanted. Anything can be earned to avoid stealing or forcefully taking things from others.

39. Teach your child to "take turns" sharing possessions (e.g., each child may use the remote control car for 15 minutes, one child bats while the other throws the ball, players change places after three hits, etc.).

40. Make certain your child understands that toys, games, etc., that are forcefully taken from others will be taken away from him/her for a period of time.

41. Provide your child, brothers/sisters, friends, etc., with more than one of those things are forcefully taken.

42. Increase supervision of your child and those activities that are likely to cause your child to forcefully take things from others.

43. Make certain when your child has a friend over that there are plenty of things with which to play.

44. Make certain other children do not take things forcefully from your child; that may result in your child attempting to forcefully take things from others.

45. Make certain when your child visits a friend that personal possessions are taken along to prevent the need to forcefully take things from others.

1. Establish rules for interacting with younger brothers and/or sisters (e.g., be patient, play cooperatively, share materials, etc.). These rules should be consistent and followed by everyone in the home. Talk about the rules often and reward your child for following the rules.

2. Attempt to be patient with others. If you are impatient, your child will learn to be impatient also.

3. Reward your child for being patient with younger brothers and/or sisters. Possible rewards include verbal praise (e.g., "Thank you for being patient while your sister learned the rules of the game we played."), a kiss on the cheek, a hug, having a friend over to play, staying up late, watching a favorite TV show, and playing a game with a parent. (See Appendix for Reward Menu.)

4. If there are other children or adolescents in the home, reward them for being patient with others.

5. Remind your child how it felt when learning something new and help your child see how younger brothers and/or sisters may feel in the same situation.

6. Show your child how to be patient with younger brothers and/or sisters by being patient yourself (e.g., talk in a calm voice, avoid demonstrating frustration or anger, etc.).

7. Give your child suggestions of things to do (e.g., count to 10, say the alphabet, walk away from the situation and then return, etc.) in order to be more patient.

8. When your child is impatient, explain exactly what he/she is doing wrong, what should be done and why.

For example: You overhear your child telling his younger sister to hurry. Go to your child and say, "William, you are yelling at Kim. You need to wait patiently because it takes her a little longer to button her coat than it takes you to button yours."

9. Write a contract with your child.

For example: I, William, will be patient with Kim for three days in a row. When I accomplish this, I can stay up late on Friday night.

The contract should be written within the ability level of your child and should focus on only one behavior at a time. (See Appendix for an example of a Behavior Contract.)

10. Make certain that your child sees the relationship between his/her behavior and the consequences which follow (e.g., hurting others feelings, others' avoiding him/her, etc.).

11. Remove your child from interacting with younger brothers and/or sisters when he/she becomes impatient.

12. Do not make your child play with younger brothers and/or sisters if he/she does not want to play with them.

13. Provide supervision when your child interacts with younger brothers and/or sisters.

14. Have your child spend short periods of time with younger brothers and/or sisters in order to be more patient with them. Gradually increase the amount of time your child spends with younger brothers and/or sisters as increased patience is demonstrated.

15. Make sure your child has a place to be alone and spend time away from younger brothers and/or sisters.

16. Teach your child how to deal with frustration in an appropriate manner.

17. Make certain that your child is not expected to have younger brothers or sisters around when friends come over or visit. Allow your older child to enjoy time alone without younger brothers or sisters around.

18. Carefully consider your child's age before expecting him/her to play cooperatively, share toys, and not fight with brothers and/or sisters.

19. Supervise your children's interactions at all times in order to correct them and to model appropriate interaction skills.

20. Make certain your child is not allowed time alone with a younger brother or sister when upset or angry.

21. Spend individual time with all of your children. Do not give more attention to the younger one(s) than to the older ones. Do not make your children compete for your attention, time, and/or praise.

22. Speak with your child about the limitations and "immature" behaviors of younger brothers and/or sisters in order to help your child become more tolerant.

23. Do not require your child to take a parental role with younger brothers and/or sisters. Your child should not be expected to feed, dress, bath, supervise, etc., younger brothers and/or sisters on a frequent basis.

24. Allow your child some time for personal activities without having a younger brother and/or sister around to interfere.

25. Give your child certain "important" responsibilities involving younger brothers or sisters (e.g., baby-sitting for 15 minutes, helping with giving baths, etc.). Reward your child for helping with a dollar, special time alone with you, etc.

26. Be consistent. Try to deal with your child and his/her behavior in a manner that is as consistent as possible (e.g., react in the same manner each time, use the same consequences, etc.).

27. Make certain your child knows the "responsibilities" of being an older brother or sister (e.g., setting a good example, helping Mom and Dad, etc.).

28. Encourage your older child to spend short periods of time with younger brothers and/or sisters. Gradually increase the time as your child demonstrates patience with the younger brothers and/or sisters.

29. Identify those areas of interactions which are difficult for your child and younger brothers and/or sisters. Remind your child to try to use patience before playing with younger brothers/sisters, goes on public outings with younger brothers and/or sisters, etc.

30. Make certain your child does not try to get out of being with young brothers/sisters simply because your child does not demonstrate patience at all times. Encourage your child to develop patience rather than avoid interaction with brothers and/or sisters.

31. Make certain your child is not assigned responsibilities for younger brothers/sisters if he/she is not demonstrating the necessary skills.

32. Make certain that baby-sitters, guests in your home, etc., are aware of your child's tendency to be impatient with younger brothers and/or sisters.

33. Increase supervision in order to assist your child during interactions with younger brothers and/or sisters and to prevent your child from becoming upset or angry.

115 Is overly critical of self

1. Do not criticize. When correcting your child, be honest yet supportive. Never cause your child to feel bad about himself/herself.

2. Do not be overly critical of yourself. If you say unkind things about yourself, your child will learn to talk critically of himself/herself.

3. When your child is critical of himself/herself, help identify what he/she likes about himself/herself and proceed from there with a positive conversation about your child.

4. Help your child see the good points in himself/herself and talk about them often in an attempt to help your child feel better about himself/herself.

5. Encourage your child to get involved in activities in order to feel better about himself/herself (e.g., 4-H, Boy Scouts, Girl Scouts, Campfire Girls, extracurricular activities at school, etc.).

6. Do not put an emphasis on competition. Repeated failures may cause your child to criticize himself/herself.

7. Talk with your child about individual differences and discuss strengths and weaknesses of individuals your child knows.

8. Encourage your child to refrain from comparing himself/herself to others.

9. Identify the comments your child makes about himself/herself that are critical. Help your child overcome those areas of concern (e.g., by getting a new haircut, losing weight, getting involved in new activities, getting a tutor, taking swimming lessons, etc.).

10. Make certain your child is not being critical of himself/herself to get your attention (e.g., ignore self-critical comments or indicate that the critical statements are not true).

11. Encourage your child to associate with peers who are not critical of themselves or others, peers who are not overly concerned with what they look like, etc.

12. Involve your child in some extra activities in order to make several friends in all kinds of settings. Help your child feel good about himself/herself in different situations.

13. Make certain you do not contribute to your child being critical of himself/herself by discussing weight, grades, looks, etc., in public or in your child's presence.

14. Be careful not to place too much importance on clothes, looks, hair, etc. If these subjects are always the topic of conversation, your child may become overly concerned with appearance.

15. Make certain your child understands the natural consequences of being overly critical of yourself (e.g., people will not want to be around your child, others will think your child does not feel good about himself/herself, etc.).

16. Help your child to feel good about himself/herself by encouraging and helping your child decide which haircut to get, clothes to wear, classes to take, etc.

17. Remove your child from a friend or group of friends who may be overly critical of your child.

18. Make certain that teachers, baby-sitters, etc., know that your child is overly critical of himself/herself so they can be aware of how you deal with the child being critical of himself/herself.

19. Attempt new activities, sports, games, etc., with your child to help him/her feel more comfortable with a new situation.

20. Make certain your child does not get out of doing things because he/she is overly critical of himself/herself (e.g., does not work on a math assignment because your child says it cannot be completed, does not finish a session of swim lessons because your child is not good at swimming, etc.).

21. Avoid engaging your child in activities in which there is little likelihood of success and which may cause him/her to feel bad about himself/herself.

22. Compliment your child whenever possible.

23. Encourage others to compliment your child.

24. Pair your child with a younger brother/sister, younger children, etc., in order to enhance your child's feelings of success or accomplishment.

25. Help your child learn those skills necessary to improve personal appearance and hygiene.

26. Encourage your child to refrain from comparing his/her performance to others and to emphasize attention to personal improvement (e.g., maintain records of his/her progress rather than making a comparison to others).

27. Make certain that your comments take the form of constructive criticism rather than criticism that can be perceived as personal, threatening, etc. (e.g., instead of saying, ''You always make the same mistake.'' say, ''A better way to do that might be....'').

28. Encourage your child to pursue those activities in which there is the greatest likelihood of success in order to enhance your child's feelings of success.

29. Encourage your child to learn to accept improvement rather than insisting on excellence (e.g., getting one hit during a game is an improvement over striking out four times, etc.).

30. Set your child up for success by finding activities that will result in success; your child will feel more confident, self-assured, etc., and will likely find more success on his/her own.

31. Do not allow your child to remain in those activities, situations, etc., where he/she does not have a chance of success. Continued failures can be a destructive influence.

A Reminder: Failure is an inhibitor. Success is a motivator.

116 Will not take part in special family events

1. Encourage your child to participate in special events (e.g., family gatherings, parties, etc.).

2. Participate in special events with your child.

3. Do not force your child to take part in special events.

4. Reward your child for participating in special events. Possible rewards include verbal praise (e.g., "I'm so proud of you for going to your friend's party!"), a kiss on the cheek, a hug, having a friend over to play, staying up late, watching a favorite TV show, and playing a game with a parent. (See Appendix for Reward Menu.)

5. If there are other children or adolescents in the home, reward them for participating in special events.

6. Encourage your child to talk about fears with you.

7. Talk with your family doctor, a school official, a social worker, a mental health worker, etc., about your child's lack of participation in special events.

8. Talk with your child before special events take place in order to help prepare for the event.

9. Give your child a special responsibility (e.g., answering the door, serving food, cleaning, etc.) in order to make the child feel important and want to participate in special events.

10. Have the whole family participate in special events with your child.

11. Make certain that your child does not get out of doing something simply because he/she does not want to do it. Encourage your child by talking through a situation, going to the event, etc.

12. Help your child plan special events (e.g., having a slumber party, visiting relatives, etc.).

13. Make certain that your child understands that by not attending a special event he/she will have to stay home with a baby-sitter, miss a party with friends, etc.

14. Make certain that teachers, baby sitters, family members, etc., are aware that your child is unwilling to take part in special events so they will understand and help encourage your child to participate.

15. Attend special events with your child for a short period of time. Gradually reduce the amount of time you spend at special events when your child begins to feel comfortable.

16. Carefully consider your child's age and maturity level before expecting your child to take part in some special events.

17. Allow enough time for your child to prepare for a special event (e.g., talking about how much fun the birthday party will be, how much fun it will be to visit Grandma's, etc.).

18. Make positive comments when talking with your child about special events. Try to be as positive as possible at all times.

19. Sit down with your child and explain changes in the daily routine and upcoming special events a few days before they happen, if possible.

20. Involve your child in highly interesting activities at school and in the community in order to increase participation in activities (e.g., school clubs, organized sports, 4-H, Girl Scouts/Boy Scouts, etc.).

21. Do not "make fun" of your child's crying or avoiding something new.

22. Have your child attend a new situation with friends with whom he/she feels comfortable (e.g., a birthday party, a school picnic, etc.).

23. Make certain that your child feels comfortable with the instructor, other children in the activity, and the activity itself.

24. If your child begins to use "afraid of doing it" as an excuse, take your child to the activity, see your child go into the activity, leave, and come back when the activity is over. Make certain the person with whom you are leaving your child understands the situation.

25. Make certain that the activity you are encouraging your child to attempt is appropriate for your child's level of development and ability.

26. Have another child (e.g., your child's friend, a relative the same age, etc.) present during special events in order that your child will have someone with whom to interact.

27. Have your child help plan special events (e.g., family gatherings, parties, etc.) in your home (e.g., choosing refreshments, planning a schedule of events, etc.).

28. Give your child a responsibility to perform at special events in order to increase participation, interaction, etc., without experiencing the awkwardness of not knowing what to do or say to others (e.g., taking coats at the door, serving refreshments, etc.).

29. Do not embarrass your child at special events by singling him/her out, trying to get him/her to entertain, laughing at him/her, etc.

30. Allow your child to attend special events without having to socialize if it makes your child uncomfortable.

31. Carefully consider the appropriateness of having your child attend special events if there are no other children, no activities of interest, etc.

117 Is afraid of new situations

1. Do not "force" your child to do fearful things (e.g., learning to ride a bike, swim, dance, etc.).

2. Encourage your child to talk about fears with you.

3. Do not "make fun" of your child's crying or avoiding new situations.

4. Participate in new situations with your child (e.g., attend the first day of school, teach your child how to ride a bike, be near when learning to swim, etc.).

5. Talk with your family doctor, a school official, a social worker, a mental health worker, etc., if you feel your child's fear is excessive.

6. Reward your child for going to school, trying to ride a bike, participating in swim and dance lessons, etc. Possible rewards include verbal praise (e.g., "I'm so proud of you for going to school today!"), a kiss on the cheek, a hug, having a friend over to play, staying up late, watching a favorite TV show, and playing a game with a parent. (See Appendix for Reward Menu.)

7. If there are other children or adolescents in the home, reward them for not being afraid of new situations.

8. Write a contract with your child.

For example: I, William, will earn a new airplane model when I learn how to ride my bike.

The contract should be written within the ability level of your child and should focus on only one behavior at a time. (See Appendix for an example of a Behavior Contract.)

9. Carefully consider your child's age and maturity level before expecting your child to ride a bike, learn how to swim, etc.

10. Allow enough time for your child to prepare for a new activity (e.g., talk about the first day of school several months in advance, go to visit the school several weeks in advance, etc.).

11. Talk with your child's teacher or instructors about your child's fears.

12. Attempt things as a family that are new to your child.

13. Make certain that teachers, baby-sitters, family members, etc., know your child is afraid of new situations so they will not push him/her into new things.

14. Make positive comments when talking with your child about attempting new things. Try to be as positive as possible at all times.

15. Make certain that your child does not get out of doing something simply because he/she does not want to do it. Encourage your child by talking through the situation, going to the event together, etc.

16. Have your child try something new with peers with whom he/she feels comfortable (e.g., swim lessons, dancing, baseball, etc.).

17. If your child begins to use "afraid of doing it" as an excuse, take your child to the activity, see your child go into the activity, leave, and come back when the activity is over. Make certain the person with whom you are leaving your child understands the situation.

18. Provide your child with a choice (e.g., "You can go to summer camp or take swim lessons. You may decide which you want to do.") Make certain your child understands that one or the other will be done.

19. Make certain that the thing you are encouraging your child to attempt is appropriate for your child's level of development and ability.

20. Accompany your child in attempting new things. Gradually require your child to attempt things alone as he/she feels more comfortable.

21. Present learning new activities in the most attractive manner possible (e.g., the family going together to learn to swim, everyone riding a bike at the same time, etc.).

22. Do not convey your own personal fears to your child (e.g., fear of water, heights, skating, skiing, etc.).

23. Be personally available when your child is attempting something new (e.g., get in the pool with your child during the first swim lessons).

24. Provide your child with optional courses of action in order to prevent total refusal to attempt something new (e.g., if your child is afraid to have you teach swimming, obtain instructions at a pool; if your child is afraid of lessons at a pool, you can teach swimming).

25. Reduce the emphasis on competitiveness in the family or neighborhood. Fear of failure may cause your child to refuse to attempt something new.

26. Allow your child to attempt something new in private before doing it in front of others.

27. Allow your child many opportunities to attempt something new (e.g., learning to ride a bike, learning to swim, etc.). Nothing is so important that it has to be learned or mastered the first time.

28. Take another child along when your child takes part in new experiences (e.g., swimming lessons, riding a bike, etc.).

29. Take your child to meet the new teacher, swim instructor, dance instructor; visit the dentist before the actual appointment; etc., in order for your child to feel comfortable with the new situation.

118 Has little confidence in school ability

1. Help your child prepare for school-related activities (e.g., provide reminders to study for a quiz or test well in advance, ask if your child needs help with homework, set aside a specific time for studying each evening, etc.).

2. Reward your child for studying and preparing for school-related activities. Possible rewards include verbal praise (e.g., "I'm so proud of you for going ahead and trying out for the school play even though you didn't think you would be chosen for a part!"), a kiss on the cheek, a hug, having a friend over to play, staying up late, watching a favorite TV show, and playing a game with a parent. (See Appendix for Reward Menu.)

3. If there are other children or adolescents in the home, reward them for having confidence in school-related activities.

4. Determine your child's strengths and/or talents (e.g., sports, music, art, etc.) and encourage involvement in activities that will help in feeling more confident and look forward to going to school.

5. Write a contract with your child.

For example: I, William, will study for my math test for 30 minutes every day this week in order to feel more confident about the test on Friday. When I accomplish this, and get 80% or better on the test, I can invite a friend to eat pizza and spend the night.

The contract should be written within the ability level of your child and should focus on only one behavior at a time. (See Appendix for an example of a Behavior Contract.)

6. Make certain that your child sees the relationship between his/her behavior and the consequences which follow (e.g., not doing well on tests and quizzes, receiving low grades, not performing well enough to get a part in the school play, etc.).

7. Talk with your child's teacher about having your child "peer tutor" another child who is having difficulty in an area where your child is confident and does well.

8. Attempt to say mostly positive things to your child and be supportive when criticizing.

9. Help your child see that lack of confidence can negatively affect performance in school and other areas.

10. Talk with school personnel often in order to monitor your child's performance and determine if extra help is needed (e.g., tutoring, referral for special education services, etc.).

11. Do not "push" your child to make A's or B's. Do not criticize if your child has a low grade on a quiz or test. Discuss things you can do to help your child feel more confident.

12. Encourage your child to refrain from comparing himself/herself to others.

13. Identify the area in which your child is not confident and provide help to improve in that area (e.g., get a math tutor, spend extra time practicing a sport, etc.).

14. Make certain your child is not demonstrating a lack of confidence to get the attention of others.

15. Encourage your child to associate with peers who are confident in themselves.

16. Talk to teachers at school to make certain that your child is successful in school and to see if your child is having problems with schoolwork.

17. Be careful not to place too much importance on grades, tests, etc. Make certain your child knows that doing his/her best is what is important.

18. Involve your child in several extra activities outside of schoolwork.

19. Make certain you do not contribute to your child's lack of confidence in schoolwork by discussing grades, comparing work, etc.

20. Compliment your child whenever possible.

21. Make certain your child does not get out of doing things as a result of being overly critical of himself/herself (e.g., does not finish a math assignment because of feeling incapable, does not finish a session of swim lessons because of feeling incapable, etc.).

22. Encourage others to compliment your child.

23. Pair your child with a younger brother/sister, younger children, etc., in order to enhance your child's feelings of success or accomplishment.

24. Encourage your child to refrain from comparing his/her performance and to emphasize attention to personal improvement (e.g., maintain records of his/her progress rather than making a comparison to others).

25. Encourage your child to pursue those school subjects where the most success occurs in order to enhance feelings of success.

26. Make certain that your comments take the form of constructive criticism rather than criticism that can be perceived as personal, threatening, etc. (e.g., instead of saying, ''You always make the same mistake.'' say, ''A better way to do that might be....'').

27. Encourage your child to learn to accept improvements rather than insisting on excellence (e.g., getting four problems right on a math quiz is an improvement over getting just one correct, etc.).

28. Provide your child with assistance in doing homework, working on school projects, etc., in order to improve the quality of schoolwork.

29. Have another child from your child's class study and do homework with your child in order to improve the quality of schoolwork.

30. Speak with your child's teacher to request assistance in providing you and your child with the necessary information about class work, quizzes, tests, etc., in order that you can assist your child in preparing for the class work, quizzes, tests, etc.

31. Speak with your child's teacher to request information on ''study skills'' to teach your child in order to ''learn better ways to learn.'' (There are ''study skills'' programs available to schools for improving the learning skills of students.)

32. Find a tutor to assist your child in preparing for school-related activities.

33. Speak with your child's teacher to request assistance for your child in school-related activities (e.g., extra assistance, tutoring, more direct communication with home, etc.).

34. Speak with your child's teacher to request that the teacher give as many success experiences as possible (e.g., call on your child when he/she will be able to answer correctly, provide review sessions before a quiz, assign a peer to help prepare for a test, etc.).

35. Make certain your child uses time at home to study, do homework, etc., to prepare for school activities.

36. Have your child or the teacher provide you with the dates of quizzes, tests, homework or project deadlines, etc., for you to follow in making certain your child is prepared for school activities.

A Reminder: Confidence comes with success. Communicate with your child's teacher(s) in order to find ways for your child to be more successful at school.

1. Establish a rule (e.g., tell the truth). The rule should be consistent and followed by everyone in the home. Talk about the rule often.

2. Promote an open and honest line of communication with your child. Do not make your child feel frightened about telling the truth.

3. Reward your child for telling the truth. Possible rewards include verbal praise (e.g., "Thank you for telling me the truth about the grade you received on your math test!"), a kiss on the cheek, a hug, having a friend over to play, staying up late, watching a favorite TV show, and playing a game with a parent. (See Appendix for Reward Menu.)

4. If there are other children or adolescents in the home, reward them for telling the truth.

5. Be honest with others. If you lie, your child will learn to lie also.

6. Do not allow your child to lie to you. If you know that your child has done something wrong, there is no need to ask if he/she is guilty. Simply deal with the behavior in a "matter of fact" way.

7. When your child lies, explain exactly what he/she is doing wrong, what should have been done and why.

For example: Your child tells you that the bed is made. When you see that it is not made, go to your child and say, "William, you did not make your bed. The next time that I ask you if your bed is made, you need to tell me the truth. When you do not tell the truth, people will learn to not believe other things that you tell them."

8. Write a contract with your child.

For example: I, William, will tell the truth for four days in a row. When I accomplish this, I can go to a movie on Saturday.

The contract should be written within the ability level of your child and should focus on only one behavior at a time. (See Appendix for an example of a Behavior Contract.)

9. Supervise your child closely in order to determine if what he/she tells you is the truth.

10. Allow natural consequences to occur due to your child's lying (e.g., loss of privileges, others not believing, etc.).

11. Make certain that your child sees the relationship between his/her behavior and the consequences which follow (e.g., others not believing, loss of privileges, being avoided by others, etc.).

12. Do not punish your child for forgetting, doing something accidently, etc.

13. Develop a system of shared responsibility.

For example: You walk into the kitchen and find milk spilled all over the floor. Instead of trying to figure out who spilled the milk, have everyone in the room help clean up the milk.

14. Do not punish your child unless you are absolutely sure he/she has lied to you.

15. Help your child understand that telling the truth as soon as possible often prevents future problems (e.g., admitting that he/she forgot to let the dog out may prevent the dog from having an accident in the house).

16. Make certain that your child understands that he/she cannot get out of doing something because of lying (e.g., your child's chores need to be completed even when you have been told that they have been completed and then you find out that they have not).

17. Do not put your child in a situation that may cause lying (e.g., a threatening situation).

18. Make certain that your child sees the relationship between his/her behavior and the consequences which follow (e.g., others not believing what is said, being avoided by others, etc.).

19. Do not appear shocked or surprised when your child lies. Deal with his/her behavior in a calm and deliberate manner.

20. Before beginning a conversation with your child when you feel he/she has lied about something, remind your child that telling the truth the first time can save further punishment.

21. Separate your child from those children and adolescents who encourage lying.

22. Make certain that teachers, baby-sitters, etc., know that your child has difficulty with telling the truth.

23. Make certain that you do not expect too much from your child. If your child is unable to measure up to what you expect it may cause lying.

24. Deal with your child's lying privately rather than in front of others.

25. Do not rely on or encourage others to inform you of your child's lying. Do not use peer pressure to solve lying incidents.

26. Do not accept your child's lying in place of meeting responsibilities (i.e., if your child says "The bed is made," and actually it is not made, make certain that the bed gets made rather than immediately punishing for lying).

27. Discuss alternative ways in which your child could have dealt with a situation rather than by lying.

28. Help your child learn that telling the truth as soon as possible prevents future problems (e.g., admitting a mistake, forgot, etc., means that the necessary steps can be taken to correct the situation, instead of waiting until the truth is determined in some other way).

29. When your child lies about his/her behavior, calmly confront your child with the facts. Encourage an open and honest line of communication between everyone in your home. Do not make your child fearful of telling the truth even though you may not be happy about his/her behavior.

30. Do not cause your child to lie about behavior by giving him/her something too difficult to do (e.g., chores, responsibilities, coming home at an early hour, etc.).

31. Help your child to feel comfortable coming to you for assistance with a problem by listening and helping with a solution to the problem.

32. Avoid arguing with your child about whether or not he/she is lying; simply explain that he/she is not being completely honest about the situation.

33. Avoid arguing with your child about whether he is telling you the truth. If you do not have proof, it is better to avoid blaming someone who is innocent.

34. Always make certain that you determine the accuracy of your child's claim that something caused a problem or failure. In some cases, someone or something may legitimately be causing your child to experience problems or failures.

35. Make certain your child understands that not being honest when confronted will result in more negative consequences than telling the truth. Be certain to be very consistent in this approach.

36. Make certain that your child understands that making inaccurate statements (lying) does not prevent consequences (e.g., the bed has to be made if it was not; an assignment that was supposedly completed and lost, still has to be done and turned in; etc.).

37. Reduce or remove punishment for accidents, forgetting, and situations with inadequate evidence. Punishment in these situations may cause your child to lie.

38. Avoid putting your child in a situation in which there is opportunity to lie, deny, exaggerate, etc. (e.g., highly competitive activities, situations with limited supervision, etc.).

39. Encourage your child to call on you for support, assistance, etc., whenever help is needed (e.g., when out late, in an uncomfortable situation on a date, etc.) instead of lying to avoid an unpleasant experience. This requires that negative consequences will not be delivered if your child tells the truth.

40. Avoid making accusations which would increase the probability of your child lying. If it is known that your child is responsible, an admission of guilt is not necessary to deal with the situation.

41. Make certain that punishment is not so severe as to cause your child to lie in order to avoid the punishment (e.g., coming in late should not result in being grounded for three weeks; a more appropriate punishment would be to come in an hour earlier the next time).

42. When your child does lie, make certain to take the time to explain why telling the truth is important (e.g., you may not be able to trust your child to tell the truth again, a situation which could have been resolved may have gotten worse because you were not able to help, one lie makes it necessary to tell more lies, someone may have been placed in danger, etc.).

43. Encourage your child to come to you when there is a problem (e.g., doing homework, dealing with peer pressure, etc.) in order that you can help your child and prevent the need to lie.

A Reminder: Your child will naturally make some errors in judgment. Punishing your child for everything he/she does wrong will likely encourage lying. In addition, some behavior can be ignored.

120 Cheats in games

1. Establish rules for playing competitive games (e.g., play by the rules, wait your turn, share materials, do not fight, etc.). These rules should be consistent and followed by everyone in the home. Talk about the rules often and reward your child for following the rules.

2. Do not allow your child to cheat. Immediately stop any form of cheating as soon as it begins.

3. Make sure that you play by the rules, wait your turn, share materials, and do not argue with others when playing competitive games. Set a good example for your child.

4. Reward your child for playing fairly in competitive games. Possible rewards include verbal praise (e.g., ''I am glad that you are playing fairly.'' ''I like to play cards with you when you play by the rules.'' etc.), a kiss on the cheek, a hug, having a friend over to play, staying up late, watching a favorite TV show, and playing a game with a parent. (See Appendix for Reward Menu.)

5. If there are other children or adolescents in the home, reward them for playing fairly.

6. Make sure that others do not cheat when they play competitive activities with your child.

7. Carefully consider your child's age and experience before expecting your child to play fairly.

8. Make sure your child knows the rules of the game and how to play while playing with others.

9. Supervise your child at all times when playing competitive games with others.

10. Immediately remove your child from the competitive activity when cheating occurs.

11. Make certain that your child sees the relationship between his/her behavior and the consequences which follow (e.g., others not wanting to play with him/her, making others angry, not being allowed to play, etc.).

12. When your child cheats, explain exactly what he/she is doing wrong, what should have been done and why.

For example: You see your child cheating at cards. Stop playing and say, ''William, you are cheating. You need to play fairly if you want to continue playing.''

13. When playing competitive activities, put the emphasis on personal improvement, getting along, sharing, and having fun.

14. Write a contract with your child.

For example: I, William, will play fairly at cards. When I accomplish this, I can play a game with Mother.

The contract should be written within the ability level of your child and should focus on only one behavior at a time. (See Appendix for an example of a Behavior Contract.)

15. Teach your child to ask for help, stop playing, etc., when he/she feels like cheating.

16. Discourage your child from participating in activities where other people cheat in order to win.

17. Help your child improve skills in activities in which he/she has cheated in order to reduce the need to cheat.

18. Do not put an emphasis on winning. If your child feels that winning is the most important thing, he/she may resort to cheating in order to win.

19. Limit your child's participation in competitive activities.

20. Teach your child appropriate ways in which to deal with anger, frustrations, etc., so your child does not feel the need to cheat.

21. Help your child accept the fact that self-improvement is more important than being the best, ''winning,'' ''beating'' someone else, etc. (e.g., improving his/her own best time in swimming is better than always trying to ''beat'' someone else, etc.).

22. Before beginning a game or competitive activity, make sure your child knows the rules, is familiar with the game, and will be compatible with the other individuals who will be playing.

23. Be a model for participating for enjoyment rather than always needing to "win" or "beat" someone else.

24. Encourage your child to engage in less competitive activities (e.g., reading, clubs, scouting, student council, etc.).

25. Encourage your child to participate in more individualized sports (e.g., aerobics, swimming, track and field, golf, etc.).

26. Help your child to have self-confidence and satisfaction in personal self-worth and successes by pointing out strengths, emphasizing positive aspects, etc.

27. Reduce the emphasis on competition among brothers and sisters in your family. Competitiveness learned in the home will be demonstrated at school and elsewhere.

28. Deal with your child's behavior consistently each time there is a problem with cheating (e.g., when your child cheats, remove him/her from the situation and do not allow him/her to return, etc.).

29. Deal with your child's cheating privately rather than in public.

30. Do not take action unless you know for certain that your child is cheating.

31. Talk to your child before going to school, a friend's house, a sporting event, etc., about the importance of playing by the rules, letting everyone have a turn, etc.

32. Make certain that teachers, baby-sitters, etc., know that your child has a tendency to cheat.

33. Increase supervision when your child is involved in competitive situations to help prevent cheating.

34. Encourage your child to take up a hobby; assist in developing the hobby into a success.

35. Make sure that activities are not so difficult as to make cheating necessary to win, to be a member of the team, to participate, etc.

36. Encourage your child to interact with less competitive friends (e.g, older, younger, opposite sex, etc.).

37. Help your child prepare for school assignments (e.g., homework, projects, tests, quizzes, etc.) in order to reduce the need to cheat.

38. Play games with your child and help him/her do well so there is no need to cheat to be successful.

39. Encourage your child and others to engage in activities where winning is not a high priority (e.g., *Freeze Tag*, *Kick the Can*, *Tag*, *Hide and Seek*, etc.).

40. Talk to older brothers, sisters, friends, etc., to encourage them to help your child to be successful in activities rather than always trying to "beat" him/her.

41. If your child does not win awards (trophies, plaques, certificates) in competition, provide a trophy, plaque, or certificate at home for good sportsmanship, improvement, finishing a season, etc.

42. Find competitive activities for your family where your child is likely to be the most successful member of the family (e.g., *Candy Land*, *Memory*, *Jacks*, *Jumping Rope*, etc.).

43. Make certain your child understands that cheating in competitive activities may result in others not wanting to interact, play, compete, etc., with him/her again.

Note: Some enjoyable noncompetitive activities are: building, cooking, camping, reading, hiking, scouting, fishing, aerobics, skating, boating, playing at the swimming pool, movies, library, magic tricks, coloring, painting, shopping, slumber parties, bike riding, playing at the neighborhood park, running errands, writing, etc.

121 Exaggerates the truth

1. Establish rules (e.g., tell the truth, make accurate statements, etc.). These rules should be consistent and followed by everyone in the home. Talk about the rules often.

2. Make sure that you do not exaggerate the truth. It is very important to tell the truth and make accurate statements if you want your child to do the same.

3. Reward your child for telling the truth and making accurate statements. Possible rewards include verbal praise (e.g., "Thank you for telling the truth; I really appreciate it!"), a kiss on the cheek, a hug, having a friend over to play, staying up late, watching a favorite TV show, and playing a game with a parent. (See Appendix for Reward Menu.)

4. If there are other children or adolescents in the home, reward them for telling the truth and making accurate statements.

5. Carefully consider your child's age before expecting him/her to make accurate statements.

6. When your child exaggerates the truth, explain exactly what he/she is doing wrong, what should have been done and why.

For example: You overhear your child exaggerating the truth to a friend. Go to your child and say, "William, you are exaggerating the truth. You need to make more accurate statements or people will not believe you."

7. Write a contract with your child.

For example: I, William, for one week, will make accurate statements when reporting information. When I accomplish this, I can have a friend spend the night.

The contract should be written within the ability level of your child and should focus on only one behavior at a time. (See Appendix for an example of a Behavior Contract.)

8. Attempt to have an open and honest relationship with your child. Encourage your child to tell the truth and do not use threats (e.g., "You had better tell the truth, or else.") to make him/her tell the truth.

9. Do not put your child in a situation (e.g., a competitive activity) in which there may be a chance to exaggerate the truth.

10. Supervise your child at all times in order to reduce his/her need to exaggerate the truth.

11. Do not punish your child for accidents, forgetting, and situations with inadequate evidence. If you punish your child in these situations, he/she may exaggerate the truth more often in order to avoid punishment.

12. If your child exaggerates the truth, make sure that he/she is still held responsible for his/her behavior. For example, if you know that your child has not completed chores, require him/her to complete the chores even though your child says that the chores have been completed.

13. Do not take action unless you know for certain that your child is exaggerating the truth.

14. Make certain that your child sees the relationship between his/her behavior and the consequences which follow (e.g., others not believing what he/she says, being avoided by others, etc.).

15. Allow natural consequences to occur when your child exaggerates the truth.

16. Promote an open and honest line of communication with your child.

17. Do not make your child exaggerate the truth to get your attention or to impress you. Let your child know that you are most impressed when he/she puts forth the best effort possible.

18. Help your child understand that telling the actual truth often prevents future problems (e.g., being honest about not finishing all of the chores will prevent problems when chore responsibilities are checked).

19. Remind your child before going to school, to a friend's house, to a sporting event, etc., that it is important to be completely honest with yourself and other people.

20. Make certain your child understands that exaggerating the truth may lead to telling more lies (e.g., telling friends that he/she is going to get a more expensive 10-speed bike than the one your child is really getting, will later result in the need to lie about not getting the more expensive bike).

21. Make certain that your child understands that he/she cannot get out of doing something when exaggerating the truth (e.g., your child's chores need to be completed even though you have been told that they have all been completed when they actually have not).

22. Do not appear shocked or surprised when your child exaggerates the truth. Deal with the behavior in a calm and deliberate manner.

23. Help your child to understand that by exaggerating the truth he/she may even come to believe what he/she exaggerates and that exaggerating may become a habit.

24. Separate your child from other children who exaggerate to impress, to get out of doing things, etc.

25. Make certain that teachers, baby-sitters, etc., know that your child has a tendency to exaggerate the truth.

26. Deal privately with your child's exaggerating the truth, rather than in front of others.

27. Help your child understand that in order to be satisfied with personal efforts, your child should not need to exaggerate the truth to impress others.

28. Encourage your child to avoid activities that cause exaggeration about abilities, possessions, etc.

29. Try to prevent competitiveness in information-sharing in order that your child will not feel the need to exaggerate in order to be accepted by others.

30. Do not exaggerate your child's abilities, possessions, etc., to others.

31. Try to make your child feel good about himself/herself by making positive comments, spending more time with him/her, and accepting the way he/she is.

32. Encourage your child to refrain from "one-upmanship" with friends (e.g., when friends talk about a new possession, it may be more desirable to say, "You're lucky." or "That's great." rather than "That's nothing, my dad's going to buy me a....").

33. Help your child learn that telling the truth as soon as possible prevents future problems (e.g., admitting a mistake, forgot, etc., means that the necessary steps can be taken to correct the situation instead of waiting until the truth is determined in some other way).

34. Avoid putting your child in a situation in which there is the opportunity to lie, deny, exaggerate, etc. (e.g., highly competitive activities, situations with limited supervision, etc.).

35. Make certain that expectations, chores, responsibilities, etc., are within your child's developmental level and abilities.

36. Always make certain that you determine the accuracy of your child's claim that something caused him/her to have a problem or failure. In some cases, someone or something may legitimately be causing your child to experience problems or failures.

37. Stress to your child that others' feelings can be hurt by being boastful/exaggerating the truth. Always having done something bigger or more costly will make others feel inadequate, inferior, etc.

38. Make certain your child understands that exaggerating the truth will usually result in embarrassment when friends, family, teachers, etc., eventually learn the truth.

122 Uses things without asking

1. Establish rules (e.g., ask permission to borrow things, return things when you are finished using them, etc.). These rules should be consistent and followed by everyone in the home. Talk about the rules often and reward your child for following the rules.

2. Supervise your child at all times in order to prevent you child from using things that belong to others without first asking permission.

3. Make sure that you ask permission to use things that belong to others in order to help your child learn to do the same.

4. Reward your child for asking permission to use things that belong to others. Possible rewards include verbal praise (e.g., "I appreciate it when you ask to use my blow dryer!"), a kiss on the cheek, a hug, having a friend over to play, staying up late, watching a favorite TV show, and playing a game with a parent. (See Appendix for Reward Menu.)

5. If there are other children or adolescents in the home, reward them for asking permission to use things that belong to others.

6. Make certain that your child sees the relationship between his/her behavior and the consequences which follow (e.g., others not wanting to play, not being able to use things that belong to others, etc.).

7. When your child does not ask to use things that belong to others, explain exactly what he/she is doing wrong, what should have been done and why.

For example: You see your child using his/her sister's bike. Go to your child and say, "William, you did not ask permission to use Kim's bike. You need to ask permission to use things that belong to others if you want them to share things with you."

8. Make sure that your child returns all items that have been taken without permission as soon as possible. If it is not possible to return an item, then your child should purchase another one like it and return it as soon as possible.

9. Immediately remove your child from an activity when things are taken without asking permission.

10. Write a contract with your child.

For example: I, William, for four days in a row, will ask to use things that belong to others. When I accomplish this, I can have a friend spend the night.

The contract should be written within the ability level of your child and should focus on only one behavior at a time. (See Appendix for an example of a Behavior Contract.)

11. Teach your child the concept of borrowing by allowing your child to borrow things from you and requiring him/her to ask permission before doing so.

12. Do not accuse your child of failing to ask to use things that belong to others unless you are absolutely certain that he/she has not asked permission.

13. Teach your child rules for the care and handling of others' property (e.g., always ask permission to use things that belong to others, treat the property with care, inform an adult if the property is damaged, return property in the same or better condition).

14. Make certain your child has things of his/her own so it is not necessary to take those things from others.

15. Allow your child to earn those items that have been taken without asking in the past, when your child does ask before borrowing.

16. Deal with your child's taking without asking privately rather than in front of others.

17. Do not rely on or encourage others to inform you of your child's taking things without asking. Do not use peer pressure to solve such incidents.

18. Increase supervision of your child when playing, visiting at someone's home, etc.

19. Do not encourage your child to take things without asking by allowing your child to go to a friend's house without supervision, go into a brother's/sister's room alone, etc.

20. Inform others (e.g., your child's teacher) of the behavior in order that they can encourage your child not to steal.

21. Put all objects that you do not want your child to have in a place where he/she cannot get to them (e.g., a locked medicine cabinet, high cabinets, a locked tool box, etc.).

22. Do not leave objects laying around that you do not want your child to take. Put them away as soon as you are finished using them.

23. Clearly mark those things your child is not allowed to handle or use with ''Warning: Poison'' ''Do Not Touch'' labels, etc. (See Appendix for ''Poison'' labels and ''Do Not Touch'' labels.)

24. Do not allow your child to be involved with children or adolescents who take things without asking.

25. Do not encourage your child to use something that he/she has not asked to borrow by allowing your child to continue using the item; stop your child and have the child return the item that has been taken.

26. Remind your child before going to school, to a friend's house, to a store, etc., that he/she should always ask before borrowing something that belongs to others.

27. Set an example for your child by asking for things in a positive manner. Use key words and phrases (e.g., ''May I please use your pencil?'' ''May I borrow your paintbrush?'' etc.).

28. Be consistent. Try to deal with your child and the behavior in a manner that is as fair as possible (e.g., react in the same manner, use the same consequences, etc.).

29. Make certain your child understands that things that are lost, broken, or destroyed must be replaced by him/her.

30. Make sure that your child is not taking things that belong to others because the items are needed at school (e.g., paper, pencils, crayons, scissors, etc.). Make sure that you give your child the materials needed at school or other organized activities, (e.g., 4-H, Boy Scouts/Girl Scouts, etc.).

31. Identify those things your child has been taking from others and provide him/her with those items as reinforcers for appropriate behavior.

32. Make certain your child understands that the things that are wanted can be earned. Anything can be earned to avoid stealing, forcefully taking things from others, or borrowing without asking.

33. Provide your child, brothers and/or sisters, friends, etc., with more than one of those things that are taken without asking.

34. Increase supervision of your child and those activities in which he/she is likely to take without asking.

35. Make certain when your child visits a friend that personal possessions are taken along to prevent the need to borrow without asking.

36. Teach your child to ask to use things that belong to others. When your child asks to use your things, allow the use of those things with your supervision.

37. Provide your child with a version of the item that is used without asking permission (e.g., tools, sewing kit, tape, pens, pencils, etc.).

1. Establish rules (e.g., ask permission to borrow things, share, return things when you are finished using them, etc.). These rules should be consistent and followed by everyone in the home. Talk about the rules often and reward your child for following the rules.

2. Supervise your child at all times when visiting someone's home, going to the store, etc.

3. Make sure that you return items to their owner when you are finished using them in order to help your child learn to do the same.

4. Reward your child for not stealing. Possible rewards include verbal praise (e.g., "I appreciate your returning the bike to your friend, Joe!"), a kiss on the cheek, a hug, having a friend over to play, staying up late, watching a favorite TV show, and playing a game with a parent. (See Appendix for Reward Menu.)

5. If there are other children or adolescents in the home, reward them for not stealing.

6. Make certain that your child sees the relationship between his/her behavior and the consequences which follow (e.g., others not wanting to play, having to replace things are stolen, etc.).

7. When your child steals, explain exactly what he/she is doing wrong, what should be done and why.

For example: Your child's teacher tells you that your child stole another child's box of crayons. Go to your child and say, "William, I know that you took another child's box of crayons today at school. The next time you need something, you should ask to borrow it and then return it when you are finished using it, or people will not let you borrow things from them."

8. Make sure that your child is not stealing things that are needed at school (e.g., paper, pencils, crayons, scissors, etc.). Make sure that you give your child the materials needed at school or other organized activities, (e.g., 4-H, Boy Scouts, Girl Scouts, etc.).

9. Write a contract with your child.

For example: I, William, will not steal things for five days in a row. When I accomplish this, I can earn a toy car.

The contract should be written within the ability level of your child and should focus on only one behavior at a time. (See Appendix for an example of a Behavior Contract.)

10. Allow your child to earn those items that have been stolen in the past when your child does not steal.

11. Immediately remove your child from an activity when stealing.

12. Teach your child the concept of borrowing by allowing him/her to borrow things from you and requiring your child to return them when finished using them.

13. Do not accuse your child of stealing something unless you are absolutely certain that the item has been stolen.

14. It is not necessary that your child admit to stealing something. If you know your child has stolen something, deal with the situation accordingly. Insisting on an admission of guilt is a separate issue from stealing.

15. Make sure that your child returns all items that are stolen as soon as possible. If it is not possible to return an item, then your child should purchase another one like it.

16. Deal with your child's stealing privately rather than in front of others.

17. Do not rely on or encourage others to inform you of your child's stealing. Do not use peer pressure to solve incidents of stealing.

18. Do not encourage your child to steal by allowing him/her to go into a store unsupervised or by leaving valuables, such as jewelry, money, etc., unattended.

19. Increase supervision of your child when playing, visiting at someone's home, etc.

20. Inform others (e.g., your child's teacher, baby-sitter, etc.) of your child's stealing behavior in order that they can encourage him/her not to steal.

21. Teach your child rules for the care and handling of others' property (e.g., always ask permission to use things that belong to others, treat the property with care, inform an adult if the property is damaged, return property in the same or better condition, etc.).

22. Make certain your child has things that others have in order not to be tempted to take those things from others.

23. Remind your child before going to school, to a friend's house, shopping, etc., about taking things that do not belong to him/her.

24. Put all objects that you do not want your child to have in a place where he/she cannot get to them (e.g., a locked medicine cabinet, high cabinets, a locked tool box, etc.).

25. Do not leave objects laying around that you do not want your child to take. Put them away as soon as you are finished using them.

26. Make it a rule in your house, out in public, etc., that everyone needs to ask before borrowing something from someone else.

27. Make certain your child understands that things that are lost, broken, or destroyed must be replaced by him/her.

28. Set an example for your child by asking for things in a positive manner. Use key words and phrases (e.g., "May I please use your pencil?" "May I borrow your paintbrush?" etc.).

29. Identify those things your child has been taking from others and provide those items as reinforcers for appropriate behavior.

30. Make certain your child understands that the things that are desired can be earned. Anything can be earned to avoid stealing or forcefully taking things from others.

31. Teach your child to "take turns" sharing possessions (e.g., each child may use the remote control car for 15 minutes, one child bats while the other throws the ball, players change places after three hits, etc.).

32. Make certain that other children do not take things from your child which results in your child taking things from others.

33. Make certain when your child visits a friend that personal possessions are taken along to prevent the need to steal.

34. Teach your child to ask to use things that belong to others. When your child asks to use your things, be certain to let your child use those things with your supervision.

35. Have your child earn money to buy those things he/she would otherwise steal.

36. Make certain your child is aware of the natural consequences of stealing (e.g., embarrassment, being fined, suspension from school, loss of freedom, incarceration, etc.).

37. Make certain that others do not make it easy for your child to steal (e.g., purses are not to be left unattended, money is not to be left sitting out, valuables should not be readily available, etc.).

38. When your child asks for things (e.g., bike, stereo, video games, etc.) immediately discuss that things can be earned instead of making your child think there is no way to get them. If your child thinks there is no chance of your help in obtaining new things, your child may see stealing as the only alternative.

39. Listen carefully to your child when he/she asks for things and share this information with relatives who may use the information (e.g., for gift giving, birthdays, holidays, etc.).

40. Take part in activities with your child (e.g., camping, sports, shopping, hobbies, etc.) to make sure you are aware of what your child is doing with personal time, who friends are, what his/her interests are, etc.

A Reminder: A child should always know that those things that are desired can be earned by doing chores, taking care of responsibilities, etc. If your child will honestly work for those things desired, he/she should have the opportunity to earn those things.

124 Plays one adult against another

1. Establish a rule about going from one adult to another adult asking for favors or permission to do something (e.g., go to a movie, eat a snack, watch TV, etc.). This rule should be consistent and followed by everyone in the home. Talk about the rule often and reward your child for not playing one adult against another.

2. Reward your child for not playing one adult against another. Possible rewards include verbal praise (e.g., "Thank you for not asking your Dad if you could borrow the car after I told you no."), a kiss on the cheek, a hug, having a friend over to play, staying up late, watching a favorite TV show, and playing a game with a parent. (See Appendix for Reward Menu.)

3. If there are other children or adolescents in the home, reward them for not playing one adult against another.

4. Do not allow your child to go from one adult to another asking for something. If this happens, go to your child and say, "William, I told you that you could not have a snack and now you are asking your father for one. The next time you ask for something and are given an answer, you are not to go to another adult. If this happens again, you will lose your TV privileges for three days!"

5. Make sure that you support the decisions made by other adults in the home.

For example: If your child asks to borrow the car, say, "Did you ask your father? What did he say?" Then stick with the answer Father gave.

6. Do not send your child to another adult if you do not want to make a decision regarding something he/she wants. If you are not ready to make a decision, tell your child to let you think about it and to come back in 15 minutes.

7. Make certain all adults involved in your child's life (e.g., parents, teachers, etc.) are in communication concerning important decisions (e.g., rules, expectations, responsibilities, permission given or not given, assignments, etc.) in order to reduce the possibility of your child playing one adult against another.

8. Write a contract with your child.

For example: I, William, for three days in a row, will not play one adult against another. When I accomplish this, I can earn $1 toward buying an airplane model.

The contract should be written within the ability level of your child and should focus on only one behavior at a time. (See Appendix for an example of a Behavior Contract.)

9. Make certain that your child sees the relationship between his/her behavior and the consequences which follow (e.g., others not believing or trusting him/her).

10. Be sure to explain the reason you are denying your child's request immediately after telling him/her "no."

11. Be consistent in expecting your child not to go from one adult to another. Do not discipline your child one time and then ignore the behavior the next time.

12. When denying your child's request, allow something in exchange (e.g., eat an apple instead of a candy bar, rent a video and have some friends over instead of going to the movies).

13. Decide on a consequence for playing one adult against another (e.g., losing TV or phone privileges, not being able to leave the yard for a day, etc.) and enforce the consequence each time your child plays one adult against another.

14. After denying your child's request, remind him/her not to go to another adult and ask for the same or a similar thing.

15. Make baby-sitters, teachers, guests in your home, etc., aware of your child's tendency to play one adult against another.

16. Establish the rule that what one adult says is the final word. Asking another adult for permission to do something after being told "no" will not be tolerated.

17. Inform baby-sitters, grandparents, guests in your home, etc., of all privileges your child has.

18. When decisions are made in your home concerning discipline, rules, etc., make certain all concerned adults (family members, friends, etc.) are informed.

19. When your child reports to you that another adult did or said something that causes you concern, immediately contact that adult for information.

20. Make certain your child knows that you will communicate with other adults to clarify or confirm what your child tells you concerning what other adults said or did.

21. Ask your child's teacher to report directly to you by phone, note, etc., your child's behavior and/or performance on a weekly basis in order that your child cannot play you against the teacher or the teacher against you.

22. Remember that what your child tells you about what other adults (teachers, friends, parents, etc.) do or say may be taken out of context or misunderstood by your child. Check with the other adult before drawing a conclusion.

23. Just as you would give your child the benefit of the doubt, be certain to give adults the benefit of the doubt when your child is concerned.

A Reminder: Your child cannot play one adult against the other if open communication with all concerned adults is maintained.

125 Is demanding

1. Establish a rule requiring your child to ask for things in a pleasant manner (e.g., "Would you get me a drink, please?" "May I please borrow a dollar?" "Could you please give me a ride to the roller rink?" etc.) This rule should be consistent and followed by everyone in the home. Talk about the rule often.

2. Make sure that you are not demanding. Help your child learn to ask for things in a pleasant manner by doing so yourself.

3. In a pleasant manner, ask your child to do chores, do favors for you, etc.

4. Reward your child for asking for things in a pleasant manner. Possible rewards include verbal praise (e.g., "I appreciate it when you say 'please' when you ask me to do something for you!"), a kiss on the cheek, a hug, having a friend over to play, staying up late, watching a favorite TV show, and playing a game with a parent. (See Appendix for Reward Menu.)

5. If there are other children or adolescents in the home, reward them for asking for things in a pleasant manner.

6. When your child is demanding, explain exactly what he/she is doing wrong, what he/she should be done and why.

For example: Your child is demanding that you get him/her a drink. Go to your child and say, "William, you are demanding. You need to ask for things in a pleasant manner if you want others to do things for you."

7. Show your child how to ask for things in a pleasant manner.

8. Make certain that your child sees the relationship between his/her behavior and the consequences which follow (e.g., others ignoring and avoiding him/her, etc.).

9. Allow natural consequences to occur due to your child's failing to ask for things in a pleasant manner (e.g., others ignoring and avoiding him/her, loss of friends, not getting what he/she wants, etc.).

10. Write a contract with your child.

For example: I, William, for five days in a row, will not be demanding when I ask someone to do something for me. When I accomplish this, I can stay up until 11:00 p.m. on Friday night.

The contract should be written within the ability level of your child and should focus on only one behavior at a time. (See Appendix for an example of a Behavior Contract.)

11. Encourage your child to do things. Allow your child to earn those favors that are desired when he/she does not demand things from others.

12. Make certain that your child is able to get those things that are needed without having to ask others for help. Your child should be able to reach food, dishes, shampoo, clothes, etc., without needing someone's help.

13. Do not give in to your child's demands.

14. Immediately remove your child from the activity, interaction, etc., when your child begins to demand things of others.

15. Make certain you ask people to do things for you in a nice way (e.g., "Would you please get me a drink of water?" "Please water the dog." etc.).

16. Ignore your child unless he/she can ask you to do something in a nice, polite way.

17. Make certain that the baby-sitter, guests in your home, etc., know not to give in to your child's demands.

18. Do not appear shocked or surprised when your child becomes demanding. Deal with the behavior in a calm, deliberate manner.

19. Be consistent in dealing with your child's demanding behavior (e.g., if your child cannot nicely ask a favor of you, do not give in and do what he/she wants you to do).

20. Talk to your children in the manner in which you want them to talk to you. Treat them with respect and do not "talk down" to them.

21. Remind your child before guests arrive in your home of the consequences for being demanding. Let your child know that you refuse to give in to demands just because others will be present.

22. Make certain that you do not give in to your child's demands simply to quiet him/her. Deal with the behavior consistently.

23. Remind your child before going into a shopping center, grocery store, etc., of the consequences for being demanding.

24. Separate your child from those children and adolescents who encourage him/her to demand things.

25. Make certain that the consequences delivered for inappropriate behavior are not too extreme and are directly related to the inappropriate behavior (e.g., demanding you to give him/her a dollar will result in not getting any money at all, demanding that you go to the skating rink will result in not going skating at all, etc.).

26. Make certain that your child's demands are not met by someone else (i.e., if you deny your child a dollar, make certain he/she does not go elsewhere to get the money).

27. Make certain that baby-sitters, grandparents, neighbors, etc., understand the importance of maintaining consistency in discipline with your child.

28. Remain calm when your child becomes demanding. Getting upset may make you feel as though you should give in to the demands.

29. Do not surprise your child with requests, chores, etc. Be consistent in expectations so your child knows his/her responsibilities and has no reason to argue (e.g., trash is taken out each evening, dishes are washed on Tuesdays and Thursdays, etc.).

30. Tell your child each time he/she becomes demanding. Bring it to his/her attention by saying, "You are demanding things, William!"

31. After giving your child directions, let your child know that there will not be a discussion (e.g., by walking away, starting a new task, etc.). If your child does not follow the direction, deliver consequences in a consistent manner.

32. Children often talk back, have the last word, etc., in order to get the attention of others. Make certain that your child gets your attention when behaving appropriately.

33. Along with a request or directive, provide an incentive statement (e.g., "Since you always do a good job of setting the table, would you please set it for dinner tonight?" "Would you please use your organizational skills to clean out the kitchen cupboards and reorganize them for me?" etc.).

34. Discuss with your child before leaving home what it is that might be needed (e.g., a soft drink at the grocery, a dollar to spend at the ball game, etc.). Explain to your child that no demands will be met in public. All requests must be discussed beforehand.

35. "Demanding" is not acceptable behavior. Tell your child when he/she is "demanding," and that unless he/she asks politely, you will not consider the demand.

36. Make certain your child understands that he/she may earn, for appropriate behavior, those things he/she demands, but that you will not "give in" to those things that are demanded.

A Reminder: Your child will stop demanding if you do not give in to his/her demands.

126 Is jealous

1. Attempt to spend some time alone with your child each day in order to help him/her feel important, special, loved, etc.

2. Help your child decide on one ability (e.g., drawing, singing, playing an instrument, athletic skills, etc.) that he/she would like to develop in order to feel good about himself/herself.

3. Establish rules for interacting with others (e.g., make positive comments, share materials, wait your turn, etc.). These rules should be consistent and followed by everyone in the home. Talk about the rules often and reward your child for following the rules.

4. If there are other children or adolescents in the home, reward them for making positive comments, sharing materials, waiting their turn, etc.

5. Make positive comments when talking with your child. Try to be as positive as possible at all times.

6. Being jealous of someone can be normal. However, if your child talks a lot about someone else and seems overly jealous, then you should consider talking with a professional about the matter.

7. When your child is jealous of someone, explain exactly what he/she is doing wrong, what should be done and why.

For example: You hear your child talking very unkindly about someone else to a best friend. Go to your child and say, ''Kim, you are being very unkind. If you can't say something nice about someone, then you shouldn't say anything at all. If you want others to like you, you need to stop saying unkind things.''

8. Make certain that your child sees the relationship between his/her jealousy of others and the consequences which follow (e.g., others avoiding your child, loss of friendships, hurting others' feelings, etc.).

9. Encourage your child to talk with you when feeling jealous of others in order to help your child understand his/her feelings.

10. Make sure that you do not appear jealous of others. Attempt to say only kind things about others.

11. Make certain that you are always complimentary of others who have been successful, gotten something new, etc.

12. Before going to someone's home, having a friend over, etc., remind your child that it is important to be complimentary of others and is not necessary to compare himself/herself to others.

13. Teach your child appropriate ways in which to deal with anger, frustration, over-competitiveness, etc.

14. Make certain that your child sees the relationship between his/her behavior and the consequences which follow (e.g., others not wanting to play with him/her, being removed from the activity, etc.).

15. Encourage your child to participate in more individualized sports (e.g., aerobics, swimming, track and field, golf, etc.).

16. Help your child to have self-confidence and satisfaction in personal self-worth and successes by pointing out strengths, emphasizing positive aspects, etc.

17. Encourage your child to play and interact with friends who are not highly competitive.

18. Encourage your child to refrain from ''one-upmanship'' with friends (e.g., when friends talk about a new possession, it may be more desirable to say ''You're lucky.'' or ''That's great.'' rather than ''That's nothing, my dad's going to buy me a...'').

19. Identify the things that appear to make your child jealous of others. Talk to your child and explain that some people have talents in one area and that he/she may be talented in another area.

20. Encourage your child to associate with peers who are not jealous of others.

21. Make certain your child is not critical of himself/herself to get your attention (e.g., ignore self-critical comments or indicate that the critical statements are not true).

22. Do not reinforce your child's jealously by buying something just because he/she is jealous of a friend for having new clothes, a new bike, his/her own car, etc.

23. Be careful not to place too much importance on clothes, looks, hair, etc. If these subjects are always the topic of conversation your child may become overly concerned with appearance.

24. Avoid engaging your child in activities in which he/she may not succeed and which may cause your child to feel bad about himself/herself.

25. Compliment your child whenever possible.

26. Encourage others to compliment your child.

27. Encourage your child to refrain from comparing personal performance to others and to emphasize attention to personal improvement (e.g., maintain records of progress rather than making a comparison to others).

28. Pair your child with a younger brother/sister, younger children, etc., in order to enhance your child's feelings of success or accomplishment.

29. Expose your child to other children with similar ability levels in order to reduce the likelihood of jealousy (e.g., encourage your child to play touch football rather than tackle, play T-ball rather than hard ball, take beginner swim lessons rather than advanced beginner, etc.).

30. Arrange for your child to earn (for appropriate behavior) those things that make him/her jealous of others.

31. Help your child find activities in which he/she may be successful, therefore reducing the need to be jealous.

32. When your child indicates that someone else has something that is desirable, point out to your child those things he/she has that others may not have.

A Reminder: It is easy to feel "left out" or be jealous of what others have. You may need to be more aware to include your child, avoid others getting new things unless your child gets a "little something," etc., until your child grows to better handle such situations.

127 Does not share

1. Establish rules for interacting with others (e.g., share materials, wait your turn, allow others to participate, play fairly, etc.). These rules should be consistent and followed by everyone in the home. Talk about the rules often and reward your child for following the rules.

2. Do not allow your child to fail to share. Immediately correct your child when failing to share.

3. Teach your child to share by sharing things yourself. Allow your child to borrow things from you, and you borrow things from your child.

4. Reward your child for sharing. Possible rewards include verbal praise (e.g., ''Thank you for sharing with your brother!''), a kiss on the cheek, a hug, having a friend over to play, staying up late, watching a favorite TV show, and playing a game with a parent. (See Appendix for Reward Menu.)

5. If there are other children or adolescents in the home, reward them for sharing.

6. Make sure that others share with your child when they are interacting.

7. Carefully consider your child's age and experience before expecting him/her to share.

8. Do not expect your child to share everything with others. Your child should have some belongings that are not shared with others.

9. Supervise your child in order to help your child learn to share.

10. Immediately remove your child from playing with others when he/she does not share.

11. When your child does not share, explain exactly what he/she did wrong, what should have been done and why.

For example: You see your child refusing to share a toy with another child. Go to your child and say, ''William, you are not sharing. You need to share or others will not want to play with you.''

12. When playing with others, put the emphasis on getting along, sharing, and having fun.

13. Write a contract with your child.

For example: I, William, will share with others. When I accomplish this, I can play a game with Dad.

The contract should be written within the ability level of your child and should focus on only one behavior at a time. (See Appendix for an example of a Behavior Contract.)

14. Teach your child to ask for help, stop playing, etc., when he/she does not want to share.

15. Discourage your child from playing with others who do not share.

16. Make certain that your child sees the relationship between his/her behavior and the consequences which follow (e.g., others not wanting to play with him/her, making others angry, not being allowed to play, etc.).

17. Reduce competition between your child and brothers and/or sisters and friends. Competitive activities are likely to inhibit sharing and working together.

18. Have objects and materials at home that everyone can use (e.g., communal property - property that belongs to everyone.)

19. Help your child see the natural rewards of sharing (e.g., others sharing in return, personal satisfaction, friendships, etc.).

20. Make sure that shared materials are returned to your child in order to develop a positive attitude about sharing.

21. Arrange for your child to be involved in many activities with other children to help him/her learn the skills necessary to interact appropriately with them.

22. Make certain that your child does not get away with refusing to share things with others. Have your child give things to others for a short period of time that he/she is unwilling to share.

23. Remind your child before going to a friend's house, having a friend over, etc., about sharing.

24. Encourage your child to share by giving each child a time limit to play with a toy, game, etc. (e.g., 10 minutes each).

25. Show your child how to play cooperatively, share, talk in an acceptable manner, and not resort to fighting with others.

26. Do not allow your child to play with those children with whom he/she has trouble getting along.

27. Supervise your child's interactions with friends in order to stop inappropriate behavior and model appropriate behavior.

28. Do not allow your child to play stimulating activities which might cause trouble getting along with friends.

29. When your child has had trouble getting along with friends, sit down and talk about the alternative things that could have been done to get along better with friends.

30. Talk with your child about appropriate ways to deal with anger and frustration (e.g., compromise, walk away from the situation, talk about the problem with an adult, etc.).

31. Do not make your child play with a certain child or group of children. Allow your child to pick his/her own friends.

32. Encourage your child to play with children or adolescents who get along well with others.

33. Be consistent. Try to deal with your child and his/her behavior in a manner that is as consistent as possible (e.g., react in the same manner each time, use the same consequences, etc.).

34. Encourage neighborhood children who frequently play at your house to bring toys, riding toys, games, etc., so your child is not always expected to share personal toys with neighborhood children.

35. Treat your child with respect. Always talk in an objective manner and use a calm, quiet voice without losing your temper.

36. Make sure your child understands that the privilege of having a friend over or going to a friend's house will be taken away if he/she is not nice to friends.

37. Provide your child and others with enough "things" that sharing will not be necessary. Gradually reduce the number of things as your child learns to share.

38. Supervise your child in activities with friends which require sharing (e.g., painting, coloring, etc.) and be sure many materials are available in order to help him/her learn to share.

39. Make certain that your child takes "things" to other friend's homes so sharing does not become a problem.

40. Make certain that others share with your child when it is an appropriate time, game, possession, etc.

41. Have your child practice sharing when a friend is over to play (e.g., each child plays with a certain toy for 10 minutes each and then they trade).

42. Create and reinforce activities in which your child and others work together for a common goal (e.g., a clubhouse, fort, etc.) rather than individual success or recognition. Point out that larger accomplishments are realized through group effort rather than individual effort, thus making sharing necessary.

43. Make certain that your child knows that some things are not owned (e.g., swings, slides, animals, etc.) and that those things must be shared.

44. Make certain your child understands that if shared materials are used up, worn out, broken under normal use, they will be replaced.

45. Make certain that if your child shares, other children will not take advantage of him/her.

46. Make certain that materials your child shares are returned. When your child learns that shared materials will be returned, he/she will be more likely to share in the future.

47. Establish rules for sharing (e.g., ask for things you wish to use, exchange things carefully, return materials when not in use, offer to share materials with others, take care of shared materials, call attention to materials that need repair). Reiterate rules often and reinforce students for following rules.

48. Practice sharing with your child by letting him/her use your things, return them and use them again. Repeat this activity with some of your child's possessions.

49. Teach your child the concept of sharing by borrowing from others and loaning things to others.

A Reminder: Not all possessions have to be shared. Adults are not expected to share many of their personal possessions (e.g., their car, golf clubs, tennis rackets, etc.); therefore, children should not be expected to share all of their possessions.

128 Cries when does not get own way

1. Model for your child acceptable ways of behaving when he/she does not get his/her way. Your child will learn how to behave by watching you.

2. Teach your child acceptable ways to behave when he/she does not get his/her way (e.g., compromising, accepting the decision, walking away from the situation, asking an adult to help solve the conflict, etc.).

3. Reward your child for not crying when he/she does not get his/her way. Possible rewards include verbal praise (e.g., ''I'm so proud of you for not crying when I told you it was time for bed.''), a kiss on the cheek, a hug, having a friend over to play, staying up late, watching a favorite TV show, and playing a game with a parent. (See Appendix for Reward Menu.)

4. If there are other children or adolescents in the home, reward them for not crying when they do not get their own way.

5. Ignore your child's crying when the child is crying because he/she did not get his/her way. Do not let the child have his/her way when he/she cries.

6. Be consistent. Try to deal with your child and the behavior in a manner that is as fair as possible.

7. When your child starts to cry, explain exactly what he/she is doing wrong, what should be done and why.

For example: It is 8:25 p.m. You tell your child that bedtime is in five minutes, and your child begins to cry. Go to your child and say, ''William, you are crying because you do not want to go to bed. You need to stop crying and go to bed because your bedtime is at 8:30.''

8. Make certain that your child sees the natural consequences of crying when he/she does not get his/her own way (e.g., others not wanting to be around, being called names by peers, etc.).

9. Carefully consider your child's age before expecting him/her not to cry.

10. Write a contract with your child.

For example: I, William, will not cry when I do not get my way, for three days in a row. When I accomplish this, I can buy a new kite.

The contract should be written within the ability level of your child and should focus on only one behavior at a time. (See Appendix for an example of a Behavior Contract.)

11. Walk away from your child when the crying begins because he/she did not get his/her own way.

12. Teach your child how to solve problems when involved in a conflict situation (e.g., walking away, asking an adult for help, compromising, apologizing, etc.).

13. Tape record your child crying because he/she did not get his/her way. Let the child listen to the tape, and then discuss the tape.

14. Show your child how to accept angry feelings when things do not go his/her way (e.g., counting to 10, saying the alphabet, etc.).

15. Immediately remove your child from the attention of others when he/she begins to cry when he/she does not get his/her way.

16. Make certain you do not give in to your child's crying just because there are others present. Maintain consistency at all times.

17. Before going into a grocery store, shopping mall, friend's house, etc., remind your child of the consequences of crying when not getting his/her way.

18. Make certain that your child does not go to another adult after you have said ''no.''

19. After telling your child that he/she cannot do or have something, explain the reason.

20. Be consistent in expecting your child to ask for things and then be able to react to disappointment without crying. Do not ''give in'' one time and expect appropriate behavior the next time.

21. Offer another suggestion to your child after you have said "no" to something (e.g., if your child wants to spend the night at someone else's and cannot do that, suggest the friend come to your house; if your child wants a new toy but cannot get one, suggest getting it for a birthday present or earning it for good behavior; etc.).

22. Make certain that your child knows beforehand what to expect in various situations (e.g., how much money your child can spend at the store, how long he/she can visit a friend, when he/she has to come home, etc.).

23. Separate your child from peers who cry when they do not get their own way.

24. Make certain there is consistency in the types of consequences delivered when your child cries because he/she does not get his/her own way (e.g., going to his/her room, sitting in a chair, etc.).

25. Make certain baby-sitters, grandparents, teachers, etc., understand the importance of maintaining consistency in discipline with your child.

26. Remain calm when your child starts crying. By getting upset, you may lose control of the situation.

27. Discuss with your child before leaving home what might be needed (e.g., a soft drink at the grocery, a dollar to spend at the ball game, etc.). Make the child understand that no demands will be met in public. All requests must be discussed beforehand.

28. Make certain that you do not give in to your child's crying.

29. Make certain your child understands that by not crying, the things that are desired may be earned, but you will not "give" those things when your child cries about them.

30. Encourage your child to use problem-solving skills: (a) identify the problem, (b) identify goals and objectives, (c) develop strategies, (d) develop a plan for action, and (e) carry out the plan.

31. Teach your child alternative ways to communicate unhappiness (e.g., talking about a problem, asking for help, etc.).

32. Reduce the emphasis on competition. Repeated failure may cause your child to become upset and cry.

33. Provide your child with alternative activities, games, etc., in which to engage in case some activities prove upsetting.

34. Give your child additional responsibilities (e.g, chores, errands, privileges, etc.) so that alternative activities will be available if he/she does not get to do what is desired.

35. Discourage your child from engaging in those activities which cause him/her unhappiness.

A Reminder: Your child will stop crying to get his/her own way if you do not give in to the crying.

1. Make certain that your child sees the relationship between his/her behavior and the consequences which follow (e.g., others avoiding your child, making fun, not believing anything he/she says, etc.).

2. Encourage your child to avoid activities that cause bragging about abilities, possessions, etc.

3. Make sure that you do not brag or exaggerate about your abilities, possessions, etc. If you do, your child will learn to brag also.

4. Supervise your child when possible in order to make certain he/she makes accurate statements.

5. Reward your child for not bragging about his/her abilities, possessions, etc. Possible rewards include verbal praise (e.g., ''I appreciate it when you do not brag!''), a kiss on the cheek, a hug, having a friend over to play, staying up late, watching a favorite TV show, and playing a game with a parent. (See Appendix for Reward Menu.)

6. If there are other children or adolescents in the home, reward them for not bragging about their abilities, possessions, etc.

7. Do not brag about your child's abilities, possessions, etc., to others.

8. Try to prevent competitiveness in information-sharing in order that your child will not feel like he/she needs to brag in order to be accepted by others.

9. When your child starts to brag, explain exactly what he/she is doing wrong, what should have been done and why.

For example: You overhear your child bragging to another child. Go to your child and say, ''William, you are bragging. You need to make accurate statements if you want others to believe you.''

10. Do not put your child in a situation, such as a competitive activity, in which there is a need to brag.

11. Write a contract with your child.

For example: I, William, will not brag about my new bike for three days in a row. When I accomplish this, I can have a slumber party.

The contract should be written within the ability level of your child and should focus on only one behavior at a time. (See Appendix for an example of a Behavior Contract.)

12. Try to make your child feel good about himself/herself by making positive comments, spending one-to-one time with your child, and accepting him/her the way he/she is.

13. Carefully consider your child's age before expecting him/her to make accurate statements.

14. Attempt to have an open and honest relationship with your child. Encourage him/her to always tell the truth.

15. Make certain that your child sees the relationship between his/her behavior and the consequences which follow (e.g., others not believing what he/she says, being avoided by others, etc.).

16. Do not make your child feel the need to exaggerate the truth to get your attention or to impress you. Let your child know that you are most impressed when he/she puts forth his/her best effort.

17. Help your child understand that bragging often promotes future problems. For example, when your child brags about being the best swimmer and then is not the winner, your child must deal with people making fun, calling names, etc.

18. Do not appear shocked or surprised when your child brags. Deal with the behavior in a calm and deliberate manner.

19. Remind your child before going to school, to a friend's house, to a sporting event, etc., that it is important to be completely honest with yourself and other people.

20. Deal with your child's bragging privately rather than in front of others.

21. Separate your child from other children or adolescents who brag to impress, compete, etc.

22. Help your child accept satisfaction with his/her own "best effort" and not feel a need to brag to impress others.

23. Reduce the emphasis on competition and "winning." Emphasize working together, having fun, making new friends, etc.

24. Supervise your child closely when engaged in competitive activities in order to suggest alternative ways in which to behave.

25. Before beginning a game or competitive activity, make sure your child knows the rules, is familiar with the game, and will be compatible with the other individuals who will be playing.

26. Encourage your child to engage in less competitive activities (e.g., reading, clubs, scouting, student council, etc.).

27. Encourage your child to participate in activities, sports, etc., for self-improvement rather than to "win" or "beat" someone else (e.g., try to improve a batting average or defensive skills rather than being disappointed if the team does not win).

28. Encourage your child to refrain from "one-upmanship" with friends (e.g., when friends talk about a new possession, it may be more desirable to say "You're lucky." or "That's great." rather than "That's nothing, my dad's going to buy me a...").

29. Reduce the emphasis on competition among brothers and sisters in your family. Competitiveness learned in the home will be demonstrated at school and elsewhere.

30. Help your child to understand that by exaggerating the truth he/she may even come to believe what he/she exaggerates and that exaggerating may become a habit.

31. Encourage your child to avoid activities that cause exaggeration about abilities, possessions, etc.

32. Make certain your child engages in activities in which success can be experienced in order that satisfaction with success may replace the need to brag (i.e., when you know you are capable there is no need to brag).

33. Heighten your child's awareness of bragging by calling attention each time bragging begins and reiterating the inappropriateness of bragging in front of others.

34. Have your child earn or work toward those things he/she brags about having or getting (e.g., a bike, remote control car, etc.). Your child can work to earn part or all of the money to buy the item for good behavior, doing chores, completing homework, etc.

A Reminder: Genuine success is the result of hard work and effort, making bragging unnecessary.

1. Establish rules (e.g., do not whine when a decision has been made; talk about what you want, but do not whine or beg, etc.). These rules should be consistent and followed by everyone in the home. Talk about the rules often and reward your child for following the rules.

2. Reward your child for not whining. Possible rewards include verbal praise (e.g., ''Thank you for not whining when I told you to feed the dog.''), a kiss on the cheek, a hug, having a friend over to play, staying up late, watching a favorite TV show, and playing a game with a parent. (See Appendix for Reward Menu.)

3. If there are other children or adolescents in the home, reward them for not whining.

4. Carefully consider your child's age before expecting him/her to not whine.

5. Be certain to call whining to your child's attention each time it occurs.

6. Tape record your child whining, let him/her listen to the tape, and then discuss his/her reaction to the tape.

7. Show your child how to ask for things and discuss feelings without whining.

8. Write a contract with your child.

For example: I, William, for five nights in a row, will not whine when told to go to bed. When I accomplish this, I can stay up late on Saturday night.

The contract should be written within the ability level of your child and should focus on only one behavior at a time. (See Appendix for an example of a Behavior Contract.)

9. Make certain that your child sees the relationship between his/her behavior and the consequences which follow (e.g., others not wanting to play, having to leave the room, being made fun of by others, etc.).

10. Immediately remove your child from the attention of others when whining begins.

11. Do not ''give in'' to what your child wants when he/she whines.

12. Be consistent in expecting your child to ask for things and react to disappointment without whining. Do not ''give in'' one time and expect appropriate behavior the next time.

13. Make certain your child knows beforehand what to expect in various situations (e.g., how much money your child can spend at the store, how long he/she can visit a friend, when to be home, etc.).

14. Show your child how to control angry feelings when things do not go his/her way (e.g., count to 10, say the alphabet, etc.).

15. Make certain you do not give in to your child's whining because there are others present. Maintain consistency at all times.

16. Remind your child of the consequences of whining before going into a grocery store, shopping mall, friend's house, etc.

17. Make certain that your child does not go to another adult after you have said ''no.''

18. After telling your child that he/she cannot do or have something, explain the reason.

19. Offer another suggestion to your child after you have said ''no'' to something (e.g., if your child wants to spend the night at someone else's and cannot do that, suggest that he/she have the friend come to your house; if your child wants a new toy but cannot get one, suggest getting it for a birthday present or earning it for good behavior; etc.).

20. Separate your child from peers who whine.

21. Make certain there is consistency in the types of consequences delivered for whining (e.g., sitting in a chair, going to his/her room, etc.).

22. Make certain you do not give in when your child whines.

23. Make certain that baby-sitters, grandparents, teachers, etc., understand the importance of maintaining consistency in the discipline of your child.

24. Remain calm when your child starts whining. By getting upset, you may lose control of the situation.

25. Ignore your child when whining begins (e.g., leave the room, continue with what you are doing, talk to someone else, etc.).

26. If your child whines about such things as not getting to go to a movie or not getting a new toy, have him/her earn such items/activities for appropriate behavior. Do not "give in" to your child if he/she is whining.

27. Teach your child alternative ways to communicate unhappiness (e.g., talk about a problem, ask for help, etc.).

28. Provide your child with alternative activities, games, etc., in which to engage in case some activities prove upsetting.

29. Give your child additional responsibilities (e.g., chores, errands, privileges, etc.) that will have alternative activities if your child cannot do what he/she wants to do.

30. Make certain you do not expect too much from your child (e.g., long shopping trips). Plan your trips so your child gets to stop for a soda or a treat, shop for something personal, etc.

31. Identify those things your child wants (e.g., to ride in the shopping cart, to go home, to ride in the front seat, etc.). Identify what your child must do to earn the things that are desired (e.g., sit quietly in the shopping cart, assist you in finding what you need in the store, ride quietly in the car, etc.).

32. Discourage your child from engaging in those activities which cause unhappiness.

33. Make certain you do not ignore your child's needs, making it necessary for him/her to whine to get things needed or genuinely wanted (e.g., new tennis shoes, new bike, etc.).

34. Do not surprise your child with such things as going to the dentist, going shopping, a change in schedule, etc. If your child knows what to expect, he/she will be less likely to whine.

35. Make certain your child understands responsibilities in order to prevent the "why do I have to?" whining. Explain everyone's contributions to the family chores, sharing, etc.

36. Teach your child to communicate wants and needs by having your child state what is desired and explain why he/she wants it (e.g., "I want a new bike because mine is broken." "I need a new dress because this one is too small." etc.).

A Reminder: If you "give in" to whining, your child will whine.

131 Does not find things to do

1. Carefully consider your child's age before expecting the child to entertain himself/herself.

2. Take things (e.g., books, tape recorder and tapes, colors, puzzles, etc.) when going somewhere in the car, going to the doctor's office or dentist's office, etc.

3. Reward your child for finding things to do. Possible rewards include verbal praise (e.g., ''I'm so proud of you for finding something to do while I was talking to my friend on the phone!''), a kiss on the cheek, a hug, having a friend over to play, staying up late, watching a favorite TV show, and playing a game with a parent. (See Appendix for Reward Menu.)

4. If there are other children or adolescents in the home, reward them for finding things to do.

5. When your child has difficulty finding something to do, explain exactly what he/she is doing wrong, what should have been done and why.

For example: Your child comes to you complaining of boredom. Get your child's attention and say, ''You are complaining that you are bored. You are old enough to entertain yourself and I have jobs I need to get done before dinner time.''

6. Make a list of things for your child to do when having difficulty thinking of things to do.

7. Maintain a collection of games, activities, puzzles, etc., for your child to use when things cannot be found to do.

8. Have jobs or responsibilities with which your child can help when he/she cannot find something to do (e.g., dusting, vacuuming, helping with dinner, etc.).

9. Arrange for your child to be involved in a variety of activities outside of the home (e.g., scouting, sports, school-related activities, etc.).

10. Help your child plan special activities in advance (e.g., having a slumber party, visiting relatives, etc.).

11. Give your child responsibilities around the house (e.g., taking care of pets, setting the table, cleaning, etc.).

12. Set aside a special time each day to spend with your child.

13. Help your child get involved in a hobby (e.g., coloring, painting, sewing, putting models together, etc.).

14. Establish a routine for your child that provides activities throughout the entire day.

15. Plan family activities for the evening.

16. Do not leave a lot of unstructured time for your child.

17. Make a list of activities for your child and have it available when a baby-sitter stays, friends come over, etc.

18. Set out games, toys, etc., each morning for your child to use that day. The games should vary each day so your child does not get bored with the same games.

19. Make certain your child is involved with outside activities and that there is plenty to do outside the home.

20. Encourage your child to get involved with peers in the neighborhood, at school, etc.

21. Discourage your child from engaging in those activities which cause unhappiness.

22. Make arrangements to have friends over to play, have your child go to a friend's house, go on a special outing, etc.

23. Provide your child with a full schedule of activities each day (e.g., games, swimming, having friends over, helping with lunch or dinner, etc.).

24. Plan evenings and weekends in advance in order to avoid your child ''having nothing to do.''

25. Provide your child with a wide variety of activities to choose from on any given day (e.g., games, renting movies, having friends over, going to the park, going for a walk, etc.).

26. Find a hobby your child will enjoy alone or with others (e.g., putting models together, building a clubhouse).

27. Find a group your child can join (e.g., craft club, scouting, swim club, etc.) to give your child plenty to do and friends with whom to interact.

28. Enroll your child in a community day camp during the summer in order to provide a full schedule of activities.

29. Go through old toy boxes and storage places to find forgotten toys, games, puzzles, books, etc., to use and enjoy.

30. Get a list of summer Parks and Recreation programs available to your child for enjoyment.

31. Get a list of community recreation programs that are available throughout the school year for your child.

32. Check the community calendar throughout the year for special events and activities.

33. Make a list of those things your child most enjoys and have your child choose those things he/she wants to do for the day, week, etc. (e.g., visiting a friend, having a friend over, skating, swimming, renting movies, etc.).

34. Arrange for your child's friends to come to your home for special activities (e.g., games, crafts, picnics, a rented movie, etc.).

35. Involve your child in library programs (e.g., go twice a week for story time, check out books, etc.).

A Reminder: You may need to plan afternoons, evenings, weekends, etc., in advance for "things to do," friends to have over, etc.

132 Wants everything in stores and on TV

1. It is normal for children to want things that they see in stores and on TV. However, if your child is constantly begging for things in stores or while watching TV, this behavior needs to be corrected.

2. Establish a rule for your child to follow when shopping and/or watching TV (e.g., do not beg for things you see or want). This rule should be consistent and followed by everyone in the home. Talk about the rule often and reward your child for following the rule.

3. Reward your child for not begging or constantly asking for things. Possible rewards include verbal praise (e.g., "I'm very proud of you for not begging for things when we went to the mall today."), a kiss on the cheek, a hug, having a friend over to play, staying up late, watching a favorite TV show, and playing a game with a parent. (See Appendix for Reward Menu.)

4. If there are other children or adolescents in the home, reward them for not begging for things they see in stores or on TV.

5. When your child begins to beg, explain exactly what he/she is doing wrong, what should have been done and why.

For example: You are at the grocery store and your child keeps asking for a treat. Stop and say, "William, you are begging. You need to stop begging or we will go home."

6. Before going into a store, explain how you expect your child to act and identify exactly what can be earned (e.g. candy bar) if he/she behaves appropriately while you are in the store.

7. Write a contract with your child.

For example: I, William, will not beg for things when we go to the mall today. If I don't beg, I can buy a Superball before we leave the mall.

The contract should be written within the ability level of your child and should focus on only one behavior at a time. (See Appendix for an example of a Behavior Contract.)

8. Immediately leave the store when your child begins to beg for things.

9. Allow your child to do something else while you are shopping (e.g., go to a movie with a friend, stay with a baby-sitter, play at a friend's house, etc.).

10. Give your child responsibilities while you are shopping (e.g., pushing the cart, adding up prices on a calculator, carrying packages, etc.).

11. Turn off the TV when your child starts to beg for things.

12. Allow your child to earn money when performing chores, so he/she can buy things that are desired.

13. Allow your child to earn something that is desired by not begging in stores.

14. Make certain that you do not give in to your child's demands simply to quiet him/her. Deal with the behavior consistently.

15. Make certain that consequences delivered for inappropriate behavior are not too extreme and are directly related to the inappropriate behavior (e.g., for demanding a toy on a store shelf your child will not be allowed to get the toy unless it is asked for nicely and you discuss a way to earn the toy, decide on the toy as a holiday or birthday present, etc.).

16. Make certain that baby-sitters, grandparents, neighbors, etc., understand the importance of maintaining consistency in the discipline of your child.

17. Make certain that your child's demands are not met by another adult (e.g, after saying "no" to a toy seen on TV, do not allow your child to go to his/her grandparents and have them get the toy).

18. Discuss with your child before leaving home what it is that might be needed (e.g., a soft drink at the grocery, a dollar to spend at the ball game, etc.). Explain that no demands will be met in public. All requests must be discussed beforehand.

19. "Demanding" is not acceptable behavior. Tell your child that he/she is "demanding" and unless you are asked politely you will not consider the demand.

20. Make certain your child understands that he/she may earn, for appropriate behavior, those things that are demanded, but that you will not "give in" to those things that are demanded.

21. After telling your child that he/she cannot do or have something, explain the reason.

22. Be consistent in expecting your child to ask for things and then be able to react to disappointment without crying, arguing, etc. Do not "give in" one time and expect appropriate behavior the next time.

23. Have your child make a list of those things that are desired in order to tell grandparents, aunts, uncles, etc., for holidays, birthdays, etc.

24. Before going into a store, explain to your child that this is an adult shopping trip and he/she should not ask to get things.

25. Make certain your child does not get everything that is seen in a store or on TV.

26. When going shopping, determine in advance what your child may be allowed to purchase. Make certain your child understands this and agrees to it.

27. Encourage your child to "save up" for "something special" rather than having to have everything that is seen in stores or on TV.

28. Have your child earn money and spend it during shopping trips.

29. Make certain your child is earning money for doing chores, performing responsibilities, etc., in order to purchase the things that are seen and desired.

A Reminder: One advantage to your child wanting what he/she sees in stores and on TV is that you can provide an opportunity for your child to earn those things through hard work, doing chores, taking care of responsibilities, etc.

133 Uses public situations to get own way

1. Immediately remove your child from a public place when he/she begins to demonstrate inappropriate behavior (e.g., crying, yelling, kicking, demanding, etc.).

2. Establish rules for public behavior (e.g., follow directions, stay with an adult, be polite to others, etc.). These rules should be consistent and followed by everyone in the home. Talk about the rules often and reward your child for following the rules.

3. Reward your child for demonstrating acceptable behavior in public. Possible rewards include verbal praise (e.g., "Thank you for not begging for a treat in the store!"), a kiss on the cheek, a hug, having a friend over to play, staying up late, watching a favorite TV show, and playing a game with a parent. (See Appendix for Reward Menu.)

4. If there are other children or adolescents in the home, reward them for demonstrating acceptable behavior in public.

5. Before going to a public place, talk with your child concerning the behavior you expect to see and what the consequences for unacceptable behavior will be.

6. Be consistent when expecting your child to behave in public. Decide on a consequence for inappropriate behavior (e.g., crying) and use the consequence each time your child cries in order to get something.

7. Write a contract with your child.

For example: I, William, will not ask for treats when we go to the grocery store today. When I accomplish this, I can get a candy bar as we leave the store.

The contract should be written within the ability level of your child and should focus on only one behavior at a time. (See Appendix for an example of a Behavior Contract.)

8. Do not take your child to places that are not geared for a child (e.g., shopping for furniture, having taxes figured, visiting someone at the hospital, going to a wedding, etc.).

9. Make certain that your child sees the relationship between his/her behavior and the consequences which follow (e.g., not being able to go to the pool the next time, having to leave the store when he/she cries, not being invited to go places with friends, etc.).

10. When your child behaves inappropriately in public, explain exactly what he/she is doing wrong, what should have been done and why.

For example: You are in the checkout line at the grocery store and your child begins to scream and cry for a candy bar. Stop what you are doing and say, "William, you are screaming because you want a candy bar. You need to stop screaming. You know that is not the behavior you are expected to demonstrate. The next time you want a candy bar, you need to ask politely."

11. When possible, use checkout lanes that do not have candy and toys located near them.

12. Allow your child to earn a treat by behaving in public. Discuss this possibility with him/her before going out in public.

13. Supervise your child at all times when in public.

14. Do not "give in" to your child's crying just to keep him/her quiet while you are in public.

15. Show your child how to control angry feelings when things do not go his/her way (e.g., count to 10, say the alphabet, etc.).

16. Immediately remove your child from the attention of others when crying begins because he/she does not get his/her way.

17. Make certain you do not give in to your child's crying just because there are others present. Maintain consistency at all times.

18. Make certain that your child does not go to another adult after you have said "no."

19. After telling your child that he/she cannot do or have something, explain the reason.

20. Make certain that baby-sitters, grandparents, teachers, etc., understand the importance of maintaining consistency in discipline with your child.

21. Be consistent in expecting your child to ask for things and react to disappointment without crying. Do not "give in" one time and expect appropriate behavior the next time.

22. Tell your child before going into the store that he/she may earn a piece of gum, a candy bar, etc. (Be specific so your child will not cry over which treat you decide to give for demonstrating appropriate behavior.)

23. Make certain your child knows beforehand what to expect in various situations (e.g., how much money can be spent at the store, how long your child can visit a friend, when to be home, etc.).

24. Ignore your child when crying, whining, nagging, etc., and trying to take advantage of a situation in order to get something.

25. Teach your child to communicate wants and needs by stating what is desired (e.g., "May I please have a piece of gum?" etc.).

26. Make certain you do not expect too much from your child (e.g., long shopping trips). Plan your trips so your child gets to stop for a soda or a treat, shops for something special, etc.

27. When your child behaves inappropriately in a public situation, immediately remove him/her (e.g, leave the store, go to the car, etc.) until the problem is resolved.

28. Identify places where your child uses public situations to get his/her own way (e.g., checkout lines) and establish rules for your child to follow (e.g., help with the shopping, ride quietly in the shopping cart, etc.) in order to earn what is desired (e.g., gum or a candy bar at the checkout line).

A Reminder: If you "give in" to your child in a public place to avoid a scene or embarrassment, your child learns to manipulate you. Be firm and your child's behavior is likely to stop or be reduced significantly.

134 Will not eat at mealtimes

Note: This problem is that the child does not eat the food that is served at mealtimes. The problem is not that the child simply prefers to not eat a few foods which are served infrequently (e.g., brussel sprouts, asparagus, etc.).

1. Establish mealtime rules (e.g., eat within 30 minutes, eat what is served, use good manners, etc.). These rules should be consistent and followed by everyone in the home. Talk about the rules often and reward your child for following the rules.

2. Remind your child of the mealtime rules when sitting down to eat.

3. Reward your child for following the mealtime rules. Possible rewards include verbal praise (e.g., "I'm proud of you for finishing your meal within the time limit."), a kiss on the cheek, a hug, having a friend over to play, staying up late, watching a favorite TV show, and playing a game with a parent. (See Appendix for Reward Menu.)

4. If there are other children or adolescents in the home, reward them for eating at mealtime.

5. Serve all of your meals at the same times each day.

6. Do not allow your child to eat snacks between meals.

7. Sit next to your child when eating in order to supervise his/her eating habits and model appropriate mealtime behavior.

8. When your child is not eating at mealtime, explain exactly what he/she is doing wrong, what should be done and why.

For example: Your child is crying because he does not like what has been served for dinner. Get his attention and say, "William, you need to stop crying and eat your dinner. It is not considerate to cry while we are trying to eat."

9. Immediately remove your child from the attention of others when your child will not eat at mealtime.

10. Do not pay attention to your child when he/she does not eat during mealtime. If you give your child attention, he/she may not eat in order to get your attention.

11. Write a contract with your child.

For example: I, William, for five days in a row, will complete each of my meals within 30 minutes. When I accomplish this, I can have a model airplane.

The contract should be written within the ability level of your child and should focus on only one behavior at a time. (See Appendix for an example of a Behavior Contract.)

12. Ask your child what kinds of foods are preferred and try to serve some of the favorites at each meal.

13. Carefully consider whether or not mealtimes fit into your child's schedule. Activities such as sports, piano lessons, dancing, etc., may interfere with your current mealtimes.

14. Attempt to schedule mealtimes to meet your child's active schedule.

15. Remove distractions (e.g., turn off the TV or radio) in order to help your child eat during mealtimes.

16. Establish a set amount of time for eating meals (e.g., 20 minutes), and remove food and plates from the table when the time has elapsed.

17. Make sure that you eat during mealtimes in order to model appropriate eating habits for your child.

18. Have your child help in planning meals.

19. Do not allow your child to have dessert if he/she does not eat during mealtime.

20. Make certain that your child sees the relationship between his/her behavior and the consequences which follow (e.g., going hungry, being removed from the table, etc.).

21. Allow natural consequences to occur as a result of your child's failure to eat at mealtimes.

22. Put small amounts of food on your child's plate. Allow your child to have more when he/she finishes.

23. Make certain you do not substitute foods for your child when he/she does not want what is served (e.g., the family is having meat loaf, but your child wants a hotdog).

24. Remind your child before dinner is served that having dessert or a snack before bedtime depends on whether he/she finishes his/her dinner.

25. Make certain that baby-sitters, grandparents, visitors in your home, etc., are aware of your expectations and consequences and the importance of maintaining consistency.

26. Schedule snack times several hours before mealtimes.

27. As a reward for your child eating at meal-time and eating what is served, allow your child to help plan favorite meals for a week.

28. Allow your child to help you prepare meals.

29. When preparing meals, take into consideration that some foods are low in popularity and either may be deleted from the menu or will not be required to be eaten by everyone.

30. Have some foods on your menu which may be eaten "voluntarily" (e.g., low popularity foods) and other foods which are required to be eaten (e.g., main courses, staples, etc.). Have at least one "optional" food at every meal that your child does not have to eat.

31. For the child who eats slowly, remind him/her that in order to get dessert, he/she must finish dinner at a reasonable time.

32. If dessert is to be used as a reward for eating, finishing on time, etc., it must be a desirable dessert and one chosen by your child.

33. Make certain your child does not find a way to eat between meals when not eating what was served at mealtime.

A Reminder: Do not force all foods on your child. All of us have a few foods we would rather not eat.

135 Will not cooperate when angry or upset

1. Model for your child acceptable ways of behaving when angry or upset. Your child will learn how to be cooperative when angry or upset by watching you.

2. Establish rules (e.g., wait your turn, share, ask for help when necessary, treat others in a friendly manner, walk away from a situation when you are getting angry or upset, etc.). These rules should be consistent and followed by everyone in the home. Talk about the rules often and reward your child for following the rules.

3. Reward your child for being cooperative when angry or upset. Possible rewards include verbal praise (e.g., "I'm very proud of you for sharing with your sister even though you were upset with her!"), a kiss on the cheek, a hug, having a friend over to play, staying up late, watching a favorite TV show, and playing a game with a parent. (See Appendix for Reward Menu.)

4. If there are other children or adolescents in the home, reward them for being cooperative when angry or upset.

5. Immediately remove your child from the activity or situation when he/she becomes uncooperative.

6. Encourage your child to talk about feelings when angry or upset.

7. When your child is uncooperative, explain exactly what he/she is doing wrong, what should be done and why.

For example: Your child refuses to watch his sister's favorite TV show because he is angry that he can't watch the show he wants. Go to your child and say, "William, you need to stop complaining. You can either watch Kim's show, or you can find something else to do. If you want to watch TV, then you need to be quiet."

8. Make certain that your child sees the relationship between his/her behavior and the consequences which follow (e.g., being avoided by others, being removed from activities, not being included in special activities, etc.).

9. Write a contract with your child.

For example: I, William, for two days in a row, will be cooperative when I am angry or upset. When I accomplish this, I can see a movie on Sunday afternoon.

The contract should be written within the ability level of your child and should focus on only one behavior at a time. (See Appendix for an example of a Behavior Contract.)

10. Teach your child how to solve problems when involved in a conflict situation (e.g., compromise, ask an adult for help, express feelings in a controlled manner, apologize, etc.).

11. Allow natural consequences to occur as a result of your child's uncooperativeness (e.g., not being included in special activities, being avoided by others, etc.).

12. Do not "force" your child to be cooperative.

13. Pay as little attention as possible to your child's behavior when being uncooperative.

14. Help your child understand why he/she is being uncooperative and teach acceptable ways to show anger, frustration, etc.

15. Help your child identify what he/she can do to calm down (e.g., walk away, talk about feelings in a socially acceptable way, seek help from an adult, etc.).

16. Avoid confrontations which may lead to arguing by giving your child options (e.g., say, "You can either set the table or wash the dishes tonight. Which do you want to do?").

17. Be flexible in helping your child be able to do those things he/she wants to do (e.g., if you do not think it would be appropriate for your child to spend the night at a friend's house, allow the friend to spend the night at your house).

18. Carefully consider your child's age before expecting him/her to be cooperative when angry or upset.

19. Before going into public places, a friend's house, etc., remind your child what can be done (e.g., count to 10, walk away, say the alphabet, etc.) in order to avoid becoming angry or upset.

20. Encourage your child to express feelings and teach him/her how to talk about feelings in a controlled manner.

21. Do not "give in" when your child is angry or upset; by "giving in" to your child, you are reinforcing inappropriate behavior.

22. Make certain your child understands that things which are destroyed, broken, etc., when he/she is angry or upset must be replaced.

23. When your child refuses to participate in a situation because he/she is angry or upset, do not reinforce inappropriate behavior by trying to talk your child into coming back to the situation, "giving in" to his/her way, etc. Ignore your child until he/she is willing to come back to the situation and be cooperative.

24. Make certain your child is allowed to voice an opinion in a situation in order to avoid becoming angry or upset.

25. Immediately remove your child from the attention of others when he/she becomes uncooperative when angry or upset.

26. After telling your child that he/she cannot do or have something, explain the reason.

27. Be consistent in expecting your child to react to disappointment without becoming uncooperative. Do not "give in" one time and expect your child to behave appropriately the next time.

28. Make certain there is consistency in the type of consequence delivered for refusing to cooperate when angry or upset (e.g., going to a room, sitting in a chair, etc.).

29. Make certain that baby-sitters, grandparents, teachers, etc., understand the importance of maintaining consistency in the discipline of your child.

30. If your child becomes upset or angry about such things as not getting to go to a movie or not getting a new toy, have him/her earn such items/activities for appropriate behavior. Do not "give in" to your child if he/she is being uncooperative

31. Encourage your child to use problem-solving skills: (a) identify the problem, (b) identify goals and objectives, (c) develop strategies, (d) develop a plan for action, and (e) carry out the plan.

32. Teach your child alternative ways to communicate unhappiness (e.g., talking about a problem, asking for help, etc.).

33. Provide your child with alternative activities, games, etc., in which to engage in case some activities prove upsetting.

34. Give your child additional responsibilities (e.g., chores, errands, privileges, etc.) in order to have alternative activities if he/she does not get to do what is desired.

35. Discourage your child from engaging in those activities which cause unhappiness.

36. Help your child choose activities that do not cause him/her to become angry, frustrated, anxious, etc.

37. Intervene early when your child begins to get angry or upset in order to prevent him/her from behaving uncooperatively and to prevent future problems (e.g., take your child out of the store, leave the home you are visiting, etc.).

38. Teach your child to verbalize feelings before losing control (e.g., "The work is too hard." "Please leave me alone, you're making me angry." etc.).

39. Reinforce your child for demonstrating self-control based on the length of time he/she can be successful. Gradually increase the length of time required for reinforcement as your child demonstrates success.

40. Prevent frustrating or anxiety-producing situations from occurring (e.g., give your child chores, responsibilities, etc., only on the appropriate ability level).

41. Make necessary adjustments in the environment to prevent your child from experiencing stress, frustration, and anger.

42. Monitor the behavior of others (e.g., brothers, sisters, friends, etc.) to make certain they are not teasing or otherwise stimulating your child to become upset or angry.

43. Teach your child ways to deal with conflict situations (e.g., talking, reasoning, asking an adult to intervene, walking away, etc.).

44. Look for the warning signs (e.g., arguing, loud voices, etc.) that your child is getting upset or angry and intervene to change the activity.

45. Provide constant, positive reinforcement for appropriate behavior. Ignore as many inappropriate behaviors as possible.

46. Prevent your child from becoming overstimulated by an activity (e.g., monitor or supervise your child's behavior to limit overexcitement in physical activities, games, parties, etc.).

47. Supervise your child closely in situations in which he/she is likely to act impulsively (e.g., maintain close physical proximity, maintain eye contact, etc.).

48. Help your child to be able to identify when he/she is getting angry so something can be done to calm down (e.g., walk away, talk about feelings in a socially acceptable way, seek help from an adult, etc.).

49. After asking your child to do something, explain why it needs to be done and your reason for asking him/her to do it.

50. Show your child how to ask permission to use something and how to react whether he/she is told "yes" or "no."

51. Intervene early when your child begins to have problems with friends to prevent the problem from getting out of control (e.g., send your child to a room, send friends home, etc.).

52. Remind your child when you go in a store that there is no need to ask for things, whine, beg, etc.

53. Establish a rule that your child is not to ask for permission to do things with friends standing around, in public places, etc.

54. Require your child to ask permission in private, where you can discuss the request.

55. When your child must be informed that he/she will not get his/her way, make certain that options are given, alternatives offered, etc., (e.g., "Matt cannot come over tonight, but he can come over on Friday night since Saturday is not a school day." "I won't give you a remote control car, but you can earn one over the next two weeks by doing chores." etc.).

56. Teach your child the value of compromise in order that both parents and child can be satisfied with outcomes (e.g., you will not "give" your child a remote control car because "everyone" else has one and he just "has" to have one; but your child can earn the car in the next two weeks for working around the house, helping clean the garage, etc.).

A Reminder: While you want to avoid "giving in" to your child, you may want to allow a few moments when he/she is angry or upset before requiring cooperation.

136 Will not go to sleep after going to bed

1. Turn down the TV, turn off the radio, talk in a quiet voice, etc., in order to help your child go to sleep.

2. Talk to your family doctor, a school official, a social worker, a mental health professional about your child's inability to go to sleep after going to bed.

3. Encourage your child to talk with you about any problems that cause difficulty in sleeping.

4. Reward your child for going to sleep after going to bed. Possible rewards include verbal praise (e.g., "I'm so proud of you for going to sleep last night!"), a kiss on the cheek, a hug, having a friend over to play, staying up late, watching a favorite TV show, and playing a game with a parent. (See Appendix for Reward Menu.)

5. If there are other children or adolescents in the home, reward them for going to sleep after going to bed.

6. Have your child engage in quiet activities (e.g., watching TV, listening to quiet music, talking with a parent, etc.) at least one-half hour before going to bed.

7. Read a story in order to help your child go to sleep.

8. Allow your child to listen to the radio (on low volume) in order to help him/her go to sleep.

9. Encourage your child to read a book in bed until he/she goes to sleep.

10. Make sure your child sees the relationship between his/her behavior and the consequences which follow (e.g., not sleeping will make it difficult to get up in the morning, he/she will not feel well, health may be impaired, etc.).

11. Determine whether or not your child is going to bed too early. Your child may not need to go to bed as early as he/she has been.

12. Do not encourage naps too close to bedtime.

13. Set up a bedtime routine and have your child go to bed at the same time each night.

14. Read your child a story that has a happy ending and is not threatening, frightening, or otherwise stimulating.

15. Lie down with your child for a short period of time to help him/her relax and go to sleep.

16. Let your child keep on a night-light or have the door cracked if it increases a feeling of security.

17. Encourage all of your children to go to bed at the same time.

18. Make certain your child does not watch any movies, TV programs, etc., that may make it hard for him/her to sleep.

19. Make certain your child is not in an activity that may cause him/her to be "wound up" before bedtime (e.g., running, playing in a sporting event, etc.).

20. Make certain that older brothers or sisters, friends, etc., have not told your child something that might make your child fear going to his/her room alone.

21. Do not bring up a subject that may be exciting to your child before bedtime (e.g., a special trip, a new toy, etc.); he/she may become too excited to sleep.

22. Do not bring up a subject before your child goes to bed that may prove upsetting (e.g., a parent leaving on a business trip, denying permission to go to friend's house the following day, etc.).

23. Encourage your child to talk to you about any anxious feelings (e.g., school, swim lessons, going to a certain friend's house, etc.).

24. Do not allow your child to have drinks before bedtime that might keep him/her up late (e.g., soda, iced tea, coffee, etc.).

25. Do not let your child start watching a movie or TV show that will not be over before bedtime.

26. Make certain your child gets up in the morning at a regular time.

27. In order to prevent your child from being overstimulated before bedtime, turn off the family TV well before bedtime (e.g., 30 minutes, one hour, etc.).

28. Require quiet time before your child goes to bed (e.g., silent reading, coloring, story time). Avoid "roughhousing," highly stimulating TV shows, etc.

29. When it is time for your child to go to bed supervise your child in turning out the lights, turning off the TV or radio, getting into bed, etc.

30. If your child is not able to go to sleep due to watching an exciting TV program just before bedtime, videotape that program for your child to watch the next evening at an earlier hour.

A Reminder: As long as your child is quiet, resting, and not exhausted during the day, the failure to go to sleep after going to bed may not be a problem.

1. Establish specific bedtimes (e.g., 8:00 p.m. on school nights and 10:00 p.m. on Friday and Saturday nights). These bedtimes should be consistent and all children in the home should have consistent bedtimes.

2. Establish a "bedtime routine."

For example:
6:45 p.m. - take bath, brush teeth, dress for bed
7:15 p.m. - watch TV or listen to quiet music
7:45 p.m. - listen to story read by parent
8:00 p.m. - lights off

The bedtime routine should be consistent and followed every night.

3. Reward your child for going to bed on time. Possible rewards include verbal praise (e.g., "I am so proud of you for not arguing with me and getting to bed on time!"), a kiss on the cheek, a hug, having a friend over to play, staying up late, watching a favorite TV show, and playing a game with a parent. (See Appendix for Reward Menu.)

4. If there are other children or adolescents in the home, reward them for going to bed on time.

5. Make "bedtime" a special, positive time for you and your child. Arrange your schedule so you can spend 15-20 minutes talking, reading, etc., with your child prior to bedtime.

6. Go through your child's bedtime routine with your child in order to make sure the routine is followed and to show exactly what you expect.

7. When your child does not go to bed on time, explain exactly what he/she is doing wrong, what should be done and why.

For example: Your child's bedtime is 8:00 p.m. It is 8:10 p.m. and your child is watching TV. Go to your child, get his/her attention and say, "William, it is 8:10 and you are not in bed. You need to turn off the TV and go to bed. When you do not get to bed on time, you do not get enough sleep and then you are tired and grouchy the next day at school."

8. Remind your child when it is time to go to bed.

9. Write a contract with your child.

For example: I, William, will go to bed at 8:00 p.m. for five nights in a row. When I accomplish this, I can stay up late on Saturday night.

The contract should be written within the ability level of your child and should focus on only one behavior at a time. (See Appendix for an example of a Behavior Contract.)

10. Make certain that your child sees the relationship between his/her behavior and the consequences which follow (e.g., losing privileges, being tired and grouchy the day after going to bed late, being avoided by others, etc.).

11. Have your child watch a brother and/or sister get ready for and go to bed on time.

12. Get ready for bed at about the same time that you expect your child to go to bed. This will help your child go to bed on time.

13. Have your child earn the privilege of staying up late on a weekend night by going to bed on time throughout the week.

14. When it is time for your child to go to bed, supervise your child in turning out the lights, turning off the TV or radio, getting into bed, etc.

15. Have your child engage in quiet activities (e.g., watching TV, listening to quiet music, talking with a parent, etc.) at least one-half hour before going to bed.

16. Read a story in order to help your child go to sleep.

17. Allow your child to listen to the radio (on low volume) in order to help him/her go to sleep.

18. Encourage your child to go to his/her room and read a book until falling asleep.

19. Lie down with your child for a short period of time to encourage him/her to go to bed.

20. Do not encourage naps too close to bedtime.

21. Let your child keep on a night-light or have the door cracked if it increases a feeling of security.

22. Encourage all of your children to go to bed at the same time.

23. Do not let your child start watching a movie or TV show that will not be over before bedtime.

24. Make certain your child is not involved in an activity that may cause him/her to be "wound up" before bedtime (e.g., running, playing in a sporting event, etc.).

25. Make certain that older brothers or sisters, friends, etc., have not told your child something that might cause fear going to his/her room alone.

26. Do not allow drinks before bedtime that might keep your child up late (e.g., soda, iced tea, coffee, etc.).

27. If your child will not go to bed on time because of distracting stimuli, like the radio or TV, then the radio or TV must be turned off or removed from the room.

28. In order to prevent your child from being overstimulated before bedtime, turn off the family TV well before bedtime (e.g., 30 minutes, 1 hour, etc.).

29. Require quiet time before your child goes to bed (e.g., silent reading, coloring, story time). Avoid "roughhousing," highly stimulating TV shows, etc.

30. Make certain your child gets up in the morning at a regular time.

31. Read your child a story that has a happy ending and is not threatening, frightening, or otherwise stimulating.

32. Make certain your child does not watch any movies, TV programs, etc., that may make it hard to sleep.

33. Make certain your child is aware of the consequences that will be delivered for not going to bed on time (e.g., loss of privileges, loss of opportunity to do those things that may keep your child from going to bed on time, etc.).

34. Provide reminders to your child when it gets near the time to go to bed (e.g., 1 hour before bedtime, 45 minutes before bedtime, 30 minutes before bedtime, 15 minutes before bedtime, etc.).

35. Determine what it is that your child is doing instead of going to bed (e.g., watching TV) and remove that variable (e.g., turn off the TV each evening at 9:00 p.m.).

36. Along with a directive statement, provide an incentive statement (e.g., "If you go to bed on time tonight, we will go to the park tomorrow." etc.).

37. If your child is not going to bed on time and is watching a particular TV program, video-tape that program for your child to watch the next evening at an earlier hour.

A Reminder: If there are fun activities going on, who wants to go to bed?

1. Establish a specific time for your child to get up each morning.

2. Wake up your child each morning and do not leave the room until he/she is out of bed.

3. Allow a favorite or special breakfast food if your child gets up on time.

4. Reward your child for getting up on time. Possible rewards include verbal praise (e.g., "Thanks for getting up when I called you!"), a kiss on the cheek, a hug, having a friend over to play, staying up late, watching a favorite TV show, and playing a game with a parent. (See Appendix for Reward Menu.)

5. If there are other children or adolescents in the home, reward them for getting up on time.

6. Have your child perform a responsibility that is enjoyable immediately after getting out of bed (e.g., feeding the dog, setting the table, helping fix breakfast, etc.).

7. When your child does not get up on time, explain exactly what he/she is doing wrong, what should be done and why.

For example: You tell your child it is time to get up and get ready for school. Ten minutes later he/she is still in bed. Go to your child's room, tell your child that he/she is 10 minutes late getting up, and that he/she needs to get up immediately to avoid being late for school.

8. If your child has trouble waking up, wake him/her 20 minutes before needing to be out of bed and getting ready for the day.

9. Give your child an alarm clock to help him/her get up on time.

10. Turn on the TV or radio in order to help your child get up on time.

11. Make certain that your child sees the relationship between his/her behavior and the consequences which follow (e.g., being late for school, losing a turn in the bathroom, eating a cold breakfast or no breakfast, etc.).

12. Write a contract with your child.

For example: I, William, will get up at 7:00 a.m. each morning for five days in a row. When I accomplish this, I can have a friend spend the night on Saturday.

The contract should be written within the ability level of your child and should focus on only one behavior at a time. (See Appendix for an example of a Behavior Contract.)

13. Allow natural consequences to occur due to your child's failure to get up on time (e.g., missing out on a special activity, having to eat a cold breakfast, eating no breakfast, being late for school, etc.).

14. Talk with your child about why he/she is not getting up on time. Your child may be avoiding school, interacting with others, riding the bus, etc.

15. Make sure that you are up and out of bed in order to help your child get up on time.

16. Make sure that your child is going to sleep at an appropriate hour to ensure that he/she is getting enough sleep.

17. Make sure that your child is not being kept awake by loud talking, the TV, the radio, etc.

18. Set more than one alarm for your child.

19. Do not provide your child with an alarm equipped with a "snooze" button.

20. Have your child set the alarm 10 minutes early, so this will not develop into a habit of being late when going places.

21. Have your child prepare school or work clothes, materials for school or work, lunch, etc., the night before so he/she does not have several things to do when waking.

22. Do not allow your child to have a TV, telephone, etc., in his/her room that may cause staying up late at night.

23. Encourage your child to keep the same morning wake-up habits on weekends and during the summer months in order to get used to waking up at a certain time each day.

24. Set an example for your child by getting up on time.

25. Do not expect your child to wake up too early each morning.

26. Do not allow drinks before bedtime that might keep your child up late (e.g., soda, iced tea, coffee, etc.).

27. If your child is not going to sleep at night because of distracting stimuli, such as the radio or TV, then the radio or TV must be turned off or removed from the room.

28. Make certain your child gets up in the morning at a regular time.

29. Encourage your child to talk with you about any problems that may be causing difficulty in sleeping.

30. Make certain your child is aware of the consequences that will be delivered for not getting up on time (e.g., loss of privileges, loss of opportunity to do those things that your child would do if he/she had gotten up earlier, etc.).

31. Determine what it is that prevents your child from getting up on time (e.g., watching TV late at night) and remove the variable (e.g., turn off the TV each evening at 9:00 p.m.).

32. Do not allow your child to stay up late on some nights (e.g., Friday, Saturday) and expect him/her to easily get back into a routine of going to bed on time and getting up on time.

33. In order to get your child up on time, begin waking him/her well before it is time to get up (e.g., if your child is to get up at 7 o'clock, set the alarm for 6:30, call him/her at 6:45, etc.).

34. If your child is not going to bed on time because he/she is watching a particular TV program, videotape that program for your child to watch the next evening at an earlier hour.

35. Make certain there is something enjoyable waiting for your child when getting up on time (e.g., a good breakfast, a breakfast of choice, a favorite juice, the opportunity to watch cartoons while eating breakfast, etc.).

36. Make certain that your child is not failing to get up on time in order to avoid something unpleasant (e.g., investigate school to determine if there is a problem with academics, an undesirable social situation, an unpleasant class or instructor, etc.).

37. Communicate with school personnel (e.g., teachers or principal) to determine if there is something enjoyable for your child to do at school when he/she gets up on time and gets to school on time (e.g., raising the flag, doing chores for a teacher, assisting the custodian in opening the school and unlocking doors, etc.).

A Reminder: You cannot get up on time if you do not go to bed at a reasonable hour.

139 Does not put things away

1. Establish a rule (e.g., return belongings to their proper places after you are finished using them). This rule should be consistent and followed by everyone in the home. Talk about the rule often and reward your child for following the rule.

2. Reward your child for putting away things. Possible rewards include verbal praise (e.g., "Thanks for putting your bike in the garage after you were finished riding it!"), a kiss on the cheek, a hug, having a friend over to play, staying up late, watching a favorite TV show, and playing a game with a parent. (See Appendix for Reward Menu.)

3. If there are other children or adolescents in the home, reward them for putting away their things.

4. Carefully consider your child's age and experience before expecting him/her to put away things without help.

5. Show your child how to put away things before expecting him/her to do so on his/her own.

6. Act as a model for putting away things by doing so yourself.

7. When your child does not put away something, explain what he/she is doing wrong, what should be done and why.

For example: You are driving into the driveway and your child's bike is blocking the way. Stop the car, get out, go to your child and say, "William, you forgot to put your bike in the garage. You need to move your bike off the driveway and put it in the garage because it is blocking the driveway."

8. Write a contract with your child.

For example: I, William, for three days in a row, will put my bike in the garage when I am not riding it. When I accomplish this, I can have a friend spend the night on Saturday.

The contract should be written within the ability level of your child and should focus on only one behavior at a time. (See Appendix for an example of a Behavior Contract.)

9. Give your child a list of personal belongings and the places where they should be stored when not using them. Have your child place a star or check mark beside each belonging that is put away after using and allow your child to trade the stars or check marks for rewards.

10. Make certain that your child sees the relationship between his/her behavior and the consequences which follow (e.g., failure to put away things may result in their being lost, broken, damaged, etc.).

11. Allow natural consequences to occur due to your child's failure to put away things (e.g., things will be lost, damaged, stolen, etc.).

12. Tell your child when to put away things.

13. Set aside time each day for everyone in the home to put away their own things.

14. Make sure that your child can reach the places where personal belongings should be when not in use.

15. Make sure your child puts away toys before getting out other playthings.

16. Limit the use of belongings until your child can care for them properly.

17. Do not allow the use of those things that your child does not put away.

18. Show your child how to return things to their proper places before expecting him/her to perform the responsibilities independently.

19. Provide your child with a list of those things that need to be put away daily.

20. Discuss your child's responsibilities at the beginning of each day so he/she knows what is expected.

21. Help your child begin to put away personal belongings.

22. Let your child know that materials not put away at the end of the day may be taken away for a period of time due to lack of responsibility.

23. Make a list of your child's frequently used items and/or materials and have your child make sure that each item and/or material is put in its designated place each day.

24. Make certain there is a designated place for all items in and around the home.

25. Require your child to put his/her coat, gloves, hat, etc., in a designated place upon entering the home.

26. Make certain that responsibilities given to your child are appropriate for your child's level of development and ability.

27. Provide your child with shelving, containers, organizers, etc., for possessions. Label the storage areas and require your child to keep possessions together.

28. Make certain your child understands that things which are lost, broken, destroyed, etc., must be replaced by him/her.

29. Do not buy additional toys, games, etc., for your child if he/she is not able to take care of things he/she already has.

30. Limit the use of those things your child is not responsible for putting away, returning, etc.

31. Assist your child in putting away things. Gradually reduce the amount of help given to your child as he/she demonstrates success.

32. Do not expect your child to pick up toys and games that friends have left out; encourage friends to help your child.

33. Tell baby-sitters or others who are involved with your child that he/she is responsible for picking up and putting away personal materials.

34. Require your child to put away things even though he/she did not do so at the established time.

35. Post a list of your child's responsibilities (e.g., put away things in your room, bring in things at night, put away clothes, etc.). Have your child put a check next to each chore that is completed and reward your child for completing chores.

36. Show your child the proper way to take care of things (e.g., shining shoes, hosing off a bike, taking care of doll, etc.). This will teach your child a sense of responsibility with personal belongings.

37. Have your child pay for things that are desired (e.g., a baseball mitt, a new doll, a new pair of jeans, etc.). If your child has spent some of his/her own money on the item, your child may be more willing to take care of it.

38. Allow your child to do something enjoyable after caring for personal belongings (e.g., watch TV, play a game with a parent, play with a friend, etc.).

39. Post a list of your child's responsibilities so he/she can review the list daily. (See Appendix for Sample List.)

40. Along with a directive, provide an incentive statement (e.g., "You may watch TV after you put your clothes where they belong.").

41. Require your child's room to be neat and organized so there will always be a place to put toys, games, clothes, etc.

42. Set aside time each day when your child is expected to put away things (e.g., 7:00 p.m. each evening).

43. Tell your child exactly what he/she is to put away (e.g., "You need to put away your bike, skateboard, and tennis racquet before going to bed." etc.).

44. Have your child put away things right after using them instead of later (e.g., put the skateboard away as soon as you get home rather than before bedtime).

46. Make certain your child is paying attention to you when you tell him/her to put away things. Have your child look directly at you and have your child repeat the direction to check for understanding.

A Reminder: Ultimately, you are doing your child a favor by requiring him/her to put away things. It is far better to learn to be responsible during childhood than adulthood.

140 Is not concerned about appearance

1. Make sure that you wear clothes that match, tie your shoes, comb your hair, etc., in order to model an acceptable appearance for your child.

2. Teach your child how to care for his/her personal appearance.

3. Help your child care for his/her personal appearance by identifying clothes that match, how to comb hair, how to tie a pair of shoes, etc.

4. Remind your child to care for his/her personal appearance.

5. Do not allow your child to leave the house unless clothes match, pants are zipped, shoes are tied, etc.

6. Reward your child for caring for his/her personal appearance. Possible rewards include verbal praise (e.g., ''I'm so proud of you for wearing clothes that match!''), a kiss on the cheek, a hug, having a friend over to play, staying up late, watching a favorite TV show, and playing a game with a parent. (See Appendix for Reward Menu.)

7. If there are other children or adolescents in the home, reward them for caring for their personal appearance.

8. When your child does not care for his/her personal appearance, explain exactly what he/she is doing wrong, what should be done and why.

For example: Your child's shoes are untied. Get your child's attention and say, ''William, your shoes are untied. You need to tie them so you will not trip and fall.''

9. Write a contract with your child.

For example: I, William, will comb my hair and brush my teeth before leaving for school each day. When I do this for five days in a row, I can ask a friend to go to the movies Saturday afternoon.

The contract should be written within the ability level of your child and should focus on only one behavior at a time. (See Appendix for an example of a Behavior Contract.)

10. Make certain that your child sees the relationship between his/her behavior and the consequences which follow (e.g., offending others, being avoided by others, etc.).

11. Make a list of the things your child needs to do (e.g., bathe daily, brush teeth three times a day, keep hair combed and neat, keep shoes tied, keep pants zipped, etc.). Post this list in several places in order to help your child care for his/her appearance. (See Appendix for Sample List.)

12. Make sure that your child has the materials needed in order to care for his/her appearance (e.g., comb and brush; clothes that match; shoe strings that are long enough to tie easily; clothes with buttons, zippers, and snaps that are in proper working order; etc.).

13. Require your child to correct his/her appearance if it is unacceptable.

14. Make sure your child has enough time to care for his/her appearance. Do not rush through the steps necessary to have acceptable appearance.

15. Set an example for your child by caring about your personal appearance (e.g., combing your hair, bathing daily, etc.).

16. Go shopping and let your child pick out clothes he/she might like to have. Help your child earn the clothes in return for demonstrating concern for personal appearance for a certain period of time.

17. Help your child decide on a haircut or hairstyle your child would like to have. Take your child to get a haircut and help your child keep the hair ''styled.''

18. Encourage your child to take Home Economics, a health class, etc., in school to learn the importance of personal hygiene.

19. Help your child pick out clothes that match before putting them on to wear to school or outdoors.

20. Talk to your daughter about the appropriate amount of makeup, hair spray, perfume, etc., to wear and about the importance of taking care of herself.

21. Teach your child which colors go together, what to wear with plaids, which shoes to wear, etc., so your child will be able to dress himself/herself.

22. Make certain that your child understands that others might "make fun" if he/she does not comb hair, zip pants, tie shoes, etc.

23. Teach your child how to comb hair, zip pants, tie shoes, etc.

24. Compliment your child for taking the time to pick out clothes that match, tying shoes, etc.

25. Encourage others to compliment your child when time has been taken to pick out clothes that match, shoes are tied, etc.

26. Have your child practice matching clothes in order for you to provide feedback on what is appropriate.

27. Provide your child with a full-length mirror.

28. Set aside time to practice hair-combing, putting on makeup, shaving, using deodorant, etc.

29. Have your child choose what he/she will wear the next day and get your approval before going to bed.

30. Help your child create "outfits" that go together and that your child can wear without trying to "match" on his/her own.

A Reminder: Some of what your child does about his/her appearance is influenced by peers, fads, etc., and may require your tolerance.

141 Does not keep own room clean

1. Establish rules for keeping a clean room (e.g., make your bed daily, put clothes and toys where they belong, dust and sweep floor once a week, straighten your room daily, etc.). These rules should be consistent and followed by everyone in the home. Talk about the rules often.

2. Reward your child for keeping his/her room clean. Possible rewards include verbal praise (e.g., "Thank you for making your bed this morning!"), a kiss on the cheek, a hug, having a friend over to play, staying up late, watching a favorite TV show, and playing a game with a parent. (See Appendix for Reward Menu.)

3. If there are other children or adolescents in the home, reward them for cleaning their rooms.

4. Carefully consider your child's age and experience before expecting him/her to keep his/her room clean without assistance.

5. Show your child how to keep his/her room clean. Assist in making your child's bed and help put clothes and toys where they belong, dust and sweep the floor with your child, etc.

6. When your child does not keep his/her room clean, explain exactly what he/she is doing wrong, what should be done and why.

For example: It is 10:30 a.m. and your child has not made his/her bed. Go to your child and say that he/she has not yet made the bed and that he/she needs to make the bed now because it is to be made by 8:30 a.m. each day.

7. Write a contract with your child.

For example: I, William, will make my bed by 8:30 a.m. each day for one week. When I accomplish this, I can stay up until 11:00 p.m. on Friday night.

The contract should be written within the ability level of your child and should focus on only one behavior at a time. (See Appendix for an example of a Behavior Contract.)

8. Make certain that your child sees the relationship between his/her behavior and the consequences which follow (e.g., a dirty room results in a loss of privileges).

9. Have your child organize and clean his/her room often in order to keep it from becoming an overwhelming job for your child to complete.

10. Make sure that your child has enough storage space in which to put toys, materials, etc., when not using them.

11. Prevent things that may distract your child from cleaning his/her room (e.g., turn off the TV, have friends go home, etc.).

12. Act as a model for your child by keeping your room clean.

13. Develop a routine of checking your child's room each morning to make sure the bed is made, toys and clothes are picked up, etc.

14. Require your child to clean his/her room at specific times (e.g., every Tuesday and Saturday).

15. Give your child a checklist of things to do when cleaning his/her room and mark off each item completed.

16. Limit the number of toys, materials, etc., that your child has in order to help successfully organize and keep his/her room clean.

17. Do not buy additional toys, games, etc., if your child is not able to take care of possessions.

18. Limit the use of those things in your child's room for which he/she is not responsible (e.g., toys, clothes, shoes, etc.).

19. Post a list of your child's responsibilities for his/her room (e.g., make bed, hang up clothes, put toys away, etc.). (See Appendix for Sample List.)

20. Discuss your child's responsibilities at the beginning of each day so he/she knows what is expected.

21. Help your child begin cleaning his/her room by providing cleaning supplies, getting hangers for clothes, etc.

22. Set aside time each day when everyone in the family works to clean their rooms.

23. Let your child know that materials not put away at the end of the day may be taken away for a period of time due to lack of responsibility.

24. Make a list of your child's frequently used items and/or materials and have your child make sure that each item and/or material is put in its designated place each day.

25. Make certain there is a designated place for all items in your child's room.

26. Teach your child to return things to their places by putting things back where they belong after you use them.

27. Provide your child with shelving, containers, organizers, etc., for personal possessions. Label the storage areas and require your child to keep possessions together.

28. Assist your child in performing responsibilities. Gradually require your child to independently assume more responsibility as he/she demonstrates success.

29. Provide a list of those things your child should do regularly in his/her room (e.g., put dirty clothes in the clothes hamper, put clean clothes in drawers, put shoes in closet, etc.).

30. Explain exactly what it is your child is to do in his/her room to clean it (e.g., "You need to hang up your clothes." "Pick up your toys." "Make your bed." etc.).

31. Have your child put clothes away right after taking them off, make the bed right after getting up in the morning, etc.

32. Help your child "clean out" those things he/she does not need in order to be able to keep the room clean.

33. Point out to your child the natural consequences of not cleaning his/her room (e.g., clothes are not put in the hamper to be washed, possessions get lost in the mess, etc.).

34. Do not allow food or drink in your child's room if it is not cleaned up when he/she is finished eating and drinking.

35. Help your child make his/her bed, put clean clothing away, pick up dirty clothing, etc. Gradually reduce the amount of help you provide your child as your child demonstrates success in cleaning his/her own room.

36. Make part of your child's allowance contingent upon cleaning his/her room.

37. Set aside 30 minutes a week for your child to clean his/her room.

38. Do not allow friends in your child's room unless it is clean.

39. Do not allow friends in your child's room while he/she is cleaning.

A Reminder: Keeping a room clean does not have the same importance for a child as it does for an adult. You may want to settle for a semblance of order and cleanliness rather than perfection.

1. Make sure that your child is eating nutritionally balanced meals and is getting enough sleep at night.

2. Talk with a family doctor, social worker, mental health professional, etc., about your concerns.

3. Reward your child for interacting with others and showing an interest in things. Possible rewards include verbal praise (e.g., "I'm so proud of you for helping me fix dinner. I really appreciate your help!"), a kiss on the cheek, a hug, having a friend over to play, staying up late, watching a favorite TV show, and playing a game with a parent. (See Appendix for Reward Menu.)

4. If there are other children or adolescents in the home, reward them for interacting with others and showing an interest in things.

5. Write a contract with your child.

For example: I, William, will try to spend more time playing with my friends in the neighborhood. Each time that I spend at least 30 minutes playing with someone, I can have a dime.

The contract should be written within the ability level of your child and should focus on only one behavior at a time. (See Appendix for an example of a Behavior Contract.)

6. Do not emphasize competition. Fear of failure in games and activities may cause your child to avoid interacting with others.

7. Keep your child busy (e.g., involve him/her in social clubs such as 4-H or Boy Scouts/Girl Scouts, give special responsibilities to perform in and around the house, etc.).

8. Encourage your child to talk to you when feeling unhappy, frustrated, anxious, etc.

9. Make certain that your child sees the relationship between his/her behavior and the consequences which follow (e.g., being avoided by others, not being included in special activities, hurting someone's feelings, etc.).

10. Encourage your child to develop any interests or hobbies (e.g., learning to play an instrument, taking dance lessons, etc.).

11. Participate in activities with your child.

12. Interact with your child frequently in order to involve him/her in interactions and activities.

13. Encourage your child to play or associate with peers who are outgoing, motivated, willing to attempt new things, etc.

14. Find exciting activities, hobbies, etc., to increase your child's interest (e.g., activities such as baseball, soccer, swimming, mountain bike riding, building models, scouting, etc.).

15. Do not allow your child to spend hours or entire afternoons watching TV, videotapes, etc.

16. Get involved in activities with your child (e.g., hunting, fishing, golf, tennis, swimming, etc.).

17. Be a model for your child by keeping busy, having projects, attempting new activities, etc.

18. Keep your child involved in activities throughout the summer months and on weekends.

19. Plan family activities (e.g., bike riding, roller skating, swimming, etc.) that will increase your child's interest, level of activity, involvement, etc.

20. Limit your child's TV watching to one hour per day.

21. Encourage your child to invite friends over to play, build things, work on projects, etc.

22. Involve your child in winter aerobics, exercise classes, etc., at your local YMCA, YWCA, community center, etc.

23. Find powerful rewards your child can earn by hard work (e.g., a bike, go-cart, skateboard, etc.).

24. Find family projects that will increase your child's interest, level of activity, involvement, etc. (e.g., building a clubhouse for the children, building a play area, etc.).

25. Plan activity-oriented weekends to get your child out of the house, away from the TV, etc. (e.g., sight-seeing, bike trips, hiking, etc.).

26. Find a year-round sport in which your child can become involved (e.g., swimming, gymnastics, aerobics, etc.).

27. Find activities your child can succeed in doing (e.g., scouting, clubs, etc.) in order to stimulate a desire to be a participant.

A Reminder: Success is a motivator while failure is an inhibitor. If your child is to be active and involved, he/she needs to find activities that result in success.

143 Does not want to take a bath, wash hair, brush teeth, change clothes, etc.

1. Establish hygiene rules (e.g., bathe daily, wash hair daily, brush teeth after each meal and before bed, change clothes when they are dirty, use deodorant as needed, etc.). These rules should be consistent and followed by everyone in the home. Talk about the rules often.

2. Reward your child for bathing daily, washing hair, brushing teeth after meals, changing clothes, etc. Possible rewards include verbal praise (e.g., ''I'm proud of you for remembering to take a bath today!''), a kiss on the cheek, a hug, having a friend over to play, watching a favorite TV show, and playing a game with a parent. (See Appendix for Reward Menu.)

3. If there are other children or adolescents in the home, reward them for having appropriate hygiene habits.

4. Carefully consider your child's age and experience before expecting him/her to care for personal hygiene independently.

5. Teach your child to bathe, wash hair, brush teeth, change clothes, etc.

6. Remind your child to bathe regularly, wash hair, brush teeth, change clothes, etc.

7. Help your child to take care of personal hygiene when necessary.

8. Make a list of hygiene tasks, place them where your child can see them (e.g., on the bathroom mirror), and have your child mark off each one after it is completed.

9. Make certain that your child sees the relationship between his/her behavior and the consequences which follow (e.g., offending others, being avoided by others, not being able to participate in special activities, etc.).

10. Have your child practice matching clothes in order for you to provide feedback on what is appropriate.

11. When your child does not care for his/her hygiene, explain exactly what he/she is doing wrong, what should be done and why.

For example: Your child has just taken a shower but did not wash his hair. Go to your child and say, ''William, I'm glad that you remembered to take a shower, but you forgot to wash your hair. You need to get back in the shower and wash your hair because it is dirty.''

12. Write a contract with your child.

For example: I, William, for five days in a row, will brush my teeth after each meal and before I go to bed. When I accomplish this, I can go roller skating on Saturday afternoon.

The contract should be written within the ability level of your child and should focus on only one behavior at a time. (See Appendix for an example of a Behavior Contract.)

13. Do not allow your child to leave the house until having bathed, washed hair, brushed teeth, put on clean clothes, etc.

14. Develop a ''Hygiene Schedule'' and have your child follow the schedule each day.

For example:
7:00 a.m. - get up, take shower, and wash hair
7:30 a.m. - eat breakfast and brush teeth
8:00 a.m. - put on clean clothes, brush hair, and catch the bus for school
5:00 p.m. - eat dinner, help clean up, and brush teeth
8:30 p.m. - wash face, brush teeth, and go to bed

15. Make sure that your child has the materials necessary to care for hygiene needs (e.g., washcloth, soap, shampoo, toothbrush, comb, nail clippers, toilet paper, handkerchiefs, etc.).

16. Talk with your child about hygiene in private. Do not embarrass your child in front of others.

17. Make sure your child has enough time to care for hygiene. Do not rush your child through the steps necessary to have acceptable hygiene.

18. Deal with your child's hygiene skills in a matter-of-fact way. If he/she needs to bathe, quietly tell your child that bathing is needed before anything else is done each day, at the end of the day, etc.

19. Require your child to correct his/her appearance if it is unacceptable.

20. Set an example for your child by caring about your personal appearance (e.g., combing your hair, bathing daily, etc.).

21. When shopping, let your child pick out clothes he/she might like to have. Help your child earn the clothes by demonstrating concern for personal appearance for a certain period of time.

22. Help your child decide on a haircut or hairstyle he/she might like to have. Take your child to get a haircut and help your child keep the hair "styled."

23. Encourage your child to take Home Economics, a health class, etc., in school to learn the importance of personal hygiene.

24. Help pick out clothes that match before your child puts on clothes.

25. Make certain that your child understands that others might "make fun" if your child does not comb hair, zip pants, tie shoes, etc.

26. Compliment your child for being neat, clean, etc.

27. Set aside time to practice hair combing, putting on makeup, shaving, use deodorant, etc.

28. Encourage your child to wash hair, brush teeth, etc., while you do the same.

29. If your child is more comfortable taking a bath with you in the same area (e.g., upstairs, as opposed to downstairs), then set aside time to be on the same floor or in the same area as your child when he/she is expected to bathe.

30. Make certain your child is putting dirty clothes in the hamper every day and not wearing dirty clothes day after day.

31. Stress to your child the social importance of brushing teeth, washing hair, bathing, etc. Not only is inadequate hygiene offensive, but other children can be cruel.

32. Turn off the TV and stop all activities at least 1 hour before bedtime in order that your child will have time to bathe, wash hair, brush teeth, get out clean clothes for the next day, etc.

33. Have your child show you the clean clothes he/she will be wearing the next day before going to bed.

34. Require your child to have a "witness" when brushing teeth, washing hair, etc. (Brothers and sisters make great witnesses.)

A Reminder: Getting your child to bathe, brush teeth, etc., is an example of those constant struggles that all parents have to endure.

144 Is unable to perform homework independently

1. Reward your child for performing homework assignments independently. Possible rewards include verbal praise (e.g., "You are doing a great job of working on your homework."), a kiss on the cheek, having a friend over to play, staying up late, watching a favorite TV show, and playing a game with a parent. (See Appendix for Reward Menu.)

2. Speak to your child to explain: (a) what your child is doing wrong (e.g., asking for help when it is not necessary) and (b) what your child should be doing (e.g., asking for help when it is necessary).

3. Establish homework rules (e.g., turn off the TV, work quietly, ask for help only when it is needed, etc.). Talk about the rules before sitting down to do homework each evening.

4. If there are other children or adolescents in the home, reward them for doing their homework independently.

5. Reward your child for communicating needs to others based on the number of times your child can be successful. Gradually increase the number of times required for reinforcement as your child demonstrates success.

6. Write a contract with your child.

For example: I, William, will do my homework on my own for five nights in a row. When I accomplish this, I can watch 30 extra minutes of TV.

The contract should be written within the ability level of your child and should focus on only one behavior at a time. (See Appendix for an example of a Behavior Contract.)

7. Identify a sibling or a friend to act as a model for your child to imitate the performing of homework assignments independently.

8. Encourage your child to question any directions, explanations, and instructions not understood.

9. Evaluate the appropriateness of expecting your child to communicate needs to others.

10. Make yourself available during homework time in order that your child can ask questions if he/she needs to.

11. Offer your child assistance frequently throughout homework time.

12. Make certain that directions, explanations, and instructions are delivered at your child's ability level.

13. Structure the environment in order that your child is not required to communicate all needs to others (e.g., make certain your child's tasks are on his/her ability level, instructions are clear, and that you maintain frequent interactions with your child to ensure success).

14. In order to detect your child's needs, communicate with your child often.

15. Demonstrate behavior that is accepting of others (e.g., willingness to help others, making criticisms constructive and positive, demonstrating confidentiality in personal matters, etc.).

16. Communicate to your child an interest in his/her needs.

17. Teach your child communication skills (e.g., expressing needs in written and/or verbal form, etc.).

18. Encourage your child to communicate needs to others (e.g., friends' parents, grandparents, friends, etc.).

19. Communicate with grandparents, friends' parents, baby-sitters, etc., in order to inform them of your child's difficulty in communicating needs.

20. Teach your child to communicate needs in an appropriate manner (e.g., use a normal tone of voice when speaking, verbally express problems, etc.).

21. Recognize your child's attempts to communicate needs (e.g., facial expressions, gestures, inactivity, self-depreciating comments, etc.).

22. Have a friend do homework with your child in order that he/she will have a nonthreatening individual to answer questions.

23. Have your child keep a chart or graph representing the number of homework assignments completed independently.

24. Assess the degree of task difficulty in comparison with your child's ability level.

25. Break your child's homework assignments into shorter tasks to be done throughout the evening. Gradually increase the number of minutes your child works as success in demonstrated.

26. Present homework in the most interesting manner possible.

27. Reduce distracting stimuli in the immediate environment (e.g., turn off the TV, send friends home, put away all toys, etc.) when your child sits down to do homework.

28. Provide your child with step-by-step written directions for performing assignments.

29. Allow natural consequences to occur when your child will not perform homework assignments independently (e.g., homework incomplete, loss of free time, etc.).

30. Explain to your child that work not done during homework time will have to be finished during outside playtime, TV time, etc.

31. Maintain consistency in the daily routine.

32. Work the first few homework problems with your child in order to help your child get started.

33. Sit close to your child when he/she does homework.

34. Have homework time each evening when there are no other activities going on in the home.

35. Make certain your child has all necessary resources available for doing homework independently (e.g., textbooks, calculator, dictionary, paper, ruler, etc.).

36. Work on a project of your own as your child does homework each evening.

37. Make certain your child knows what is expected each evening in order to perform homework assignments (e.g., have directions for homework sent home to you, have the teacher send homework instructions home with your child, etc.).

38. Provide your child with a selection of homework assignments and require him/her to choose a minimum number of assignments to perform independently (e.g., present your child with two homework assignments from which one must be selected).

39. Communicate clearly with your child the length of time he/she has to complete homework. Your child may want to use a timer in order to complete homework within the given period of time.

40. Specify exactly what is to be done for the completion of the homework (e.g., indicate definite starting and stopping points, indicate the minimum requirements, etc.).

145 Requires repeated drill and practice to learn schoolwork

1. Reduce the emphasis on competition. Competitive activities may cause your child to hurry and make mistakes.

2. Give your child fewer concepts to learn at any one time, spending more time on each concept until your child can learn it.

3. Have a sibling or friend spend time each day engaged in drill activities with your child.

4. Have your child use the new concepts frequently throughout the day.

5. Have your child highlight or underline key words, phrases, and sentences from reading assignments, newspapers, magazines, etc.

6. Develop crossword puzzles which contain only your child's spelling words and have your child complete them.

7. Write sentences, passages, paragraphs, etc., for your child to read which reinforce new concepts.

8. Have your child act as a tutor to a younger brother/sister to teach concepts just learned.

9. Have your child review new concepts each day for a short period of time rather than two or three times per week for longer periods of time.

10. Use pictures to introduce new concepts with visual images for your child to associate with previously learned concepts.

11. Initiate a "learn a concept a day" program with your child and incorporate the concept into the assigned school activities for the day.

12. Communicate with your child's teacher to get information on concepts that are going to be taught over the next week or two in order to review the concepts at home with your child.

13. Allow your child to use devices to help him/her successfully perform tasks (e.g., calculator, multiplication tables, abacus, dictionary, etc.).

14. Provide your child with various times throughout the day when he/she can engage in drill activities with a parent, peer, brother/sister, etc.

15. Provide your child with opportunities for drill activities in the most interesting manner possible (e.g., computer programs, using a calculator, playing educational games, watching a video, listening to a tape, etc.).

16. Provide your child with a list of key words, phrases, or main points to learn for each new concept introduced in school.

17. Underline, circle, or highlight important information from any material your child is to learn (e.g., science, math, geography, etc.).

18. Provide your child with information he/she needs to learn in the most direct manner possible (e.g., a list of facts, a summary of important points, an outline of important events, etc.).

19. Tape record important information your child can listen to as often as necessary.

20. Provide your child with a pleasant, functional "office" space of his/her own in which to study, drill, do homework, etc.

21. Make fun activities contingent upon completion of a short drill or study activity (e.g., first we go over spelling words and then you may watch TV, work ten math problems before going out to play, etc.).

22. Make certain your child is only drilling over material that still needs to be learned (i.e., if 20 spelling words are assigned and your child knows 12 of them, only the remaining eight need to be written again and again).

23. Provide practice in new concepts using a computer software program that gives your child immediate feedback.

24. Make certain that your child has mastery of concepts at each level before expecting him/her to understand a new skill level.

25. Have your child practice a new skill or assignment alone or with a brother/sister, friend, parent, etc., before trying it in front of peers at school or before performing it for a grade.

146 Does not have necessary study skills

1. Identify a particular place to study which is free of clutter (e.g., desk, table, etc.).

2. Identify and use a place to study which is quiet and free from movement or other distractions (e.g., no radio or TV, away from siblings, isolated from discussions or telephone calls, etc.).

3. Choose a time for studying which allows for maximum concentration (e.g., after school, after one hour of play and relaxation, after dinner, etc.). This will be an individual preference.

4. Have your child study at the same identified time each day. In the event he/she does not have an assignment, the time should be used for reading or reviewing.

5. Provide your child with materials needed in order to be organized at his/her work area (e.g., paper, pencils, pen, ruler, eraser, pencil sharpener, tape, crayons, colored pencils, scissors, stapler, dictionary, thesaurus). This will reduce the need for your child to interrupt his/her work to look for materials.

6. Keep the identified work area at a comfortable room temperature. A room kept too warm will make your child drowsy.

7. Have your child prioritize his/her assignments on the basis of due dates and then divide study time according to the assignments. (See Appendix for Assignment Sheet and Schedule of Daily Events.)

8. As a parent, be available to help or check for completion and/or accuracy. Being available does not mean sitting with your child. It is best to be in another room while available.

9. It is vital that your child is required to follow a routine of studying and preparing for school each day.

10. Have your child plan for short study breaks (e.g., drink of water, stretching break, restroom break, etc.).

11. Require your child to review nightly for two to three nights before a test.

12. Require your child to study graphics, pictures and captions within chapters.

13. After reading a chapter, require your child to summarize the chapter with a parent by using the Outline Form. (See Appendix.)

14. When reading for content, require your child to answer "Who, What, Where, When, How, and Why" using the Outline Form. (See Appendix.)

15. Require your child to use flash cards when preparing for tests. (See Appendix for Flash Card Study Aid.)

16. If your child regularly has difficulty remembering to bring necessary materials home, a set of school texts can be kept at home for his/her use (e.g., spelling book, reading book, science book, etc.).

17. Make sure your child is aware of those specified times when he/she can watch TV, visit with a friend, etc.

18. Provide an organizer for materials in your child's room.

19. At the end of each study period, require the child to show the progress made on assignments.

20. Evaluate the appropriateness of the task to determine: (a) if the task is too difficult, and (b) if the length of time scheduled to complete the task is appropriate.

21. Have your child question any written directions, explanations, instructions he/she does not understand.

22. Assign a peer to work with your child to help him/her follow written directions.

23. Teach your child written direction-following skills (e.g., read carefully, write down important points, ask for clarification, wait until all directions are received before beginning, etc.).

24. Give directions in a variety of ways to increase the probability of understanding (e.g., if your child fails to understand written directions, present them in verbal form).

25. Provide clearly stated written directions (e.g., make the directions as simple and concrete as possible).

26. Interact frequently with your child in order to help him/her follow written directions.

27. Require that assignments done incorrectly, for any reason, be redone.

28. Follow a less desirable task with a highly desirable task, making the completion of the first necessary to perform the second.

29. Prevent your child from becoming over-stimulated by an activity (e.g., frustrated, angry, etc.).

30. Present directions in both written and verbal form.

31. Tape record directions for your child to listen to individually and repeat as necessary.

32. Work the first problem or problems with your child to make certain that he/she follows the written directions accurately.

33. Teach your child note-taking skills (e.g., copy main ideas from the board, identify main ideas from lectures, condense statements into a few key words, etc.).

34. Provide a standard format for taking notes of directions and explanations (e.g., have paper and pencil or pen ready, listen for the steps in directions or explanations, write a shortened form of directions or explanations, ask to have any steps repeated when necessary).

35. Provide a standard format for taking notes during lectures (e.g., have paper and pencil or pen ready, listen for main ideas or important information, write a shortened form of main ideas or important information, ask to have any main ideas or important information repeated when necessary, etc.).

36. Have your child practice legible manuscript or cursive handwriting during simulated and actual note-taking activities.

37. Have your child keep his/her notes organized in a folder for each subject or activity.

38. Check your child's notes before he/she begins an assignment in order to determine if they are correct and adequate for the assignment.

39. Provide your child with samples of notes taken from actual instructions, directions, lectures, etc., given in the classroom in order that he/she may learn which information is necessary for note taking.

40. Provide delivery of information in short segments for your child to take notes. Gradually increase the length of delivery as the student experiences success in note taking.

41. Make certain that the vocabulary used in delivering instructions, directions, lectures, etc., is appropriate for your child's ability level.

42. Make certain your child has all necessary materials for note taking (e.g., paper, pencil, pen, etc.).

43. Make certain your child uses any necessary aids in order to facilitate note taking (e.g., eye-glasses, hearing aid, etc.).

44. Make certain your child has adequate surface space on which to write when taking notes (e.g., uncluttered desk top).

45. As an alternative to note taking, have your child tape record instructions, directions, lectures, etc.

46. Have your child listen and take notes for the "Who, What, Where, When, How, and Why" when concepts are presented. (See Appendix for Outline Form.)

47. Have your child prepare for tests using the "Who, What, Where, When, How, and Why" method. (See Appendix for Outline Form.)

48. Have your child takes notes when directions are being given following the "What, How, Materials, and When" format. (See Appendix for Assignment Form.)

49. Provide your child with earphones to wear if auditory stimuli interferes with his/her ability to function. Gradually remove the earphones as your child functions more successfully in the presence of auditory stimuli.

50. Require your child to be productive in the presence of auditory and visual stimuli for short periods of time. Gradually increase the length of time your child is required to be productive as he/she becomes successful.

51. Provide your child with shorter tasks which do not require extended attention in order to be successful. Gradually increase the length of the tasks as your child demonstrates success.

52. Model for your child appropriate behavior in the presence of auditory and visual stimuli in the home (e.g., continuing to work, asking for quiet, moving to a quieter part of the home, etc.).

53. Provide time at the beginning of each day/activity for your child to organize his/her materials (e.g., before school, after school, end of the day, etc.).

54. Act as a model for being prepared for activities.

55. Reduce the emphasis on competition. Competitive activities may cause your child to hurry and make mistakes.

56. Give your child fewer concepts to learn at any one time, spending more time on each concept until your child can learn it correctly.

57. Have your child use new concepts frequently throughout the day.

58. Have your child highlight or underline key words, phrases, and sentences from reading assignments, newspapers, magazines, etc.

59. Write sentences, passages, paragraphs, etc. for your child to read which reinforce new concepts.

60. Have your child review new concepts each day for a short period of time rather than two or three times per week for longer periods of time.

61. Require your child to use resources (e.g., encyclopedia, dictionary, etc.) to provide information to help him/her be successful when performing tasks.

62. Encourage your child to review new concepts each evening for a short period of time.

63. Provide your child with opportunities for drill activities in the most interesting manner possible (e.g., working with a computer, using a calculator, playing educational games, watching a film, listening to a tape, etc.).

64. Allow your child to use devices to help him/her successfully perform tasks (e.g., calculator, multiplication tables, abacus, dictionary, etc.).

65. Use concrete examples in teaching your child new information and concepts.

66. Teach your child to takes notes when he/she is in an early grade (i.e., third grade).

67. Teach your child to listen and look for key words (e.g., *Christopher Columbus*, *Spain*, *New World*, etc.).

68. Teach your child to listen and look for action words (e.g., *sailed*, *discovered*, *founded*, etc.).

69. Teach your child to listen and look for direction words (e.g., *circle*, *underline*, *choose*, *list*, etc.).

70. Teach your child, when taking notes, to write the key words and main ideas that answer "Who, What, Where, When, How, and Why." Your child should then be given time periodically to go back to fill in connecting details (e.g., your child writes, "Christopher Columbus - Spain - New World - 1492," and is given time to go back to fill in "sailed from - to discover - during the year," resulting in a complete statement: "Christopher Columbus sailed from Spain to discover the New World during the year of 1492.").

71. Teach your child to divide note-taking paper in the middle, writing main ideas and key words on the left side of the paper, filling in details and connecting points on the right side of the paper. These details and connecting points may be filled in after the lecture or during a pause.

72. Teach your child to learn and use abbreviations for words frequently used, in order to take notes more effectively. (See Appendix for Selected Abbreviations and Symbols.)

73. Teach your child that it is acceptable to write notes in incomplete sentences.

74. Teach your child how to organize information into smaller units (e.g., break the number sequence 132563 into units of 13, 25, 63).

75. Use sentence dictation to develop your child's short-term memory skills. Begin with sentences of three words and increase the length of the sentences as the student demonstrates success.

76. Have your child practice making notes for specific information he/she wants and/or needs to remember.

77. Provide your child with written lists of things to do, materials he/she will need, etc.

78. Teach your child to use associative cues or mnemonic devices to remember sequences.

79. Teach your child to recognize main points, important facts, etc. (See Appendix for Outline Form.)

80. Help your child employ memory aids in order to recall words (e.g., a name might be linked to another word, for example, "Mr. Green is a very colorful person.").

81. Make certain your child receives information from a variety of sources (e.g., texts, discussions, films, slide presentations, etc.) in order to enhance your child's memory/recall.

82. Have your child memorize the first sentence or line of poems, songs, etc. Require more to be memorized as your child experiences success.

83. Have your child be responsible for helping a peer remember sequences.

84. When your child is required to recall information, provide him/her with auditory cues to help him/her remember the information (e.g., key words, a brief oral description to clue your child, etc.).

85. Teach your child not to spend too much time on any one item on timed tests.

86. Teach your child to proofread all items on a test.

87. Give your child a practice test at home.

88. Provide your child with sample questions from a test.

89. Make certain your child knows what topic/areas will be covered by a test.

147 Does not demonstrate an understanding of left-right, forward-backward, east-west, etc.

1. Make certain to use the terms *right* and *left* as a part of directions you give to your child (e.g., refer to the windows on the left side of the room, the table on the right side of the room, etc.).

2. Identify directions in your home with signs (e.g., on the ceiling of your child's bedroom put *up*, on the floor put *down*, etc.).

3. Have your child practice following directions on paper. Instruct your child to make marks on the right, left, middle, top, and bottom parts of the paper according to the directions given.

4. Avoid the problem of mirror images by standing next to your child when giving right and left directions.

5. Design an obstacle course using materials in your home. Your child can step *into* the box, crawl *over* the coffee table, walk *under* the light, etc., when trying to convey an understanding of concepts.

6. Use concrete examples when teaching concepts of *up/down, high/low, above/below*, etc. Use books, balls, your child's toys, etc., when trying to convey these concepts.

7. Hang directional signs in your child's room (e.g., turn left, games under cabinet, etc.).

8. Play *Simon Says* for directions (e.g., "Raise your left hand." "Walk behind the chair." etc.).

9. Conduct scavenger hunts. Have your child look for a pencil *in* the desk, a bowl *under* the table, a glass *on* the chair, etc.

10. Teach *north, south, east,* and *west* using the neighbor's home, the neighborhood playground, etc.

11. Have your child sort left and right gloves, shoes, paper hand and foot cut-outs, etc.

12. Label strips of paper left and right and attach them to your child's wrists.

13. Have your child practice walking forward and backward, moving toy cars and trucks forward and backward, etc.

14. Have your child identify objects which move up and down (e.g., airplanes, teeter-totter, etc.).

15. Point out doors which are labeled *push* and *pull* and activities which require *pushing* and *pulling* (e.g., opening drawers, opening doors, etc.).

16. Have your child find things that represent the concept of *in* and *out* (e.g., we pour milk in a glass and pour it *out*, we walk *in* a room and walk *out* etc.).

17. Identify objects which represent over and *under* (e.g., a bridge is *over* water; people sleep *under* blankets; birds fly *over* our heads; rugs are *under* our feet, etc.).

18. Teach the concept of *before* and *after* with examples from your child's daily routine (e.g., we wake up *before* we eat breakfast; we go to school *after* we eat breakfast; we eat dinner *after* we do our homework, etc.).

19. Teach the concept of *above* and *below* with examples in your home (e.g., the ceiling is *above* our heads and the floor is *below* our feet, etc.).

20. Emphasize activities which require the action of *off* and *on* (e.g., we turn lights *on* for light and *off* when we do not need them; we turn the stove *on* to heat things and *off* when things are hot; we put clothes *on* to go to school; leaves fall *off* a tree in the fall; etc.).

148 Performs homework so carelessly as to be illegible

1. Reward your child for performing homework assignments neatly. Possible rewards include verbal praise (e.g., "Your handwriting looks wonderful on your math assignment."), a kiss on the cheek, a hug, having a friend over to play, staying up late, watching a favorite TV show, playing a game with a parent. (See Appendix for Reward Menu.)

2. Speak to your child to explain: (a) what your child is doing wrong (e.g., turning in work which has spelling errors or spacing errors, work that is illegible, etc.) and (b) what your child should be doing (e.g., taking time to check for spelling, spacing errors, etc.).

3. Establish homework rules (e.g., work on assignment, work quietly, remain in your room, etc.). Reiterate rules often and reinforce your child for following the rules.

4. If there are other children or adolescents in the home, reward them for doing their homework neatly and taking their time.

5. Reward your child for improving the quality of handwriting based on ability. Gradually increase the amount of improvement expected for reinforcement as your child is successful.

6. Write a contract with your child.

For example: I, William, for five days in a row, will do my homework in the best handwriting I can. When I accomplish this, I can buy Matchbox car at the store.

The contract should be written within the ability level of your child and should focus on only one behavior at a time. (See Appendix for an example of a Behavior Contract.)

7. Evaluate the appropriateness of the homework to determine: (a) if the task is too difficult and (b) if the length of time scheduled to complete the task is appropriate.

8. Have a sibling or a friend work with your child in order to provide an acceptable model for your child to imitate.

9. Allow your child to perform homework in a quiet place (e.g., in a bedroom, at the library, in the dining room, etc.).

10. Have your child do smaller amounts of homework several times throughout the evening.

11. Supervise your child during homework time in order to monitor handwriting quality.

12. Provide your child with clearly stated criteria for acceptable work.

13. Have your child read/go over schoolwork with the teacher in order that your child can become more aware of the quality of work.

14. Provide your child with samples of work which may serve as models for acceptable quality (e.g., your child is to match the quality of the sample before turning in the assignment).

15. Provide your child with additional time to perform homework in order to achieve quality.

16. Teach your child procedures for doing quality work (e.g., listen to homework directions, make certain directions are understood, make certain you bring all necessary materials home, make certain that you allow yourself enough time to do your work, etc.).

17. Make certain to go over your child's homework when it is completed.

18. Allow natural consequences to occur when your child does homework assignments carelessly (e.g., require that the homework be done over until it is done neatly).

19. Provide your child with quality materials to perform homework assignments (e.g., pencil with eraser, paper, handwriting sample, etc.).

20. Provide your child with an appropriate model of handwriting to use while doing homework (e.g., sample work, teacher samples, commercial samples, etc.).

21. Provide your child with ample opportunity to master handwriting skills (e.g., instruction in letter positioning, directions, spacing, etc.).

22. Act as a model for appropriate handwriting at all times for your child.

23. Provide a multitude of opportunities for your child to practice handwriting skills (e.g., writing letters to sports and entertainment figures, relatives, and friends; writing for free information on a topic of interest; etc.).

24. Have your child trace handwriting models and fade the model as your child develops the skill.

25. Gradually reduce the space between lines as your child's handwriting improves.

26. Use primary paper to assist your child in sizing uppercase and lowercase letters. Use standard lined paper when your child's skills improve.

27. Use paper that is also vertically lined (e.g., | | | | |) to teach your child appropriate spacing skills (e.g., | K | a | t | h | y |).

28. Use adhesive material (e.g., tape, Dycem material, etc.) to keep paper positioned appropriately for handwriting.

29. Use a pencil grip (e.g., three-side, foam rubber, etc.) in order to provide your child assistance in appropriate positioning of the pencil or pen.

30. Use handwriting models with arrows that indicate the direction in which your child should correctly form the letters.

31. Make certain that everyone who works with your child maintains consistent expectations of handwriting quality.

32. Speak to your child's teacher to see if assignments could be shortened for your child. Longer assignments may cause your child to fail to perform assignments neatly. The length of the assignments may be increased as your child demonstrates success.

33. Make certain your child has a number line and alphabet strip to use as a reference for correct form of letters and numbers in order to reduce errors.

34. Recognize your child's quality work (e.g., hang assignments on the refrigerator, show papers to brothers/sisters, etc.).

35. Check your child's pencil grip to make certain that he/she is holding the pencil correctly.

36. Have your child use a different size pencil or pencil grip.

149 Demonstrates visual perception problems

1. Make certain your child's vision has been checked recently.

2. Give your child the opportunity to find objects which are the same or different in size, shape, color, etc.

3. Have your child sort objects according to size, shape, color, etc.

4. Have your child use play equipment such as a ladder, jungle gym, blocks, teeter-totter, balance beam, etc., to become more aware of body positions in space.

5. Have your child complete partially drawn figures, words, numbers, etc.

6. Have your child use paper pictures from magazines, catalogs, etc., to assemble features and body parts.

7. Have your child build an object according to a pattern (e.g., Tinker Toys, blocks, etc.).

8. Have your child engage in sequencing activities (e.g., put numbers in order, place pictures in correct order, etc.).

9. Have your child pick out specific objects from pictures around the house or in the environment while outside playing.

10. Have your child perform a variety of activities such as tracing, cutting, coloring, pasting, etc.

11. Have your child complete jigsaw puzzles (e.g., beginning with simple self-made puzzles and progressing to more complex puzzles).

12. Develop a variety of activities for your child using a pegboard.

13. Provide your child with a variety of classifying activities (e.g., from simple classifying of types of clothes, cars, etc., to more complex classifying of items that would be located at certain stores; etc.).

14. Have your child find specific shapes in the home (e.g., the door is a rectangle, the clock is a circle, etc.).

15. Provide your child with simple designs to be reproduced with blocks, sticks, paper, etc.

16. Provide your child with dot-to-dot worksheets following specific patterns, etc.

17. Have your child identify objects by looking at the outlines of objects on a cardboard silhouette, etc.

18. Reduce visual stimuli on a worksheet or in a book by covering all of the page except the activity on which your child is working.

19. Have your child repeat the names of objects, shapes, numbers, or words that are presented to him/her for a limited period.

20. Provide your child with a variety of exercises in which he/she must identify the missing body parts, common objects, etc.

21. Provide your child with a variety of visual recall tasks (e.g., your child writes numbers, shapes, and words that were shown for a specific time, etc.).

22. Use a variety of colored tiles to make a pattern. Have your child duplicate the pattern while looking at the model and then complete the design from memory without using the model.

23. Place several items on a tray (e.g., a pencil, flower, penny, and piece of gum). Allow your child to look at the items, then take the items away and have your child identify the items that were on the tray.

24. Have your child practice tracing outlines of pictures. Work pages with dotted lines of pictures, letters, numbers, etc., can be used to develop eye-hand coordination.

25. Play a matching game like *Concentration* in which hidden pictures, numbers, or shapes are turned over one at a time and your child must remember where the matching picture is located.

26. Using pictures from magazines, remove any important part of the picture and ask your child to identify the missing part.

27. Speak to your child's teacher about reducing the amount of information on a page for your child.

150 Has difficulty classifying

1. Make certain your child understands that all objects, people, ideas, actions, etc., can be grouped based on how they are alike. Provide your child with concrete examples.

2. Give your child pairs of objects and ask your child to name all the ways in which they are alike and then ways in which they are different. Proceed from simple things which can be seen and touched to more abstract ideas which cannot be seen or touched.

3. Name a category or group and ask your child to identify as many things as possible which belong in the group. Begin with large categories (e.g., living things) and move to more specific categories (e.g., things which are green).

4. Explain that each new word which is learned is an example of some category. When defining a word, it should first be put into a category (e.g., a hammer is a kind of tool, anger is a kind of emotion, etc.).

5. Present a series of objects or words and have your child tell which one does not belong in the same category as the others.

6. Present a series of objects and have your child create a category into which they fit.

7. Give your child a list of words and have your child identify the categories into which the words belong (e.g., Love and hate are both emotions. Love fits into the specific category of good feelings and hate fits into the specific category of bad or unhappy feelings.).

8. Explain that words can be categorized according to many different attributes, such as size, function, texture, etc.

9. Ask your child to help make lists of some categories which fit inside larger categories (e.g., flowers, trees, and bushes are all categories which can be included in the plant category).

10. Play a game such as "I'm thinking of an object" in which an object is described and your child must guess the item based on the answers that are given to the questions that are asked.

11. Have your child help when grocery shopping by having your child make a list of items needed in a particular food group (e.g., dairy products, meats, etc.).

12. Have your child cut out pictures for a notebook of favorite foods, television shows, or other categories, and group them in appropriate arrangements.

13. Give your child specific categories and have your child name as many items as possible within the category (e.g., objects, persons, places, etc.).

14. Give your child a series of words or pictures and have your child name the category to which they belong (e.g., objects, persons, places, etc.).

15. Give your child a series of words (e.g., objects, persons, places, etc.) your child can think of which have similar meanings. (synonyms)

16. Stop at various points during the presentation of information to check your child's comprehension.

17. Use pictures, diagrams, a chalkboard, and gestures when delivering information.

151 Does not comprehend what he/she reads

1. Make certain that the reading material your child is reading is on your child's reading level.

2. Talk to your child's teacher in order to have reading material modified or adjusted to your child's reading level.

3. Outline reading material for your child using words and phrases on your child's reading level.

4. Tape record difficult reading material for your child to listen to while reading along.

5. Talk to your child's teacher to get upcoming readings in science, social studies, basal readers, etc., to preview with your child before they are read in class.

6. Arrange for a brother/sister or a friend to study with your child for quizzes, tests, etc.

7. Use a sight word vocabulary approach in order to teach your child key words and phrases when reading directions and instructions (e.g., key words such as *circle, underline, match,* etc.

8. Use lower grade level reading books from the library for outside reading material for your child.

9. Have your child tape record lectures at school to use as an additional source of information when studying.

10. Make a list of main points from your child's reading material, written on your child's reading level.

11. Reduce distracting stimuli in order to increase your child's ability to concentrate on what he/she is reading (e.g., turn the TV off, work in the dining room or bedroom, send friends home, etc.). This is used as a means of distracting stimuli and not as a form of punishment.

12. Provide your child with a quiet place to work while doing homework (e.g., an office, a bedroom, a dining room, etc.).

13. Teach your child to identify the main points in reading material in order to assess comprehension.

14. Have your child outline, underline, or highlight important points in reading material.

15. Provide your child with written direction-following activities in order to enhance comprehension (e.g., following a recipe, following directions to put together a model, etc.).

16. Provide your child with written one-, two- and three-step direction-following activities (e.g., make your bed, pick up your clothes, take out the trash, etc.).

17. Have your child take notes while reading in order to increase comprehension.

18. Have your child read progressively longer segments of reading material in order to build comprehension skills (e.g., begin with a single paragraph and progress to several paragraphs, a chapter, a short story, a novel, etc.).

19. Have your child tape record what he/she reads in order to enhance comprehension by listening to the material.

20. Teach your child to use context clues to identify words and phrases that he/she does not know.

21. Write paragraphs and short stories requiring skills that your child is currently developing in school. These passages should be of high interest to your child by using names of family members, friends, pets, interesting experiences, etc.

22. Have your child dictate stories which are then written for him/her to read, placing an emphasis on comprehension skills.

23. Have your child read high-interest signs, advertisements, notices, etc., from newspapers, magazines, movie promotions, etc.

24. Make certain that your child is practicing comprehension skills which are directly related to high interest reading activities (e.g., adventures, romance, mystery, sports, etc.).

25. Reduce the emphasis on competition among brothers/sisters or friends. Competitive activities may make it difficult for your child to comprehend what is read.

26. Underline or highlight important points before your child reads material silently.

27. Write notes and letters to your child to provide reading material which your child will want to read for comprehension. Your child may be encouraged to write notes and letters at a time set aside each day, once a week, etc.

28. Give your child time to read a selection more than once, emphasizing comprehension, rather than speed.

29. After your child reads a passage, discuss what was read.

30. Make it a habit every evening to turn off the TV and set aside silent reading time for the family.

31. Be a model for reading for enjoyment.

32. Reduce the amount of material your child reads at one time (e.g., reduce reading material to single sentences on a page, a single paragraph, etc.). Gradually increase the amount of material as your child experiences success.

33. Avoid subjecting your child to uncomfortable reading situations (e.g., reading aloud in front of others, reading with time limits, etc.).

34. Stop your child at various points throughout the reading selection to check for comprehension.

35. Reduce the amount of information on a page if it is causing visual distractions for your child (e.g., less print to read, fewer pictures, etc.).

36. Highlight or underline important information your child should pay close attention to when reading.

152 Fails to recognize words on grade level

1. With the help of your child's teacher, create a list of words and phrases from your child's reading material which your child will not recognize (e.g., have the science teacher identify words your child will not recognize in the following week's assignment). These words and phrases will become the student's reading word list for the following week.

2. Have your child identify words and phrases which he/she does not recognize. Make these words a list to learn.

3. Make certain that your child's teacher has reading materials modified or adjusted to his/her reading level.

4. Outline reading material for your child using words and phrases on your child's reading level.

5. Teach your child to use context clues to identify words and phrases he/she does not know.

6. Emphasize that your child learn a root word sight vocabulary in order to be able to add various prefixes and suffixes to develop work attack skills.

7. Tape record difficult reading material for your child to listen to while reading along.

8. Use a highlight marker to identify key words and phrases for your child. These words and phrases become your child's sight word vocabulary.

9. Teach your child to use related learning experiences (e.g., videotapes, the museum, tape recordings, etc.).

10. Use the sight word vocabulary approach in order to teach your child key words and phrases when reading directions and instructions (e.g., key words such as *circle, underline, match*, etc.).

11. Arrange for a brother/sister or a friend to study with your child for quizzes, tests, etc.

12. Use library books on a lower grade level for extra reading material for your child.

13. Talk to your child's teachers in order to have lectures and test reviews tape recorded for your child.

14. Make a list of main points from your child's reading material, written on your child's reading level.

15. Write paragraphs and short stories requiring skill your child is currently developing at school. These passages should be of high interest to your child using family members, friends, pets, and interesting experiences.

16. Have your child dictate stories which are then written for your child; the emphasis should be placed on reading skills.

17. Have your child read high-interest signs, advertisements, notices, etc., from newspapers, movie promotions, magazines, etc., placing an emphasis on reading skills.

18. Make certain your child is practicing reading skills which are directly related to high-interest reading activities (e.g., adventures, romance, mystery, athletics, etc.).

19. Make certain that the reading demands of all subjects and assignments are within the ability level of your child. If they are not, modify or adjust the reading material to your child's ability level. A lower grade level text may be an alternative.

20. Make certain that your child's knowledge of a particular skill is being assessed rather than your child's ability to read directions, instructions, etc.

21. Have your child read aloud each day in order to provide evaluative feedback.

22. Reduce the amount of material your child reads at one time (e.g., reduce reading material to single sentences on a page, a single paragraph, etc.). Gradually increase the amount of material as your child demonstrates success.

23. Have your child practice vocabulary words from required reading material by writing them while saying the sounds.

153 Loses place when reading

1. Make certain that your child's reading material is adjusted to your child's ability level.

2. Use a highlight marker to identify key syllables, words, etc., for your child. These words and phrases become your child's sight word vocabulary.

3. Have your child point to syllables, words, etc., as he/she reads them in order to help your child recognize omissions.

4. Tape record your child's reading in order that he/she can hear omissions made.

5. Reduce the emphasis on competition among brothers/sisters or friends. Competitive activities may cause your child to hurry and omit words.

6. Have your child read aloud to you each day in order to provide evaluative feedback relative to omissions made.

7. Verbally correct your child's omissions as often as possible in order that your child hears the correct version of the reading material.

8. Make a list of those words for which your child makes omissions. Have your child practice reading these words.

9. Have your child use a paper strip to move down the page while reading each line.

10. Make a reading "window" for each text-book your child uses. Your child moves the reading "window" down and across the page while reading.

11. Enlarge the print your child is reading.

12. Reduce the amount of material your child reads at one time (e.g., reduce reading material to single sentences on a page, a single paragraph, etc.).

13. Provide a quiet place for your child to work (e.g., "office" space, the dining room, a bedroom, etc.).

14. Have your child highlight or underline the material he/she reads.

15. Have your child read aloud in order to help maintain his/her place while reading.

16. Have your child place a ruler under each line that is being read at the time. Your child then moves the ruler to the next line and so on.

17. Give your child time to read a selection more than once, emphasizing comprehension rather than speed.

18. Make certain that the reading demands of all subjects and assignments are within the ability level of your child. If they are not, modify or adjust the reading material to your child's ability level.

19. Make certain that your child's knowledge of a particular skill is being assessed rather than your child's ability to read directions, etc.

20. Reduce the amount of information on a page if it is causing visual distractions for your child (e.g., less print to read, fewer pictures, etc.).

21. Have your child point to every word read in order to hold his/her place.

154 Omits, adds, substitutes, or reverses letters, words, or sounds when reading

1. Talk to your child's teacher and make a list of words and phrases from your child's reading material which he/she will not recognize (e.g., have the science teacher identify the words and phrases your child will not recognize in the following week's assignment). These words and phrases will become a part of your child's reading activities for the following week.

2. Make certain that your child's reading material has been adjusted or modified to his/her reading level.

3. Have your child identify words and phrases that are not recognized. Make these words your child's list to be learned.

4. Emphasize that your child learn a root word sight vocabulary in order to be able to add various prefixes and suffixes to develop word attack skills.

5. Use a highlight marker to identify key syllables, words, etc., for your child. These words and phrases become your child's sight word vocabulary.

6. Use a sight word vocabulary approach in order to teach your child key words and phrases when reading directions and instructions (e.g., key words such as *circle, underline, match*, etc.).

7. Tape record pronunciations of words on which your child commonly makes errors in order that your child can hear all the sounds.

8. Have your child point to syllables while reading in order to help recognize omissions, additions, substitutions, or reversals.

9. Tape record your child's reading in order for him/her to hear omissions, additions, substitutions, or reversals.

10. Make certain your child is learning basic word lists to assist in reading.

11. Reduce the emphasis on competition among brothers/sisters, friends, etc. Competitive activities may cause your child to omit, add, substitute, or reverse letters, words, or sounds when reading.

12. Have your child read aloud to you each day in order to provide evaluative feedback relative to omissions, additions, substitutions, and reversals.

13. Verbally correct your child's omissions, additions, substitutions, and reversals as often as possible in order that your child hears the correct version of the reading material.

14. Make a list of those words for which your child makes omissions, additions, substitutions, or reversal errors. Have your child practice reading these words.

15. Have your child write those letters, words, or sounds that are often omitted, added, substituted, or reversed in order for him/her to have a greater opportunity to see the correct version.

16. Make certain your child has an alphabet strip to have a reference for the correct form of letters in order to reduce reversal-related errors when reading.

17. Teach your child to use context clues in reading (i.e., have your child use the words which are around the unknown word to help him/her figure out the word, such as "Bob ran very _____ because he was afraid.").

18. Tape record difficult reading material for your child to listen to while he/she reads along.

19. Make certain that the reading demands of all subjects and assignments are within your child's ability level.

20. Make certain that your child's knowledge of a particular skill is being assessed rather than your child's ability to read directions, instructions, etc. Reading directions, instructions, etc., to your child can increase success.

21. Reduce the amount of material your child reads at one time (e.g., reduce reading material to single sentences on a page, a single paragraph, etc.). Gradually increase the amount of material as your child experiences success.

22. Reduce the amount of information on a page if it is causing visual distractions for your child (e.g., less print to read, fewer pictures on a page, etc.).

155 Reads words correctly in one context but not in another

1. Speak to your child's teacher to make certain that your child is reading material on the appropriate reading level.

2. Highlight or underline those words your child most frequently fails to recognize in different contexts.

3. Use library books on a lower grade level as outside reading material for your child.

4. Write paragraphs and short stories using those words your child most frequently fails to recognize in different contexts. These paragraphs should be of high interest to your child using family members, friends, pets, and interesting experiences.

5. Make a reading "window" for your child. Your child moves the reading "window" down and across the page while reading.

6. Have your child list those words he/she most frequently fails to recognize into categories such as people, food, animals., etc., in order to help your child recognize those words in different contexts.

7. Teach your child to use context clues to identify words that are not understood.

8. Identify words your child does not recognize in different contexts and put these words on flash cards. Have your child match these words to the same words in sentences, paragraphs, short stories, etc.

9. Have your child maintain a list with definitions of those words he/she frequently fails to recognize in different contexts.

10. Have your child print/write words which he/she frequently fails to recognize in different contexts.

11. Highlight or underline those words in reading material which your child is unable to recognize. Have your child identify those words while reading them.

12. Reduce distracting stimuli where your child is reading in order to increase your child's ability level to concentrate (e.g., turn the TV off, send friends home, go to a quiet place to read, etc.).

13. Provide your child with a quiet place (e.g., an "office," the dining room, a bedroom, etc.) for reading.

14. Reduce the emphasis on competition among brothers/sisters, friends, etc. Competitive activities may cause your child to hurry and fail to recognize words in a particular context.

15. Provide your child with a dictionary and require him/her to find the definitions of those words that are not recognized.

16. Have your child read short sentences in order to make it easier to recognize words in different contexts. Longer sentences are presented as your child demonstrates success.

17. Provide your child with large-print reading materials in order to increase the likelihood of your child recognizing words in different contexts.

18. Use daily drill activities to help your child memorize vocabulary words.

19. Tape record difficult reading material for your child to listen to as he/she reads along.

20. Write notes and letters to your child to provide reading material which includes words your child frequently has difficulty with.

21. Have your child read aloud to you each day in order to provide evaluative feedback.

22. Reduce the amount of information on a page if it is causing visual distractions for your child (e.g., less print to read, fewer pictures to look at, etc.).

23. Require your child to read a selection each day which includes the vocabulary currently being studied.

156 Does not read independently

1. Speak to your child's teacher to make certain that your child is reading material on the appropriate reading level.

2. With the assistance of your child's teacher, modify or adjust reading material to the ability level of your child.

3. Tape record reading material for your child to listen to while reading.

4. Provide your child with a quiet place (e.g., an "office," the dining room, a bedroom, etc.) for reading.

5. Write paragraphs and short stories for your child. These passages should be of high-interest to your child using family members, friends, pets, and interesting experiences.

6. Have your child dictate stories which are then written for your child to read.

7. Have your child read high-interest signs, advertisements, notices, etc., from newspapers, magazines, movie promotions, etc.

8. Provide your child with many high-interest materials (e.g., comic books, magazines relating to sports, fashion magazines, etc.).

9. Talk to your child and discuss the types of reading material that would be interesting for him/her to read.

10. Read, or have someone read, high-interest material to your child to promote your child's interest in reading.

11. Develop a library in your home that is appealing to your child (e.g., in a tent, a bean-bag chair, etc.).

12. Provide your child with high-interest reading material that is also short in length in order that your child can finish reading the material without difficulty.

13. Encourage interest in reading by having brothers/sisters, friends, etc., share interesting things they have read.

14. Have your child write to the author of material he/she reads in order to encourage an interest in reading more material by the same author.

15. Encourage your child to read material with many illustrations and a limited amount of print. Gradually encourage your child to read material with fewer illustrations and more print.

16. Read to your child and have your child read to you.

17. Be a model for your child by reading for enjoyment.

18. Have your child read lower grade level stories to younger brothers/sisters, friends, etc., in order to enhance your child's feelings of confidence relative to reading.

19. Include predictable reading books in your child's library. Predictability can make books more appealing to beginning readers and build confidence as well.

20. Avoid subjecting your child to uncomfortable reading situations (e.g., reading in front of brothers/sisters, friends, other adults, etc.).

21. Write periodic notes to your child and encourage your child to write back.

22. Expose your child to large print materials. Large print can appear less intimidating to the child who does not choose to read.

23. Provide assistance in helping your child find reading material according to his/her interests and reading level.

24. Set aside a fixed or random time (e.g., a half-hour daily, an hour a week, etc.) for silent reading in your home. Everyone, parents included, chooses a book to read for pleasure.

25. Offer your child memberships in paperback book clubs.

26. Have your child act as a peer tutor to read to a younger brother/sister, friend, etc.

27. Make certain your child has mastery of reading skills before expecting him/her to read independently.

28. Encourage your child to find books about different subjects being taught or discussed in school (e.g., when studying electricity, encourage your child to read a book about Thomas Edison, etc.).

157 Does not discriminate between similar letters and words

1. Make certain that your child's hearing has been checked recently.

2. Each day have your child practice those letters and words that he/she can not discriminate.

3. Take every opportunity throughout the day to emphasize a designated letter or word your child cannot discriminate (e.g., identify the sound when speaking, writing, reading, etc.).

4. Use highlight markers (e.g., pink and yellow) to have your child mark the letters and words in a passage that he/she does not discriminate (e.g., all m's marked with the pink marker and all n's marked in yellow marker).

5. Make a list of words your child cannot discriminate. Have your child and a brother/sister, friend, etc., work together with flash cards to develop your child's ability to recognize the differences in the letters and words.

6. Tape record stories and paragraphs your child can listen to while reading along.

7. Have your child read aloud to you each day in order to provide evaluative feedback relative to your child's ability to discriminate letters and words.

8. Verbally correct your child as often as possible when he/she does not discriminate between letters and words in order that your child hears the correct version of the reading material.

9. Have your child use context clues in reading. These skills will be particularly helpful when your child is unable to discriminate letters and words.

10. Have your child write those letters and words that he/she has difficulty discriminating in order to have greater opportunity to conceptualize the correct version.

11. Make certain your child looks closely at word endings as well as beginnings in order to discriminate similar words (e.g., cap and cat).

12. Identify a letter or word each day which your child has difficulty discriminating. Have your child underline or highlight that letter or word each time it is read that day.

13. Make certain your child has an alphabet strip as a reference when reading or performing assignments.

14. Make certain that the reading demands of all subjects and assignments are within the ability level of your child. If they are not, modify or adjust the reading material to your child's ability level.

15. Make certain that your child's knowledge of a particular skill is being assessed rather than your child's ability to read directions, instructions, etc.

16. Have your child cut letters out of magazines or newspapers and glue the letters to make words, sentences, etc.

158 Does not know all the letters of the alphabet

1. Reward your child for knowing letters of the alphabet. Possible rewards include verbal praise (e.g., ''I'm so proud of you for knowing the first three letters of the alphabet.''), a kiss on the cheek, a hug, a special outing with a parent, etc.

2. Make certain that your child has an alphabet strip to use as a reference for the alphabet.

3. Hang the letters of the alphabet on the wall in your child's bedroom (e.g., an alphabet chart, a letter chain, etc.)

4. Each day have your child print those letters of the alphabet that he/she does not know.

5. Have your child work with a brother/sister, friend, etc., on one letter of the alphabet each day (e.g., tracing the letter, printing the letter, recognizing the letter in words in a paragraph, etc.).

6. Have your child read and write friends' first names which include letters your child does not recognize.

7. Introduce letters to the student as partners (e.g., Aa, Bb, Cc, Dd, etc.). This may make it easier for your child to remember the names of the letters.

8. Have your child say the letters of the alphabet in sequence. Repeat by rote several times a day.

9. Identify a letter your child does not know. Have your child find that letter in all the words in a paragraph or a page of a book.

10. Present the alphabet to your child on flash cards. This is an appropriate activity for a brother/sister to conduct with your child each day.

11. Start by teaching the names of the letters in your child's name only. When your child has mastered the letters in his/her first name, go on to the last name, parents' name, etc.

12. Give your child a word which begins with each letter of the alphabet (e.g., *a-apple*, *b-bad*, *c-cat*, etc.). Go over several of the words each day, stressing the alphabet letters being learned.

13. Take every opportunity throughout the day to emphasize a designated letter for that day (e.g., identify the letter when speaking, writing, reading, etc.).

14. Teach your child the alphabet song and sing it several times a day with your child.

15. Read alphabet books, listen to alphabet tapes, and watch alphabet videotapes with your child in order to add variety to the ways your child sees and hears the alphabet.

16. Use daily drill activities to help your child memorize the alphabet.

159 Understands what is read to him/her but not what he/she reads silently

1. Talk to your child's teacher to make certain that your child is reading material on the appropriate reading level.

2. With help from your child's teacher, modify or adjust reading material to your child's ability level.

3. Outline reading material which your child reads silently by using words and phrases on the ability level of your child.

4. Tape record difficult reading material for your child to listen to while reading along.

5. Use lower grade level library books for your child to read as enjoyable outside reading.

6. Make a list of main points from your child's reading material, written on your child's reading level.

7. Reduce distracting stimuli in order to increase your child's ability to concentrate on reading (e.g., turn off the TV, send friends home, have your child go to a quiet place to read, etc.). This is used as a means of reducing distracting stimuli and not as a form of punishment.

8. Provide your child with a quiet place (e.g., an "office," the dining room, the bedroom, etc.) for reading activities.

9. Have your child verbally paraphrase material that has just been read in order to assess comprehension.

10. Teach your child to identify the main points in material read in order to assess comprehension.

11. Have your child outline, underline, or highlight important points in reading material.

12. Have your child take notes while reading in order to increase comprehension.

13. Have your child read progressively longer segments of reading material in order to build comprehension skills (e.g., begin with a single paragraph and progress to several paragraphs, chapters, short stories, etc.).

14. Have your child tape record what he/she reads in order to enhance comprehension by listening.

15. Teach your child to use context clues (e.g., the general idea of what is being read) to identify words and phrases which are not known.

16. Have your child read high-interest signs, advertisements, notices, etc., from newspapers, magazines, movie promotions, etc., placing an emphasis on comprehension skills.

17. Write paragraphs and short stories requiring reading skills your child is currently developing. These passages should be of high interest to your child using family members, friends, pets, and interesting experiences.

18. Have your child dictate stories which are then written for your child to read, placing an emphasis on comprehension skills.

19. Make certain your child is practicing comprehension skills which are directly related to high-interest reading activities (e.g., adventures, romances, mysteries, athletics, etc.).

20. Have your child underline or highlight important points in reading materials.

21. Underline or highlight important points before your child reads assigned material.

22. Write notes to your child to provide reading material which your child will want to read for comprehension. Your child may be encouraged to write notes to friends or relatives at a time set aside each day, once a week, etc.

23. Give your child time to read a selection more than once, emphasizing accuracy in understanding, not speed.

24. Use a sight word vocabulary approach in order to teach your child key words and phrases when reading directions and instructions (e.g., key words such as *circle*, *underline*, *match*, etc.).

25. Make certain your child is not required to learn more information than he/she is capable of at any one time.

26. Tape record difficult reading material for your child to listen to as he/she reads along.

27. Make certain that the reading demands of all subjects and assignments are within the ability level of your child. If they are not, modify or adjust the reading material to your child's ability level.

28. Have your child read aloud when reading to himself/herself.

29. Make certain that your child's knowledge of a particular skill is being assessed rather than your child's ability to read directions, instructions, etc. Reading directions, instructions, etc., to your child can increase his/her success.

30. Reduce the amount of material your child reads at one time (e.g., reduce reading material to single sentences on a page, a single paragraph, etc.). Gradually increase the amount of material as your child demonstrates success.

31. Stop at various points while your child is reading silently in order to check comprehension.

32. Reduce the amount of information on a page if it is causing visual distractions for your child (e.g., less print to read, fewer pictures to look at, etc.).

160 Does not compose complete sentences or express complete thoughts when writing

1. Reward your child for composing complete sentences and expressing complete thoughts when writing. Possible rewards include verbal praise (e.g., "I love your writing. That is one of the best stories you have ever written."), a kiss on the cheek, a hug, etc. (See Appendix for Reward Menu.)

2. Reduce the emphasis on competition among brothers/sisters, friends, etc. Competition may cause your child to hurry and fail to complete sentences or express complete thoughts when writing.

3. Identify the qualities a good writer possesses (e.g., writing in complete sentences or thoughts, using correct vocabulary, etc.) and help your child to achieve those characteristics.

4. Have your child identify someone who he/she thinks is a good writer and tell why.

5. Have a brother/sister, friend, etc., act as a model for writing in complete sentences or thoughts. Have that child work with your child to help improve writing skills.

6. Be certain to act as a model for your child to imitate writing in complete sentences or thoughts.

7. Require your child to proofread all written work before turning it in as homework.

8. Give your child a series of written phrases and have your child tell you which phrases express a complete thought.

9. Have your child correct a series of written phrases, making each a complete sentence.

10. After reading a piece of written work, have your child explain why specific sentences do not express complete thoughts.

11. Give your child a subject and have him/her write as many complete sentences about it as possible.

12. Recognize quality work (e.g., display your child's work, congratulate your child, etc.).

13. Make groups of cards containing subjects, verbs, adjectives, etc. Have your child combine the cards in various ways to construct complete sentences.

14. Give your child several short sentences and have your child combine them in order to make one long, complete sentence (e.g., The dog is big. The dog is brown. The dog is mine. becomes The big, brown dog is mine.).

15. Give your child a list of transition words (e.g., therefore, although, because, etc.) and have your child make sentences using each word.

16. Make certain your child understands that a complete sentence has to express a complete though about a subject and what that subject is or does.

17. Have your child write a daily log, expressing thoughts in complete sentences.

18. Have your child write letters to friends, relatives, etc., in order to practice writing complete sentences or thoughts.

19. Encourage your child to read his/her written work aloud, in order to help identify incomplete sentences and thoughts.

20. Give your child a group of related words (e.g., *author*, *love*, *bestseller*, etc.) and have your child make up a paragraph including all the words.

21. Provide your child with clearly stated criteria for acceptable work (e.g., neatness, complete sentences, etc.).

22. Check your child's written work at various points throughout the assignment to make certain your child is using complete sentences in written work.

23. Provide your child with appropriate time limits for the completion of written homework assignments.

24. Read orally to your child to stimulate his/her thought and writing process.

161 Fails to correctly organize writing activities

1. Reward your child for correctly organizing writing activities. Possible rewards include verbal praise (e.g., "I love the story you wrote. You did a nice job of telling the readers exactly how things happened."), a kiss on the cheek, a hug, etc. (See Appendix for Reward Menu.)

2. Have your child practice organizational skills in writing activities by engaging in writing activities designed to cause him/her to want to be successful (e.g., writing a letter to a friend, rock star, famous athlete, etc.).

3. Have your child regularly write an account of the previous week, past weekend, etc., with primary attention given to organization (e.g., sequencing events, developing a paragraph, using correct word order, etc.).

4. Require your child to proofread all written work before turning it in as homework.

5. Have your child write a daily log, expressing thoughts in complete sentences.

6. Have your child create personal stories about topics which are of interest. Your child is more likely to try to be successfully when writing about something of interest.

7. Have your child read his/her own written work aloud to help identify errors in organization.

8. Make certain your child knows that paragraphs, essays, etc., need an introduction, a middle where information is contained, and a conclusion or ending.

9. Have your child arrange a series of statements on a topic in an appropriate order so that they make sense in a paragraph.

10. Help your child "brainstorm" ideas about a topic and then show your child how to put those ideas into outline form, combining some ideas and discarding others.

11. Provide your child with a paragraph in which a statement does not belong. Have your child find the inappropriate statement.

12. Have your child write step-by-step directions (e.g., steps in making a cake) so your child can practice sequencing events.

13. Give your child a group of related words (e.g., *author*, *read*, *love*, *bestseller*, etc.) and have your child make up an appropriately organized paragraph including each word.

14. Using a written essay that your child has not seen, cut the paragraphs apart and have your child reconstruct the essay by putting the paragraphs in an appropriate order.

15. Reduce the emphasis on competition. Competitive activities may cause your child to hurry and fail to correctly organize writing activities.

16. Reduce distracting stimuli when your child is involved in a writing activity (e.g., turn off the TV, send friends home, have your child work in a quiet place, etc.). This is meant as a means of reducing distracting stimuli and not as a form of punishment.

17. Make certain your child is not interrupted or hurried when engaging in writing activities.

18. Have your child read sentences, paragraphs, stories, etc., written by peers who demonstrate good organizational skills in writing.

19. When correcting your child's organizational skills in writing, be certain to provide evaluative feedback which is designed to be instructional (e.g., help your child rewrite for better organization, rewrite passages for your child, etc.).

20. Have your child develop an outline or "skeleton" of what he/she is going to write. From the outline your child can then practice organizational skills in writing.

21. Have your child practice writing letters, words, and sentences by tracing over a series of dots.

22. Make certain your child has a number line and alphabet strip to use as a reference for correct form of letters and numbers in order to reduce errors.

23. Require your child to proofread all written work. Reinforce your child for each correction made.

24. Recognize quality work (e.g., display your child's work, congratulate your child, etc.).

25. Use a computer or typewriter as an alternative writing tool.

26. Be certain that your child has only the necessary materials when working on homework assignments.

27. Provide your child with quality materials to perform homework assignments (e.g., pencil with eraser, paper, dictionary, handwriting sample, etc.).

162 Omits, adds, or substitutes words when writing

1. Speak to your child to explain what he/she is doing wrong (e.g., not writing in clear and complete sentences, leaving words out, etc.) and what should be done (e.g., writing in clear and complete sentences, rereading what was written, etc.).

2. Reduce the emphasis on competition. Competitive activities may cause your child to hurry and omit words when writing.

3. Have your child proofread all written work for omissions, additions, or substitutions.

4. Encourage your child to read all written work aloud in order to detect omissions, additions, or substitutions.

5. Give your child several sentences and have your child combine them to practice making complete sentences (e.g., The car is new. The car is red. The car is mine. becomes The new, red car is mine.).

6. Give your child a list of transition words (e.g., therefore, although, because, etc.) and have your child make sentences using each word.

7. Have your child write a daily log or diary expressing thoughts in complete sentences.

8. Encourage your child to create stories about topics which are of interest in order to provide more experiences in writing.

9. Have your child complete "fill-in-the-blank" stories and sentences and then read them aloud.

10. Make certain your child is aware of the types of errors that are being made (e.g., omits *is*, omits final *s*, etc.) in order to be more conscious of them when writing.

11. Make certain your child is not interrupted or hurried when engaged in writing activities.

12. Have your child engage in writing activities designed to cause a desire to be successful in writing (e.g., writing a letter to a friend, rock star, famous athlete, etc.).

13. When reviewing your child's work, be certain to provide evaluative feedback which is designed to be instructional (e.g., point out all omissions, additions, and substitutions; suggest more appropriate words, phrases, etc.; help your child rewrite work to make corrections in the omissions, additions, substitutions, etc.).

14. Give your child the scrambled words of a sentence and have your child put them in the correct order to form the sentence.

15. Give your child a group of related words (e.g., *baseball*, *fans*, *glove*, *strikeout*, etc.) and have your child make up a paragraph including each word.

16. Reduce distracting stimuli when your child is engaged in writing activities (e.g., turn off the TV, send friends home, have your child work in a quiet place, etc.). This is used as a means of reducing distracting stimuli and not as a form of punishment.

17. Make a list of your child's most common omissions, additions, and substitutions and have your child refer to the list when engaged in writing activities in order to check for errors.

18. Have your child practice writing simple sentences successfully without omissions, additions, or substitutions. Have your child write more complex sentences, paragraphs, short stories, etc., as success is demonstrated.

19. Make certain your child has written work proofread by someone (e.g., older brother/sister, parent, teacher, etc.) for omissions, additions, substitutions before turning in written work.

20. Recognize quality work (e.g., display your child's work, congratulate your child, etc.).

21. Check your child's work at various points throughout a writing homework assignment in order to detect any omissions, additions, or substitutions.

22. Require your child to proofread all written work. Reinforce your child for each correction made.

163 Spells words correctly in one context but not in another

1. Reward your child for spelling words correctly in all contexts. Possible rewards include verbal praise (e.g., "The story you wrote is great. You did a wonderful job of spelling in the story."), a kiss on the cheek, a hug, etc. (See Appendix for Reward Menu.)

2. Reduce the emphasis on competition. Competitive activities may cause your child to hurry and make mistakes in spelling.

3. Give your child fewer words to learn to spell at any one time (e.g., learn three words a night rather than spending every night of the week on every spelling word), spending more time on each word until your child can spell the word correctly.

4. Have an older brother/sister, friend, etc., spend time each day engaged in drill activities with your child on spelling words.

5. Have your child use spelling words in sentences as a practice activity.

6. Write sentences, paragraphs, etc., for your child to read which repeat his/her spelling words throughout the material.

7. Have your child write spelling words in different locations throughout your home as your child is learning the words (e.g., notes on the refrigerator, notes on your child's bedroom door, etc.).

8. Have your child use the dictionary to find the correct spelling of any word he/she cannot spell correctly. The emphasis on this situation becomes spelling accurately rather than memorizing spelling words.

9. Have your child use correct spelling in a meaningful manner which would cause your child to want to be successful (e.g., writing a letter to a friend, rock star, famous athlete, etc.).

10. Make certain your child knows why he/she is learning each spelling word (e.g., provide your child with a concrete example of how each word can be used in daily experiences).

11. Have your child identify a list of spelling words (e.g., 5, 10, 15) each week which your child wants to learn to spell. If your child is interested in cars, words from automotive magazines, advertisements, etc., can be identified.

12. Try various activities to help strengthen and reinforce the visual memory of spelling words (e.g., flash cards, lists on the refrigerator, a list in your child's room, etc.).

13. Make certain your child has had adequate practice in writing the spelling words (e.g., drill activities, sentence activities, etc.).

14. Make certain your child has adequate time to perform homework assignments.

15. Reduce distracting stimuli when your child is working on spelling activities (e.g., turn off the TV, send friends home, have your child work in a quiet room, etc.). This is used as a means of reducing distracting stimuli and not as a form of punishment.

16. Have your child maintain a folder of all spelling words. Have your child refer to the list when engaged in writing activities in order to check spelling.

17. Make certain your child learns to "use" spelling words rather than simply memorizing the spelling of words for testing purposes (e.g., have your child use the words in writing notes, sentences, letters to relatives, etc.).

18. Require your child to proofread all written work for spelling errors before turning in homework.

19. Have your child keep a dictionary of "most misspelled words" to have as a reference when uncertain of the spelling of a word.

20. Have your child write spelling words frequently over a period of time in order to increase your child's visual memory of the spelling words.

21. Make certain your child is not being required to learn too many spelling words at one time.

22. Speak to your child's teacher to make certain that your child's spelling words are seen on a routine basis, rather than infrequently, in order to assure correct spelling and use of the words.

23. Arrange with your child's teacher to use weekly vocabulary words as weekly spelling words.

24. Speak to your child's teacher to make certain that your child is able to read the words that are given as spelling words. If your child is unable to read the spelling words, it is unlikely that your child will be able to spell the words.

25. Recognize quality work (e.g., display your child's work, congratulate your child, etc.).

26. Make certain your child is not required to learn more information than your child is capable of at any one time.

164 Requires continued drill and practice in order to learn spelling words

1. Reward your child for learning spelling words. Possible rewards include verbal praise (e.g., "You have done a great job of learning your spelling words this week."), a kiss on the cheek, a hug, etc.

2. Reduce the emphasis on competition. Competitive activities may cause your child to hurry and make mistakes in spelling.

3. Give your child fewer words to learn to spell at any one time (e.g., work on three words a night rather than all spelling words each night), spending more time on each word until your child can spell it correctly.

4. Have an older brother/sister, a peer, etc., spend time each day engaged in drill activities with your child on weekly spelling words.

5. Have your child use spelling words in sentences each day.

6. Have your child highlight or underline spelling words in passages from reading assignments, newspapers, magazines, etc.

7. Develop crossword puzzles which contain only your child's spelling words and have your child complete them.

8. Have your child act as a tutor to teach spelling words to a younger brother/sister, a younger friend, etc.

9. Write sentences, passages, paragraphs, etc., for your child to read which repeat your child's spelling words throughout the material.

10. Have your child post spelling words in different locations throughout your home as your child is learning them (e.g., a list on the refrigerator, a list on a desk, in your child's room, etc.).

11. Have your child indicate when a spelling word has been mastered. As your child demonstrates that the word is mastered, remove the spelling word from the study list.

12. Use visual images such as pictires for the student to associate with the letter sound.

13. Have your child's current spelling list in his/her bedroom with the requirement that the words practiced whenever your child has a few extra minutes. Reward your child for practicing spelling words.

14. Have your child review spelling words each day for a short period of time rather than two or three times per week for longer periods of time.

15. Have your child use a dictionary to find the correct spelling of any word that is difficult to spell. The emphasis in this situation becomes spelling accurately rather than memorizing spelling words.

16. Have your child quiz brothers/sisters, friends, etc., over his/her spelling words.

17. Speak with your child's teacher to make certain that your child's spelling instruction is on a level where success can be met.

18. Initiate a "learn to spell a word a day" program with your child.

19. Use words for your child's spelling list which are commonly found in daily surroundings (e.g., commercials, hazard signs, directions, lunch menu, etc.).

20. Have your child's current list of spelling words on the refrigerator at all times.

21. Have your child use current spelling words in a meaningful manner which would cause your child to want to be successful (e.g., writing a letter to a friend, rock star, famous athlete, etc.).

22. Require your child to proofread all written work for spelling errors.

23. Have your child identify a list of words (e.g., 5, 10, 15) each week which he/she wants to learn to spell. If your child is interested in cars, identify words from automotive magazines, advertisements, etc.

24. Speak to your child's teacher to make certain that your child is able to read the words that are given as spelling words. If your child is unable to read the spelling words, it is unlikely that he/she will be able to spell the words.

25. Recognize quality work (e.g., display your child's work, congratulate your child, etc.).

26. Make certain your child is not required to learn more information than he/she is capable of at any one time.

27. Provide practice on spelling words by using a computer software program that gives your child immediate feedback.

165 Has a limited speaking vocabulary

1. If there are other children or adolescents in the home, reward them for using an extended vocabulary.

2. Tape record your child's spontaneous speech, noting specific words that are used; and then have your child make a list of other words (synonyms) which could be substituted for these words.

3. Select relevant and appropriate reading material and have your child underline each unfamiliar word. Make a list of these words and review their meanings with your child until your child can use them when speaking.

4. Reward your child for using new or more difficult words when speaking.

5. Have your child keep a diary or log of all unfamiliar words which your child encounters each day. Include their meanings.

6. Give your child a list of words and ask your child to tell the opposite of each word.

7. Have your child make up sentences or stories using new words recently learned.

8. Name a category and have your child identify things within the category. Introduce new words which belong in the same group.

9. Explain to your child where he/she can go to find word meanings (e.g., dictionary, thesaurus, encyclopedia, etc.).

10. Encourage your child to read newspapers, novels, magazines, or other materials for enjoyment.

11. Be a model for your child by reading newspapers, novels, magazines, etc.

12. Give your child a "word of the day" which is to be incorporated into conversations. Reinforce your child with praise or "points" each time the word is used.

13. During conversation, repeat phrases used by your child, revising the vocabulary to include a larger speaking vocabulary (e.g., Your child says, "The TV show was good." Repeat by saying, "I'm glad the TV show was so entertaining.").

14. Use a new word to complete a sentence. Have your child explain how the word changes the sentence meaning (e.g., I like Jerry because he is ____ (sincere, humorous, competitive).).

15. Before your child reads, prepare a list of new words which will be encountered. Help your child look up the words and practice saying them and using them in sentences.

16. Explain to your child how to use context clues to determine the meaning of words heard or seen (e.g., looking at the surrounding words and determining what type of word would be appropriate).

17. Explain to your child how to classify new words as to category, function, antonym and synonym, etc., so your child will have a way of "filing" the word to remember it.

18. Have an older brother/sister, an older friend, etc., act as a model to expand your child's speaking vocabulary.

19. Review on a daily basis new vocabulary words and their meanings. Have your child use the words daily.

20. Review on a daily basis previously learned vocabulary words and meanings. Have your child incorporate previously learned vocabulary words into daily conversation and activities.

21. Have your child maintain a notebook of all new vocabulary words to call upon for daily conversation and activities.

22. Use pictures to help your child understand the meanings of new vocabulary words.

23. Make certain your child is not expected to learn more vocabulary words and meanings than he/she is capable of comprehending.

24. Make certain your child has mastery of vocabulary words at each level before introducing new words.

25. Be certain to take time each day (e.g., after school, at the dinner table, etc.) to have each member of the family tell about their day. When your child describes his/her day, ask questions to encourage the extended use of vocabulary.

166 Does not complete statements or thoughts when speaking

1. Reward your child for using complete statements or thoughts when speaking. Possible rewards include verbal praise (e.g., "You did a nice job of telling me what you wanted for lunch.").

2. If there are other children or adolescents in the home, reward them for speaking in complete statements or thoughts.

3. Allow your child to speak without being interrupted or hurried.

4. Tape record a spontaneous monologue given by your child. Transcribe your child's speech from the tape and have your child listen to the tape. Have your child correct errors and practice speaking in more complete statements or thoughts.

5. Have your child keep a list of times and/or situations in which he/she is nervous, anxious, etc., and has more trouble with speech than usual. Help your child identify ways to feel more successful with those situations.

6. Demonstrate acceptable and unacceptable speech, using complete/incomplete statements and thoughts, and have your child critique each example.

7. When your child has difficulty during a conversation, remind your child that this occasionally happens to everyone and not to become upset.

8. When your child fails to use complete thoughts (e.g., says, "Ball," and points) elaborate on what was said (e.g., "So you want to play ball?"). This provides a model for more complete statements and thoughts.

9. Have your child role-play various situations in which good speech is important (e.g., during a job interview, etc.).

10. Make a list of the attributes that are likely to help a person become a good speaker (e.g., takes time, thinks of what to say before starting, etc.).

11. Reduce the emphasis on competition. Competitive activities may cause your child to hurry and fail to speak in complete statements or thoughts.

12. Break down the qualities a good speaker possesses (e.g., rate, diction, volume, vocabulary, etc.) and have your child evaluate the characteristics in his/her own speaking. Set a goal for improvement in only one or two areas at a time.

13. Have an older brother/sister, an older friend, etc., act as a model for speaking in complete statements or thoughts.

14. Make a list of the most common incomplete statements or thoughts your child says. Spend time with your child practicing how to make these statements or thoughts complete.

15. Verbally correct your child when complete sentences are not used so your child can hear the correct version.

16. Have your child practice saying descriptive statements or thoughts which can be used when speaking.

17. Be certain to act as a model for your child to imitate speaking in complete statements or thoughts (e.g., speak clearly, slowly, concisely, and in complete sentences, statements, and thoughts).

18. When your child is required to recall information, provide visual and/or auditory cues to help him/her remember the information (e.g., key words, expose part of a picture, etc.).

19. Be certain to take time each day (e.g., after school, at the dinner table, etc.) to have each member of the family tell about their day. When your child describes his/her day, ask questions to encourage your child to complete statements or thoughts when speaking.

167 Dysfluent speech interferes with daily communication

1. Make certain your child's hearing has been recently checked.

2. Reward your child for speaking fluently. Possible rewards include verbal praise (e.g., "Thank you for speaking clearly; it is much easier to understand what you are trying to say."), a kiss on the cheek, a hug, etc. (See Appendix for Reward Menu.)

3. Familiarize yourself and your child with the terms of fluency, dysfluency, stuttering, easy speech, etc. Keep these words as neutral as possible, without negative connotations.

4. Evaluate the appropriateness of requiring your child to speak without dysfluency (e.g., developmentally, young children experience normal dysfluency in their speech and all persons are occasionally dysfluent).

5. Provide your child with an appropriate model of slow, easy speech. Lengthen the pauses between words, phrases, and sentences.

6. Identify an older brother/sister, an older friend, etc., to act as a model for appropriate speech.

7. During conversation, calmly delay your verbal responses by one or two seconds.

8. Use a tape recorder so your child may listen to and evaluate his/her own speech.

9. Develop a list of the attributes which are likely to help a person become a good speaker and have your child practice each attribute.

10. During oral reading, underline or highlight words which are difficult for your child to say, and provide reinforcement when your child says them fluently.

11. Have your child identify the times and/or situations that are likely to make him/her nervous or uncomfortable. Discuss the reasons for this and seek solutions to the difficulty experienced.

12. Have your child speak in unison with you while you are modeling slow, easy, speech.

13. Have your child practice techniques for relaxing (e.g., deep breathing, tensing and relaxing muscles, etc.) which he/she can be employed when he/she starts to become dysfluent.

14. Have your child identify the specific words on which he/she becomes dysfluent, and practice these words or phrases.

15. Encourage your child to maintain eye contact during all speaking situations. If the child is noticeably more fluent when eye contact is averted, attempt to increase eye contact on a gradual basis.

16. Reward your child's moments of relative fluency and emphasize that these occurred when your child was speaking slowly and easily.

17. Empathize with your child and explain that he/she is not more or less valuable as a person because of stuttering. Emphasize your child's positive attributes.

18. Empathize with feelings of anger which your child may be experiencing.

19. When your child is speaking fluently, try to extend the positive experience by allowing your child ample opportunity to continue speaking.

20. Reward your child each time a question is answered or your child makes a spontaneous comment.

21. If your child is speaking too rapidly, remind your child to slow down and take more time. Develop a private signal (e.g., raising a finger, touching earlobe, etc.) to avoid calling too much attention to your child's speech in front of others.

22. Try to give your child your undivided attention so your child will not feel a need to hurry or to compete with others for attention.

23. If your child is more dysfluent when involved in another activity at the same time he/she is talking, encourage your child to stop the other activity.

24. If your child is highly excited, wait until your child is calm before requiring any verbal interactions. A high level of excitement often precipitates an anxiety level that interferes with fluency.

25. During moments of dysfluency, use nonverbal activities to relax your child (e.g., deep breathing, eyes closed, etc.).

26. Do not interrupt or finish your child's sentences even if you can anticipate what your child is going to say. This can be extremely frustrating and may decrease your child's willingness to engage in future communicative interactions.

27. Help your child learn to identify periods of dysfluency and periods of slow, easy speech.

28. Help your child learn to identify situations in which he/she is more fluent and less fluent. Determine the aspects of the fluent situations that seem to enhance fluency and try to transfer those features to the less fluent situations.

29. When your child is dysfluent during conversations, explain that this happens to everyone at times.

30. Have your child make a list of his/her strong points or the things he/she does well in order to improve his/her overall level of confidence.

31. Point out to your child that he/she is capable of fluent speech and is in control in many situations.

32. Model slow, easy speech for your child and encourage your child to speak at a similar rate. Practice with your child for a short time each day until he/she is able to match the rate.

33. Provide your child with a list of sentences and encourage your child to read at a slow rate.

34. Prepare simple oral reading passages in written form in which phrases are separated by large spaces (indicating "pauses"). Have your child practice reading the passages aloud.

35. Teach your child ways to restate or rephrase a misunderstood message rather than continuing to repeat the original message with the same error patterns.

36. When your child experiences a severe episode of dysfluency, respond by reiterating the content of your child's message to communicate that the message has been understood.

37. Meet with your child's teacher to determine the level of dysfluency at school, teachers' reactions to the dysfluency, and successful strategies the teachers might employ when dealing with dysfluent speech.

168 Does not understand the concept of skip counting

1. Have your child count nickels, dimes, quarters, etc. (e.g., 5 cents, 10 cents, 15 cents, etc.).

2. Have an older brother/sister, an older friend, etc., work with your child to help your child understand the concept of skip counting (e.g., counting Oreo cookies by two's, counting eggs by three's, etc.).

3. Have your child use a number line (e.g., a line of numbers, 1, 2, 3, 4, 5, 6, 7, 8, 9, 10, 11, 12, 13, 14, 15, 16, 17, 18, 19, 20, etc.) as he/she counts by 2's, 5's, 10's, etc., in order that your child can see the increments that are being added.

4. Have your child count by 2's, 5's, 10's, etc., and write the numbers as your child counts. Your child can then go back to the numbers that were written and see that the increment of 2, 5, 10, etc., is added to each number.

5. Have your child use tangible objects (e.g., pennies, paper clips, etc.) when counting by 2's, 5's, 10's, etc., in order to see that the total number is increasing in successive increments.

6. Have your child use a calculator when skip counting, adding 2, 5, 10, etc., to each successive number in order to see that skip counting increases by the increment used in counting (e.g., 2 + 2 = 4, + 2 = 6, + 2 = 8, + 2 = 10, etc.).

7. Make certain your child knows why he/she is learning a math concept. Provide your child with concrete examples and opportunities to apply these concepts in real-life situations.

8. Have your child use a clock in the home to count by 5's, 10's, 15's, etc.

9. Make certain your child understands number concepts (e.g., "What does 3 mean?" "What does 5 mean?" etc.) and the relationships of symbols to the numbers of objects (e.g., the number 3 means three things, the number 5 means five things, etc.), before requiring your child to solve math problems.

10. Make certain your child has a number line (e.g., a line of numbers, 1, 2, 3, 4, 5, 6, 7, 8, 9, 10, 11, 12, 13, 14, 15, 16, 17, 18, 19, 20, etc.) to use as a reference.

11. Use manipulative objects (e.g., abacus, base ten blocks, etc.) to teach your child the concept of skip counting.

12. Make certain your child is not required to learn more information than he/she is capable of at any one time.

13. Have your child act as a tutor to teach a younger brother/sister, friend, etc., a concept he/she has mastered. This can serve as reinforcement for your child.

14. Provide practice in skip counting using a computer software program that gives your child immediate feedback.

15. Make certain your child has mastery of math concepts at each level before introducing a new skill level.

169 Does not remember math facts

1. Reward your child for improving retention of math facts. Possible rewards include verbal praise (e.g., "I am so proud of you for knowing five new math facts."), a kiss on the cheek, a hug, etc. (See Appendix for Reward Menu.)

2. Reduce the emphasis on competition. Competitive activities may cause your child to hurry and make mistakes in math problems.

3. Beginning with the addition and subtraction facts, separate the basic facts into "sets," each to be memorized successively by the student.

4. Using the tracking technique to help your child learn math facts, present a few facts at a time. Gradually increase the number of facts your child must remember as your child demonstrates success.

5. Provide your child with many concrete experiences to help your child learn and remember math facts. Use popsicle sticks, tongue depressors, paper clips, buttons, etc., to form groupings to teach math facts.

6. Use fingers to teach your child to form addition and subtraction combinations. Have your child hold up fingers and add or subtract other fingers to find the correct answer.

7. Have your child use a calculator to reinforce learning of the math facts. Have your child solve several problems each day using the calculator.

8. If there is a computer available, provide practice of math facts using a computer with software programs that provide immediate feedback for your child.

9. Use daily drill activities to help your child memorize math facts (e.g., written problems, flash cards, etc.).

10. Allow your child to keep basic addition, subtraction, multiplication, and division charts to use in solving math problems.

11. Build upon math facts your child already knows, reinforcing facts your child has mastered. Add one fact at a time as your child demonstrates success.

12. Have your child perform timed drills to reinforce basic math facts. Your child "competes" against his/her best work.

13. Have your child use a number line when working addition and subtraction problems.

14. Choose one fact your child is unsuccessful with and review it several times a day. Make that fact your child's "fact of the day."

15. Have your child complete math facts and then have your child use a calculator to check and correct the problem.

16. Have an older brother/sister, an older friend, etc., work with your child each day on drill activities (e.g., flash cards).

17. Avoid going on to multiplication and division facts until addition and subtraction facts have been mastered.

18. Have your child use math fact records and tapes for math fact drill activities.

19. Use manipulative objects (e.g., peg board, abacus, base 10 blocks, etc.) to teach your child basic math facts while providing a visual image.

20. Have your child use a calculator for drill activities of basic math facts.

21. Find opportunities for your child to apply math facts in real-life situations (e.g., getting change at a restaurant, measuring the length of objects, etc.).

22. Have your child solve half of the math homework problems with a calculator and half of the problems without a calculator.

23. Make certain your child is not required to learn more information than he/she is capable of at any one time.

24. Review, on a daily basis, those skills, concepts, tasks, etc., which have been previously introduced.

170 Does not understand the concept of time

1. Reward your child for telling time correctly. Possible rewards include verbal praise (e.g., "Thank you for telling me that is was time to take you to school."), a kiss on the cheek, a hug, etc. (See Appendix for Reward Menu.)

2. If there is a computer available, provide practice in telling time using computer software programs that give immediate feedback to your child.

3. Have your child work with an older brother/sister, friend, etc., each day practicing skills required for telling time (e.g., telling time to the hour, half hour, quarter hour, etc.).

4. Make certain your child understands all the concepts involved in telling time (e.g., there are five minutes between each number on the clock; counting by 5's, 10's, 15's; the big hand and the little hand, etc.).

5. Make certain your child understands which seasons come before and after other seasons.

6. Make certain your child understands the concepts of morning, afternoon, evening, and night.

7. Make certain your child understands the concept of the length of a minute, 5 minutes, 10 minutes, 15 minutes, 1 hour, 90 minutes, 24 hours, etc.

8. Make certain your child has a standard clock in his/her room to use as a visual reference.

9. Make certain your child knows the number of hours in a day, days in a week, weeks in a year, etc.

10. Make certain your child understands the terms used in telling time (e.g., *a quarter 'til*, *half past*, *a quarter after*, etc.).

11. Make certain your child can count by common divisors of time (e.g., one minute, two minutes, three minutes, five minutes, 10 minutes, 15 minutes, 60 minutes, 90 minutes, one hour, two hours, three hours, etc.).

12. Have your child recognize when events occur in the environment (e.g., lunch, naptime, bedtime, etc.).

13. Have your child indicate when the clock is on the hour.

14. Have your child indicate when the clock is on the half hour.

15. Have your child indicate when the clock is on the quarter hour.

16. Give your child word problems involving math concepts on your child's ability level (e.g., "At 10 minutes after 9 o'clock, you will begin walking to school. It takes 10 minutes to walk to school. What time will it be when you arrive?").

17. Make certain your child has a clock with a face and hands to manipulate when learning to tell time.

18. Have your child set the hands on a clock as you indicate the time of the day.

19. Use a large face clock to set the hands and have your child indicate the time. Begin with the hours, the half hours, the quarter hours, etc.

20. Make certain your child can read a digital clock or watch.

21. If possible, provide your child with a wristwatch to wear while learning to tell time.

22. Make certain your child has a number line (e.g., a line of numbers, 1, 2, 3, 4, 5, 6, 7, 8, 9, 10, 11, 12, 13, 14, 15, 16, 17, 18, 19, 20, etc.) to use as a reference.

23. Make certain your child knows why he/she is learning a math concept. Provide your child with concrete examples and opportunities to apply these concepts in real-life situations.

24. Have your child talk through math problems as he/she is solving them in order to identify errors your child is making.

25. Recognize quality work (e.g., display your child's work, congratulate your child, etc.).

26. Make certain your child has mastery of math concepts at each level before introducing a new skill level.

27. Reduce the amount of information on a page if it is causing visual distractions for your child (e.g., fewer math problems, less print, etc.).

171 Has difficulty understanding abstract concepts

1. Make certain to use terms when speaking to your child which convey concepts to describe tangible objects in the environment (e.g., *larger, smaller, square, triangle*, etc.).

2. Identify tangible objects in the home with signs that convey abstract concepts (e.g., *larger, smaller, square, triangle*, etc.).

3. Use concrete examples when teaching abstract concepts (e.g., number of objects to convey *more than* and *less than*, rulers and yardsticks to convey concepts of *height* and *width*, etc.).

4. Play *Simon Says* to enhance under- standing of abstract concepts (e.g., ''Find the largest desk.'' ''Touch something that is a rectangle.'' etc.).

5. Conduct a scavenger hunt. Have your child look for the smallest pencil, tallest chair, etc., in your home.

6. Teach shapes using common objects in the environment (e.g., round clocks, rectangle tables, square tiles on the floor, etc.).

7. Evaluate the appropriateness of expecting your child to understand abstract concepts (e.g., is it too difficult for your child).

8. Teach abstract concepts one at a time before pairing the concepts (e.g., *dimensionality, size, space, shape*, etc.).

9. Provide repeated physical demonstrations of abstract concepts (e.g., identify things far away and close to your child, point out a small box in a large room, etc.).

10. Review, on a daily basis, those abstract concepts which have been previously talked about. Talk about new abstract concepts only after your child has mastery of those previously talked about.

11. When introducing abstract concepts, rely on tangible objects (e.g., boxes for dimensionality, family members for size, cookie cutters for shape, etc.). Do not introduce abstract concepts by using their descriptive titles such as square, rectangle, triangle, etc.

12. Have your child match the names of abstract concepts with objects (e.g., *triangle, square, circle*, etc.).

13. Give your child direction-following chores (e.g., ''Go to the swing which is farthest away.'' ''Go to the nearest sandbox.'' etc.).

14. Have a peer spend time each day with your child pointing out abstract concepts in the class- room (e.g., the rectangle-shaped light switch plate, the round light fixture, the tallest girl, etc.).

15. Make certain your child is attending to the source of information (e.g., eye contact is being made, hands are free of materials, etc.) when directions are delivered that involve abstract concepts.

16. Label abstract concepts throughout the home (e.g., triangle shapes on the walls, left and right sides of a desk, etc.) to help your child under- stand the concepts.

17. Make certain your child is not required to learn more abstract concepts than your child is capable of learning at any one time.

172 Has trouble using money to make purchases, make change, etc.

1. Reward your child for correctly solving problems involving money. Possible rewards include verbal praise (e.g., "You did a great job of figuring out the money word problems."), a kiss on the cheek, a hug, having a friend over to play, staying up late, watching a favorite TV show, and playing a game with a parent. (See Appendix for Reward Menu.)

2. Have your child use a calculator to reinforce learning to solve problems involving money. Have your child solve several problems each day using the calculator.

3. Use real-life situations for your child to practice money problems (e.g., paying for lunch in the cafeteria line, making purchases from the store, purchasing a soft drink, etc.).

4. Use actual coins in teaching your child coin values; counting by fives, tens, etc.; matching combinations of coins; etc.

5. Make certain your child recognizes all coins (e.g., penny, nickel, dime, quarter, half-dollar).

6. Make certain your child recognizes common denominations of paper money (e.g., one-dollar bill, five-dollar bill, etc.).

7. Have a peer or a sibling work with your child every day practicing coin values, paper money values, money combinations, etc.

8. Have your child match equal values of coins (e.g., two nickels to a dime, two dimes and a nickel to a quarter, five nickels to a quarter, etc.).

9. Make certain your child understands all math operation concepts involved in using money (e.g., addition, subtraction, multiplication, division, decimals, etc.).

10. Make certain your child can solve the necessary math problems involved in the use of money (i.e., your child can solve math problems of the same difficulty as those involving money).

11. Make certain your child can count by pennies, nickels, dimes, quarters, half-dollars.

12. Have your child use actual money to simulate transactions (e.g., purchasing lunch, groceries, snacks, clothing, etc.). Have your child practice acting as both a customer and a clerk.

13. Provide your child with math word problems involving the use of money, making certain the appropriate operation is clearly stated.

14. Provide your child with a daily shopping list of items and include the cost of each item. Have your child determine the cost of his/her purchase.

15. Collect a selection of menus and have your child select items for a meal and compute the cost of the items.

16. Have your child use a newspaper or catalog and make a list of things advertised which he/she would like to purchase. Have your child determine the total cost of the items selected.

17. Have your child earn a hypothetical income and engage in money-related math problems (e.g., taxes, social security, savings, rent, food, clothing, auto payments, recreation, etc.). The degree of difficulty of the problems should be matched to your child's ability level.

18. Have your child talk through money math problems while solving them in order to identify errors.

19. Make certain your child knows why he/she is learning the concept of money. Provide your child with concrete examples and opportunities to apply these concepts in real-life situations.

20. Make certain your child is not required to learn more information than your child is capable of at any one time.

21. Provide practice in solving money problems using a computer software program that gives your child immediate feedback.

22. Review, on a daily basis, those skills, concepts, tasks, etc., which have been previously introduced.

173 Has trouble with measurement in day-to-day activities

1. Reward your child for using measurement in day-to-day activities. Possible rewards include verbal praise (e.g., "You did a nice job of using the ruler to measure the space you needed for your project." etc.), a kiss on the cheek, a hug, having a friend over to play, staying up late, watching a TV show, and playing a game with a parent. (See Appendix for Reward Menu.)

2. Reduce the emphasis on competition. Competitive activities may cause your child to hurry and solve measurement problems incorrectly.

3. Discuss and provide your child with a list of words/phrases which usually indicate measurement problems (e.g., pounds, inches, millimeter, kilogram, etc.).

4. Have a peer or sibling act as a model for your child to demonstrate how to solve measurement problems.

5. Evaluate the appropriateness of your child learning measurement skills to determine: (a) if the task is too difficult and (b) if the length of time scheduled for the task is appropriate.

6. Find opportunities for your child to apply measurement facts to real-life situations (e.g., cooking, measuring lengths of objects, etc.).

7. Develop a measurement reference sheet (e.g., 12 inches = 1 foot, 8 ounces = 1 cup, etc.) for your child to keep with him/her.

8. Provide your child with enjoyable activities in measurement (e.g., computer games, math games, etc.).

9. Make certain that the language used to communicate with your child about measurement is consistent (e.g., meters, grams, etc.).

10. Make certain that your child has mastery of measurement concepts at any level before introducing a more difficult level.

11. Have your child practice measuring items in the environment to find their length, weight, etc.

12. Work the first problem or two of a measurement assignment with your child in order to make certain that your child understands directions and the operations necessary to solve the problems.

13. Have your child practice basic measurement concepts (e.g., pound, ounce, inch, foot, etc.) using everyday measurement devices found in the environment (e.g., rulers, measuring cup, etc.).

14. Make certain your child knows the basic concepts of fractions before requiring him/her to solve problems involving measurement (e.g., ¼ inch, 1½ inch, etc.).

15. Have your child complete measurement problems that he/she will want to be able to successfully perform (e.g., following a recipe to cook, building a model, etc.).

16. Have your child practice using smaller units of measurement to create larger units of measurement (e.g., twelve inches to make one foot, three feet to make one yard, eight ounces to make one cup, four cups to make one quart, etc.).

17. Have your child begin solving problems using measurement which require same and whole units (e.g., 10 pounds minus 8 pounds, 24 inches plus 12 inches, etc.). Introduce fractions and mixed units (e.g., pounds and ounces, etc.) only after your child has demonstrated success with same and whole units.

18. Have your child use a calculator to solve measurement problems, check the accuracy of the problems that have been worked, etc.

19. Have your child use computer software programs to practice measurement skills.

20. Have your child solve beginning measurement problems by using measurement devices before solving the problems on paper (e.g., 5 inches plus 4 inches using a ruler, 3 liquid ounces plus 5 liquid ounces using a measuring cup, etc.).

21. Make certain your child knows why he/she is learning measurement concepts. Provide your child with concrete examples and opportunities to apply these concepts in real-life situations.

22. Make certain your child is not required to learn more information than he/she is capable of at any one time.

23. Review, on a daily basis, those skills, concepts, tasks, etc., which have been previously introduced.

24. Have your child participate in an actual "hands on" experience by following simple recipes (e.g., making Jell-O, peanut butter cookies, etc.).

174 Confuses operational signs when working math problems (e.g., +, -, ×, ÷)

1. Speak to your child to explain: (a) what your child is doing wrong (e.g., not recognizing operational symbols) and (b) what your child should be doing (e.g., following operational symbols).

2. Evaluate the appropriateness of tasks to determine: (a) if the task is too difficult, and (b) if the length of time scheduled for the task is appropriate.

3. Have your child practice recognizing operational symbols (e.g., flash cards of ÷, +, -, ×).

4. Use a written reminder beside math problems to indicate which math operation is to be used (e.g., addition, subtraction, multiplication, division). Gradually reduce the use of reminders as your child demonstrates success.

5. Make the math operation symbols next to the problems extra large in order that your child will be more likely to observe the symbol.

6. Color code math operation symbols next to the problems in order that your child will be more likely to observe the symbols.

7. Require your child to go through math problems on each homework assignment, highlighting or otherwise marking the operation of each problem before beginning to solve the problems.

8. Work the first problem or two of the math assignment for your child in order that he/she knows what math operations to use.

9. Use a separate piece of paper for each type of math problem. Gradually introduce different types of math problems on the same page.

10. Place the math operation symbols randomly around your child's room and have your child practice identifying the operation involved as he/she points to each symbol.

11. Have your child solve his/her math problems using a calculator.

12. Provide your child with a math operation symbol reference sheet to keep and use while working on homework (e.g., + means to add, - means to subtract, × means to multiply, and ÷ means to divide).

13. Talk to your child's teacher and ask that a math operation symbol reminder be provided for your child at the top of each sheet of math problems (e.g., + means to add, - means to subtract, × means to multiply, and ÷ means to divide).

14. Have your child practice matching math operation symbols to the words identifying the operations by using flash cards (e.g., +, -, ×, ÷; add, subtract, multiply, divide).

15. Have a sibling or a friend work with your child to act as a model and provide reminders as your child solves his/her math problems.

16. Make certain your child knows why he/she is learning a math concept. Provide your child with concrete examples and opportunities to apply these concepts in real-life situations.

17. Have your child check his/her math assignments using a calculator. The calculator can also be used to reinforce the learning of math facts.

18. Make certain your child is not required to learn more information than he/she is capable of at any one time.

19. Provide practice in operational signs using a computer software program that gives your child immediate feedback.

20. Make certain your child has mastery of math concepts at each level before introducing a new skill level.

21. Highlight operational signs so that your child is sure to notice the signs before beginning the operation.

175 Does not make use of columns when working math problems

1. Reward your child for making use of columns when working math problems. Possible rewards include verbal praise (e.g., "I like the way you worked your math problems by using the columns."), having a friend over to play, staying up late, watching a favorite TV show, and play a game with a parent. (See Appendix for Reward Menu.)

2. Identify a sibling or a friend to act as a model for your child to demonstrate the use of columns when working math problems.

3. Use manipulative objects (e.g., base ten blocks, connecting links, etc.) to teach your child the use of columns when working math problems.

4. Make certain your child has the prerequisite skills to learn place value (e.g., able to count orally, write numbers to 100, etc.).

5. Make certain your child knows the concepts and terminology necessary to learn place value (e.g., *set, column, middle, left, digit*, etc.).

6. Make certain your child understands that the collective value of ten "ones" is equal to one ten and that ten "tens" is equal to one hundred.

7. Provide your child with learning experiences in grouping tangible objects into groups of tens, hundreds, etc.

8. Have your child practice labeling columns to represent ones, tens, hundreds, etc.

9. Have your child practice regrouping a number in different positions and determining its value (e.g., 372, 627, 721).

10. Make certain your child understands the zero concept in place value (e.g., there are no tens in the number "207," so a zero is put in the tens column).

11. Have your child use a calculator to solve math problems involving the use of columns.

12. Money concepts will help your child learn place value by association (e.g., $1.26 is the same as six pennies or six ones; two dimes or two tens; one dollar or one hundred).

13. Use vertical lines on graph paper to help your child visualize columns and put a single digit in a column.

14. Make certain your child understands that math problems of addition, subtraction, and multiplication move from right to left beginning with the ones column.

15. Provide your child with many opportunities to indicate the value of columns in multiple-digit numbers (e.g., 56 = __ tens and __ ones; 329 = __ hundreds, __ tens, and __ ones; etc.).

16. Teach your child the concept of filling each column and moving on to the next column from ones to tens, hundreds, thousands, etc.

17. Talk to your child's teacher about developing a marked column format on a master which can be copied for your child to use in solving all math problems (e.g., | thousands | hundreds | tens | ones |).

18. Require your child to check all of his/her math assignments for accuracy. Reinforce your child for each correction made in the use of columns.

19. Make certain your child knows why he/she is learning a math concept. Provide your child with concrete examples and opportunities to apply these concepts in real-life situations.

20. Have your child talk through math problems as he/she is solving them in order to identify errors that are being made.

21. Provide practice of using columns in math by using a computer software program that gives your child immediate feedback.

176 Fails to correctly solve math problems requiring addition

1. Reward your child for correctly solving addition problems. Possible rewards include verbal praise (e.g., "You did a great job of solving your addition problems."), having a friend over to play, staying up late, watching a favorite TV show, and playing a game with a parent. (See Appendix for Reward Menu.)

2. Provide your child with a quiet place to work (e.g., "office," desk, etc.). This is used as a means of reducing distracting stimuli and not as a form of punishment.

3. Reduce the emphasis on competition. Competitive activities may cause your child to hurry and solve addition problems incorrectly.

4. Have your child solve addition problems by manipulating objects and stating the process(es) used.

5. Discuss and provide your child with a list of words/phrases which indicate an addition operation in word problems (e.g., together, altogether, sum, in all, both, gained, received, total, saved, etc.).

6. Have a sibling or a friend act as a model for your child to demonstrate how to solve addition problems.

7. Evaluate the appropriateness of the task to determine: (a) if the task is too difficult, and (b) if the length of time scheduled to complete the task is appropriate.

8. Provide your child with many concrete experiences to help him/her learn and remember math facts. Use popsicle sticks, tongue depressors, paper clips, buttons, fingers, etc., to form groupings to teach addition facts.

9. Have your child use a calculator to reinforce learning addition. Have your child solve several problems each day using a calculator.

10. Provide practice of addition facts using a computer with software programs that give immediate feedback to your child.

11. Use daily drill activities to help your child memorize addition facts (e.g., written problems, flash cards, etc.).

12. Have your child use a calculator for drill activities of basic addition facts.

13. Have your child use a number line (e.g., a line of numbers, 1, 2, 3, 4, 5, 6, 7, 8, 9, 10, 11, 12, 13, 14, 15, 16, 17, 18, 19, 20) to solve addition problems.

14. Find opportunities for your child to apply addition facts to real-life situations (e.g., getting change in a restaurant, measuring the length of objects, etc.).

15. Have your child perform timed drills in addition in order to reinforce basic math facts. Your child "competes" against his/her own best time.

16. Develop math facts reference sheets for addition for your child to use when solving math problems.

17. Have your child solve half of his/her problems each day and use the calculator as reinforcement to complete the other half of the assignment.

18. Make certain your child understands number concepts and the relationships of numbers of objects before requiring him/her to solve math problems requiring addition.

19. Make certain your child knows the concepts of *more than*, *less than*, *equal*, and *zero*. The use of tangible objects will facilitate the learning process.

20. Have your child make sets of objects and add the sets together to obtain a sum total.

21. Provide your child with opportunities for tutoring from siblings or friends. Allow your child to tutor others when he/she has mastered a concept.

22. Reinforce your child for attempting math assignments. Emphasize the number correct, then encourage him/her to see how many more he/she can correct without help. Have your child maintain a personal chart of math performance.

23. Provide your child with enjoyable math activities (e.g., computer games, math games, manipulatives, etc.).

24. Make certain that the language used to communicate with your child about addition is consistent (e.g., ''Add the numbers.'' ''What is the total?'' or ''Find the sum.'').

25. Have your child recheck all math work. Reinforce your child for each error he/she corrects.

26. Provide your child with shorter math homework tasks, but give more of them throughout the evening (e.g., four problems given three times a night, etc.).

27. Work the first problem or two of the math homework assignment with your child in order to make certain that your child understands directions and the operation necessary to solve the problems.

28. Teach your child to use resources in the environment to help him/her solve problems (e.g., counting numbers of objects, using a calculator, etc.).

29. Have your child talk through the math problems as he/she solves them in order to identify errors your child is making.

30. Have your child add numbers of objects. Have your child then pair number symbols with the numbers of objects while he/she performs simple addition problems. Gradually remove the objects as your child demonstrates success in solving simple addition problems.

31. Make certain your child knows why he/she is learning a math concept. Provide your child with concrete examples and opportunities to apply the concept in real-life situations.

32. Make certain your child is not required to learn more information than he/she is capable of at any one time.

33. Have your child act as a tutor to teach a younger brother/sister, friend, etc., a concept he/she has mastered. This can serve as reinforcement for your child.

34. Make certain your child has mastery of math concepts at each level before introducing a new skill level.

35. Make certain that all directions, questions, explanations, and instructions are delivered in a clear and concise manner and at an appropriate pace for your child.

177 Fails to correctly solve math problems requiring subtraction

1. Reward your child for correctly solving math problems involving subtraction. Possible rewards include verbal praise (e.g., "You did a great job of solving your subtraction problems."), having a friend over to play, staying up late, watching a favorite TV show, and playing a game with a parent. (See Appendix for Reward Menu.)

2. Provide your child with a quiet place to work (e.g., "office," desk, etc.). This is used as a means of reducing distracting stimuli and not as a form of punishment.

3. Reduce the emphasis on competition. Competitive activities may cause your child to hurry and do subtraction problems incorrectly.

4. Have your child solve math problems by manipulating objects and stating the process(es) used.

5. Discuss words and phrases which usually indicate subtraction operations (e.g., *difference, between, from, left, how many more or less, how much taller, how much farther,* etc.).

6. Have a sibling or a friend act as a model for your child to demonstrate how to solve subtraction problems.

7. Evaluate the appropriateness of the task to determine: (a) if the task is too difficult, and (b) if the length of time scheduled to complete the task is appropriate.

8. Provide your child with many concrete experiences to help him/her learn and remember math facts. Use popsicle sticks, paper clips, fingers, etc., to form groupings to teach subtraction facts.

9. Have your child use a calculator to reinforce learning subtraction. Have your child solve several problems each day using a calculator.

10. Provide practice of subtraction facts using a computer with software programs that give immediate feedback for your child.

11. Use daily drill activities to help your child memorize subtraction facts (e.g., written problems, flash cards, etc.).

12. Have your child perform timed drills in subtraction to reinforce basic math facts. The student "competes" against his/her own best time.

13. Have your child use a number line (e.g., a line of numbers, 1, 2, 3, 4, 5, 6, 7, 8, 9, 10, 11, 12, 13, 14, 15, 16, 17, 18, 19, 20) to solve subtraction problems.

14. Have your child use a calculator for drill activities of basic subtraction facts.

15. Find opportunities for your child to apply subtraction facts to real-life situations (e.g., getting change in a restaurant, measuring the length of objects, etc.).

16. Have your child solve half his/her subtraction problems each day and use a calculator as reinforcement to solve the rest of the problems.

17. Make certain your child understands number concepts and the relationships of number symbols to numbers of objects before requiring your child to solve math problems requiring subtraction.

18. Make certain your child knows the concepts of *more than, less than, equal, zero,* etc. The use of tangible objects will facilitate the learning process.

19. Provide your child with opportunities for tutoring from siblings and friends. Allow your child to tutor others when he/she has mastered a concept.

20. Reinforce your child for attempting and completing work. Emphasize the number correct, then encourage your child to see how many more he/she can correct without help. Have your child maintain a personal "chart" of math performance.

21. Provide your child with enjoyable math activities (e.g., computer games, math games, manipulatives, etc.).

22. Make certain that the language used to communicate with your child about subtraction is consistent (e.g., "Subtract the numbers." "What is the difference?" etc.).

23. Have your child check all math work. Reinforce your child for each error corrected.

24. Make certain your child has mastery of math concepts at each level before introducing a new skill level.

25. Provide your child with shorter math assignments, but give more of them throughout the evening (e.g., four problems given three times throughout the evening, etc.).

26. Work the first problem or two of the math homework assignment with your child in order to make certain that he/she understands the directions and the math operation necessary to do the problems.

27. Teach your child to use resources in the environment to help him/her solve math problems (e.g., counting numbers of objects, using a calculator, etc.).

28. Have your child talk through math problems as he/she solves them in order to identify errors that are made.

29. Have your child subtract numbers of objects. Have your child then pair number symbols with the number of objects while he/she performs simple subtraction problems. Gradually remove the objects as your child demonstrates success in solving simple subtraction problems.

30. Require that your child check subtraction problems by adding (i.e., the difference plus the subtrahend equals the minuend). Reinforce your child for each error he/she corrects.

31. Make certain your child learns the concept of take away (e.g., "You have 3 toys and I take away 2 of them. How many do you have left?").

32. Make certain your child knows why he/she is learning a math concept. Provide your child with concrete examples and opportunities to apply these concepts in real-life situations.

33. Make certain your child is not required to learn more information than he/she is capable of at any one time.

34. Make certain that all directions, questions, explanations, and instructions are delivered in the most clear and concise manner and at an appropriate pace for your child.

178 Fails to correctly solve math problems requiring multiplication

1. Reward your child for correctly solving math problems requiring multiplication. Possible rewards include verbal praise (e.g., ''I like the way you solved your multiplication problems.''), a kiss on the cheek, a hug, having a friend over to play, staying up late, watching a favorite TV show, and playing a game with a parent. (See Appendix for Reward Menu.)

2. Provide your child with a quiet place to work (e.g., ''office,'' desk, etc.). This is used as a means of reducing distracting stimuli and not as a form of punishment.

3. Reduce the emphasis on competition. Competitive activities may cause your child to hurry and do multiplication problems incorrectly.

4. Have your child solve math word problems by manipulating objects and stating the process(es) involved.

5. Discuss words/phrases which usually indicate a multiplication operation (e.g., area, each, times, product, double, triple, twice, etc.).

6. Have a sibling or a friend act as a model for your child to demonstrate how to solve multiplication problems.

7. Evaluate the appropriateness of the task to determine: (a) if the task is too difficult, and (b) if the length of time scheduled for the task is appropriate.

8. Provide your child with many concrete experiences to help in learning and remembering math facts. Use popsicle sticks, tongue depressors, paper clips, buttons, fingers, etc., to form groupings to teach multiplication facts.

9. Have your child use a calculator to reinforce learning multiplication facts. Have your child solve several multiplication problems each day using a calculator.

10. Provide practice on multiplication facts using a computer with software programs that give immediate feedback for your child.

11. Use daily drill activities to help your child memorize multiplication facts (e.g., written problems, flash cards, etc.).

12. Have your child perform timed drills in multiplication to reinforce basic math facts. Your child ''competes'' against his/her own best time.

13. Have your child use a calculator for drill activities of basic multiplication facts.

14. Develop a math facts reference sheet for multiplication for your child to use when solving multiplication problems.

15. Have your child solve half of his/her multiplication problems and use the calculator as reinforcement to complete the other half of the assignment.

16. Make certain your child understands number concepts and the relationship of number symbols to numbers of objects before requiring your child to solve math problems requiring multiplication.

17. Provide your child with opportunities for tutoring from siblings or friends. Allow your child to tutor others when he/she has mastered a concept.

18. Reinforce your child for attempting and completing work. Emphasize the number correct, then encourage your child to see how many he/she can correct without help. Have your child maintain a personal chart of math performance.

19. Provide your child with enjoyable math activities (e.g., computer games, math games, manipulatives, etc.).

20. Have your child recheck all math work. Reinforce your child for each error corrected.

21. Provide your child with shorter math homework assignments throughout the evening (e.g., four problems given several times throughout the evening, etc.).

22. Work the first problem or two of the math homework assignment with your child in order to make certain that your child understands the directions and the operation necessary to solve the problems.

23. Teach your child to use resources in the environment to help in solving math problems (e.g., counting figures, counting numbers of objects, using a calculator, etc.).

24. Have your child talk through the math problems while solving them in order that you can identify errors he/she is making.

25. Make certain your child understands that multiplication is a quick way of adding, by giving him/her examples of how much longer it takes to add than to multiply.

26. Practice skip counting with 2's, 3's, and 5's.

27. Have your child count by equal distances on a number line. Demonstrate that the equal distances represent skip counting or equal addition which is the concept of multiplication.

28. Teach your child the identity element of one. Any number times one is always that number.

29. Have your child practice the multiplication tables each day with a brother/sister or a friend using flash cards.

30. Identify specific multiplication problems your child fails to correctly solve, and target these problems for additional instruction and time to be spent in tutoring and drill activities.

31. Make certain your child knows why he/she is learning a math concept. Provide your child with concrete examples and opportunities to apply these concepts in real-life situations.

32. Make certain your child is not required to learn more information than he/she is capable of at any one time.

33. Make certain that all directions, questions, explanations, and instructions are delivered in a clear and concise manner and at an appropriate pace for your child.

179 Fails to correctly solve math problems requiring division

1. Reward your child for correctly solving math problems requiring division. Possible rewards include verbal praise (e.g., "You did a great job of solving your division problems."), a kiss on the cheek, a hug, having a friend over to play, staying up late, watching a favorite TV show, and playing a game with a parent. (See Appendix for Reward Menu.)

2. Provide your child with a quiet place to work (e.g., "office," desk, etc.). This is used as a means of reducing distracting stimuli and not as a form of punishment.

3. Reduce the emphasis on competition. Competitive activities may cause your child to hurry and solve division problems incorrectly.

4. Have your child solve division problems by manipulating objects and stating the process(es) used.

5. Discuss words and phrases which usually indicate a division operation (e.g., *into*, *share*, *each*, *average*, *quotient*, *half as many*, etc.).

6. Have a sibling or a friend act as a model for your child to demonstrate how to solve division problems.

7. Evaluate the appropriateness of the task to determine: (a) if the task is too difficult, and (b) if the length of time scheduled for the task is appropriate.

8. Provide your child with many concrete experiences to help in remembering math facts. Use popsicle sticks, tongue depressors, paper clips, buttons, fingers, etc., to form groupings to teach division facts.

9. Have your child use a calculator to reinforce learning division. Have your child solve several problems each day using a calculator.

10. Provide practice of division facts using a computer with software programs that give immediate feedback to your child.

11. Use daily drill activities to help your child reinforce basic math facts. Your child "competes" against his/her own best time.

12. Have your child use a calculator for drill activities of basic division facts.

13. Use daily drill activities to help your child memorize division facts (e.g., written problems, flash cards, etc.).

14. Find opportunities for your child to apply division facts to real-life situations (e.g., money, average length of time it takes to do a job, etc.).

15. Develop math fact reference sheets for division for your child to use in solving division problems.

16. Have your child independently solve half of his/her homework problems each evening and use a calculator as reinforcement to complete the other half of the problems.

17. Make certain your child understands number concepts and the relationship of number symbols to numbers of objects before requiring your child to solve math problems requiring division.

18. Make certain that your child knows the concepts of *more than*, *less than*, *equal*, and *zero*. The use of tangible objects will facilitate the learning process.

19. Give your child several objects (e.g., one inch cubes, connecting links, etc.) and have him/her divide them into groups.

20. Provide your child with opportunities for tutoring from a sibling or friend. Allow your child to tutor others when he/she has mastered a concept.

21. Reinforce your child for attempting and completing work. Emphasize the number correct, then encourage your child to see how many more he/she can correct without help. Have your child maintain a personal chart of math performance.

22. Provide your child with enjoyable math activities (e.g., computer games, math games, manipulatives, etc.).

23. Make certain that the language used to communicate with your child about division is consistent (e.g., "Divide the numbers." "What is the divisor?" "What is the dividend?" etc.).

24. Have your child recheck all math work. Reinforce your child for each error corrected.

25. Make certain your child has mastery of math concepts at each level before introducing a new skill level.

26. Provide your child with shorter math tasks throughout the evening (e.g., four homework problems given several times throughout the evening, etc.).

27. Work the first problem or two of the homework assignment with your child in order to make certain that he/she understands the directions and the operations necessary to solve the problems.

28. Teach your child to use resources in the environment to help him/her solve math problems (e.g., counting figures, counting numbers of objects, using a calculator, etc.).

29. Have your child talk through math problems as he/she solves them in order to identify errors your child is making.

30. Have your child learn to divide numbers of objects. Then have your child pair number symbols with the number of objects while solving simple division problems. Gradually remove the objects as your child demonstrates success in solving simple division problems.

31. Teach your child the identity element of one. Any number divided by one is always that number.

32. Have your child practice the division tables each day with a brother/sister or a friend using flash cards.

33. Identify specific division problems your child fails to correctly solve and target problems for additional instruction and time to be spent in tutoring and drill activities.

34. Make certain your child knows why he/she is learning a math concept. Provide your child with concrete examples and opportunities to apply the concept in real-life situations.

35. Make certain your child is not required to learn more information than he/she is capable of at any one time.

36. Make certain that all directions, questions, explanations, and instructions are delivered in a clear and concise manner and at an appropriate pace for your child.

180 Fails to correctly solve math problems requiring regrouping (e.g., borrowing and carrying)

1. Reward your child for correctly solving math problems requiring regrouping. Possible rewards include verbal praise (e.g., "You did a good job of solving your math problems that required regrouping."), a kiss on the cheek, a hug, having a friend over to play, staying up late, watching a favorite TV show, and playing a game with a parent. (See Appendix for Reward Menu.)

2. Reduce the emphasis on competition. Competitive activities may cause your child to hurry and make mistakes in regrouping.

3. Have your child solve math problems by manipulating objects to experience regrouping.

4. Have a sibling or a friend act as a model for your child and demonstrate how to correctly solve math problems that require regrouping.

5. Evaluate the appropriateness of the task to determine if your child has mastered the skills needed for regrouping.

6. Provide your child with many concrete experiences to help your child learn and remember regrouping skills. Use popsicle sticks, tongue depressors, paper clips, buttons, base 10 blocks, etc., to form groups to teach regrouping.

7. Provide practice in regrouping using a computer software program that gives immediate feedback to your child.

8. Use daily drill activities to help your child with regrouping (e.g., written problems, flash cards, etc.).

9. Have your child perform timed drills to reinforce regrouping. Your child "competes" against his/her own best time and score.

10. Find opportunities for your child to apply regrouping to real-life situations (e.g., getting change in a restaurant, figuring how much items cost when added together while shopping, etc.).

11. Develop a regrouping reference sheet for your child to use when solving math problems which require regrouping.

12. Have your child solve half of his/her math problems each day and use the calculator as reinforcement to complete the other half of the math assignment.

13. Make certain your child understands number concepts and the relationship of number symbols to numbers of objects before requiring him/her to solve math problems requiring regrouping.

14. Make certain your child knows the concepts of *more than*, *less than*, *equal*, and *zero*. The use of tangible objects will facilitate the learning process.

15. Have your child practice the concept of regrouping by "borrowing" and "carrying" from objects in columns set up like math problems.

16. Provide your child with opportunities for tutoring from a sibling or friend. Allow your child to tutor others when he/she has mastered a concept.

17. Reinforce your child for attempting and completing work. Emphasize the number correct, then encourage him/her to see how many more your child can correct without help. Have your child maintain a personal chart of math performance.

18. Provide your child with a few problems several times throughout the evening (e.g., four homework problems given three times a night, etc.).

19. Work the first problem or two of the math homework assignment with your child in order to make certain that your child understands the directions and the operation necessary to solve the problems.

20. Have your child talk through math problems as he/she solves them in order to identify errors that are being made.

21. Require your child to check subtraction problems by adding (i.e., the difference plus the subtrahend equals the minuend). Reinforce your child for each error corrected.

22. Make certain your child has a number line (e.g., a line of numbers, 1, 2, 3, 4, 5, 6, 7, 8, 9, 10, 11, 12, 13, 14, 15, 16, 17, 18, 19, 20) to use as a reference.

23. Have your child talk through math problems while solving them in order that you can identify errors he/she is making.

24. Have your child check his/her math assignments using a calculator. The calculator can also be used to reinforce the learning of math facts.

25. Use manipulative objects (e.g., base 10 blocks) to teach your child regrouping.

26. Develop a math reference sheet for your child to keep with him/her (e.g., steps used in doing subtraction problems, addition problems, etc.).

27. Make certain your child understands the concept of place value and that problems move right to left beginning with the ones column.

28. Make certain your child is not required to learn more information than he/she is capable of at any one time.

29. Make certain your child has mastery of math concepts at each level before introducing a new skill level.

181 Works math problems from left to right instead of right to left

1. Reward your child for working math problems from right to left. Possible rewards include verbal praise (e.g.,"You did a great job of solving your math problems."), a kiss on the cheek, a hug, staying up late, watching a favorite TV show, and playing a game with a parent. (See Appendix for Reward Menu.)

2. Reduce the emphasis on competition. Competitive activities may cause your child to hurry and make mistakes in math problems.

3. Have a brother/sister or a friend work with your child each day on working math problems from right to left.

4. Develop a math reference sheet for your child (e.g., steps used in doing addition problems, subtraction problems, multiplication problems, division problems).

5. Have your child check math assignments using a calculator.

6. Use large colored arrows to indicate where your child should begin to work math problems (e.g., right to left).

7. Work the first problems for your child as he/she watches, in order to provide demonstration and set an example.

8. Put your child's math problems on graph paper or vertically lined paper to emphasize columns, with directions to begin each problem at the right.

9. Make certain your child has mastered place value concepts and understands that columns to the left are higher values than those to the right.

10. Require your child to solve math problems by place value (e.g., begin with the ones column, the tens column, hundreds column, etc.).

11. Have your child use a calculator to solve math problems.

12. Speak to your child to explain: (a) what he/she is doing wrong (e.g., working math problems from left to right) and (b) what he/she should be doing (e.g., working math problems from right to left).

13. Write the place value above each math problem in order to remind your child to begin with the ones column to solve the problems.

14. Display a large poster with a message that indicates reading begins to the left and math problems begin on the right (e.g., READING BEGINS ON THE LEFT. MATH BEGINS ON THE RIGHT.).

15. Make certain your child has a number line (e.g., a list of numbers, 1, 2, 3, 4, 5, 6, 7, 8, 9, 10, 11, 12, 13, 14, 15, 16, 17, 18, 19, 20) to use as a reference.

16. Make certain your child knows why he/she is learning a math concept. Provide your child with concrete examples and opportunities to apply these concepts in real-life situations.

17. Have your child talk through math problems while solving them in order to identify errors your child is making.

18. Recognize quality work (e.g., display your child's work, congratulate your child, etc.).

19. Provide practice in math using a computer software program that gives your child immediate feedback.

20. Make certain your child has mastery of math concepts at each level before introducing a new skill level.

21. Reduce the amount of information on a page if it is causing visual distractions for your child (e.g., fewer math problems, less print, etc.).

182 Fails to follow necessary steps in math problems

1. Reward your child for following the necessary steps when solving math problems. Possible rewards include verbal praise (e.g., ''You did a nice job on your math homework problems tonight.''), a kiss on the cheek, a hug, having a friend over to play, staying up late, watching a favorite TV show, and playing a game with a parent. (See Appendix for Reward Menu.)

2. Evaluate the appropriateness of the task to determine: (a) if the task is too difficult and (b) if the length of time scheduled for the task is appropriate.

3. Reduce the emphasis on competition. Competitive activities may cause your child to hurry and fail to follow necessary steps in math problems.

4. Make certain that your child recognizes all math operation symbols (e.g., ×, -, +, ÷).

5. Use written reminders beside math problems to indicate which step is to be done. Gradually reduce the use of reminders as your child demonstrates success.

6. Put all math problems involving the same steps on a single line, on a separate piece of paper, etc.

7. Make the math operation symbols next to math problems extra large in order that your child will be more likely to observe the symbol.

8. Color code math operation symbols next to the problems in order that your child will be more likely to observe the symbol.

9. Work the first problem or two of a math homework assignment for your child in order that he/she will know what steps to use.

10. Use a separate piece of paper for each type of math problem, gradually introducing different types of problems on the same page.

11. Provide your child with a list of steps necessary for the problems your child is attempting to solve. Have your child keep a list as a reference while solving math problems.

12. List the steps in solving math problems on your child's bulletin board, on a poster, etc.

13. Have a brother/sister or a friend work with your child while he/she learns to follow the steps in math problems.

14. Have your child check his/her answers to math problems on a calculator.

15. Have your child act as a tutor for a younger brother/sister or friend who is learning new math concepts. Explaining steps in basic math problems will help your child cement his/her own skills.

16. Have your child equate math problems to real-life situations in order that he/she will better understand the steps involved in solving the problems (e.g., 4×25 is the same as 4 baskets of apples with 25 apples in each basket. How many apples do you have?).

17. Make certain your child has a number line (e.g., a list of numbers, 1, 2, 3, 4, 5, 6, 7, 8, 9, 10, 11, 12, 13, 14, 15, 16, 17, 18, 19, 20) to use as a reference.

18. Have your child talk through math problems as he/she is solving them in order to identify errors your child is making.

19. Develop a math reference sheet for your child to use (e.g., steps used in doing subtraction, multiplication, addition, and division problems).

20. Have your child check his/her math homework assignments using a calculator. The calculator can also be used to reinforce the learning of math facts.

21. Use vertical lines or graph paper in math to help your child keep math problems in correct order.

22. Make certain your child is not required to learn more information than he/she is capable of at any one time.

23. Provide practice in math using a computer software program that gives your child immediate feedback.

24. Make certain your child has mastery of math concepts at each level before introducing a new skill level.

25. Reduce the amount of information on a page if it is causing visual distractions for your child (e.g., fewer problems on a page, less print, etc.).

1. Make certain that your child's inability to read is not the cause of his/her difficulty solving math word problems.

2. Reward your child for correctly solving math word problems. Possible rewards include verbal praise (e.g., "I like the way you solved all of your math word problems."), a kiss on the cheek, a hug, having a friend over to play, staying up late, watching a favorite TV show, and playing a game with a parent. (See Appendix for Reward Menu.)

3. Have your child question any directions, explanations, or instructions not understood.

4. Provide your child with a quiet place to work (e.g., "office," desk, etc.). This is used as a means of reducing distracting stimuli and not as a form of punishment.

5. Reduce the emphasis on competition. Competitive activities may cause your child to hurry and solve math word problems incorrectly.

6. Have your child read the math word problems first silently and then aloud and identify the mathematical operation required.

7. Work math word problems that require a one-step process with your child, making certain that the sentences are short and concise.

8. Teach your child to look for "clue" or "key" words in word problems that indicate mathematical operations.

9. Have your child orally analyze the steps that are required to solve word problems (e.g., "What is given?" "What is asked?" "What operation(s) are used?" etc.).

10. Represent the numerical amounts, in concrete forms, that are presented in the word problems (e.g., problems involving money can be represented by providing your child with the appropriate amount of real or play money).

11. Have your child write a number sentence (e.g., 4 + 3 = 7) after reading a math word problem. This process will help your child see the numerical operation prior to finding the answer.

12. Have your child create word problems for number sentences. Place the number sentence on a piece of paper and have your child tell or write word problems that could be solved by the number sentences (e.g., 4 + 3 = 7: four apples and three apples equals seven apples).

13. Have your child restate math word problems in his/her own words.

14. Ask your child to identify the primary question that must be answered to solve the given word problem. Continue this activity using more difficult word problems containing two or more questions. Make sure your child understands that questions are often implied rather than directly asked.

15. Have your child make up his/her own word problems. Direct your child to write problems involving specific operations. Brother/sister, friends, parents, etc., could solve the word problems. Your child can also provide answers to his/her own problems.

16. Supplement your child's textbook problems with self-made problems. These problems can deal with everyday experiences. Include your child's name in the word problems to make them more realistic and meaningful to your child.

17. Use word problems that are of interest to your child and related to his/her experiences.

18. Make certain your child reads through the entire word problem before attempting to solve it.

19. Teach your child to break down each math word problem into specific steps.

20. Have your child make notes to "set the problem up" in written form as he/she reads the math word problem.

21. Have your child simulate situations which relate to math word problems (e.g., trading, selling, buying, etc.).

22. Have your child solve math word problems by manipulating objects and stating the process(es) used.

23. Help your child recognize common patterns in math word problems (e.g., how many, add or subtract, etc.).

24. Discuss words/phrases which usually indicate a subtraction operation (e.g., *difference between, from, left, how many more or less, how much taller, farther, heavier, withdrawal, spend, lost, remain, more*, etc.).

25. Discuss words/phrases which usually indicate a division operation (e.g., *into, share, each, average, monthly, daily, weekly, yearly, quotient, half as many*, etc.).

26. Discuss and provide your child with a list of words/phrases which usually indicate an addition operation (e.g., *together, altogether, sum, in all, both, gained, received, total, won, saved*, etc.).

27. Discuss words/phrases which usually indicate a multiplication operation (e.g., area, each, times, product, double, triple, twice, etc.).

28. Teach your child to convert words into their numerical equivalents to solve word problems (e.g., two weeks = 14 days, one-third = ⅓, one year = 12 months, one quarter = 25 cents, one yard = 36 inches, etc.).

29. Allow your child to use a calculator when solving math word problems.

30. Require your child to read math word problems at least twice before beginning to solve them.

31. Have your child begin solving basic word problems which combine a math problem and word problems such as:

$$\begin{array}{r} 7 \text{ apples} \\ \text{and} \quad 3 \text{ apples} \\ \hline \text{equals } 10 \text{ apples} \end{array}$$

Gradually change the problems to math word problems as your child demonstrate success.

32. Before introducing completed word problems, present your child with phrases to be translated to numbers (e.g., six less than ten equals 10 - 6).

33. Have a brother/sister or a friend act as a model for your child to demonstrate how to solve math word problems.

34. Talk to your child's teacher to reduce the number of assigned problems given to your child at one time (e.g., 5 problems instead of 10, etc.).

35. Demonstrate for your child how to solve word problems by reading the problem and solving the problem on paper step-by-step.

36. Speak with your child to explain: (a) what he/she is doing wrong (e.g., using the wrong operation, failing to read the problem carefully, etc.) and (b) what he/she should be doing (e.g., using the appropriate operation, reading the problem carefully, etc.).

37. Evaluate the appropriateness of the task to determine: (a) if the task is too difficult and (b) if the length of time scheduled to complete the task is appropriate.

38. Correlate word problems with computation procedures just learned at school (e.g., multiplication, operations with multiplication word problems, etc.).

39. Teach your child the meaning of mathematical terms (e.g., sum, dividend, etc.). Frequently review the terms and their meanings.

40. Highlight or underline key words in math word problems (e.g., references to the operation involved, etc.).

41. Provide your child with a checklist to follow in solving math word problems (e.g., what information is given, what question is asked, what operation(s) is used).

42. Make certain your child has a number line (e.g., a line of numbers, 1, 2, 3, 4, 5, 6, 7, 8, 9, 10, 11, 12, 13, 14, 15, 16, 17, 18, 19, 20) to use as a reference.

43. Make certain your child knows why he/she is learning to solve math word problems. Provide your child with concrete examples and opportunities to apply these concepts in real-life situations.

44. Have your child talk through math word problems as he/she is solving them in order to identify errors your child is making.

45. Develop a math reference sheet for your child (e.g., steps used in doing subtraction, multiplication, addition, and division problems).

46. Have your child check his/her word problems using a calculator. The calculator can also be used to reinforce the learning of math facts.

47. Make certain your child knows the concepts of *more than*, *less than*, *equal*, and *zero*. The use of tangible objects will facilitate the learning process.

48. Recognize quality work (e.g., display your child's work, congratulate your child, etc.).

49. Make certain your child is not required to learn more information than he/she is capable of at any one time.

50. Have your child act as a tutor to teach a brother/sister, friend, etc., a math concept he/she has mastered. This can serve as reinforcement for your child.

51. Provide practice in solving math word problems using a computer software program that gives your child immediate feedback.

52. Make certain your child has mastery of math concepts at each level before introducing a new skill level.

53. Have your child manipulate objects (e.g., apples, oranges, toy cars, toy airplanes, etc.) as you describe the operation.

184 Fails to form letters correctly when printing or writing

1. Reward your child for making correct letters. Possible rewards include verbal praise (e.g., "Your handwriting is beautiful."), a kiss on the cheek, a hug, having a friend over to play, staying up late, watching a favorite TV show, and playing a game with a parent. (See Appendix for Reward Menu.)

2. Evaluate the appropriateness of the task to determine: (a) if the task is too difficult and (b) if the length of time scheduled to complete the task is appropriate.

3. Check your child's posture. Have your child sit erect in an appropriately sized chair with feet touching the floor, his/her back pressed against the back of the chair, shoulders slightly inclined, arms resting comfortably on the desk, and elbows just off the lower edge of the desk.

4. Check your child's writing position. A right-handed person writing in cursive should tilt the paper to the left so the lower left-hand corner points toward the midsection. As writing progresses the paper should shift, not the writing arm.

5. Check your child's grasp. The pencil should be between the thumb and first two fingers, holding the instrument one inch from its tip.

6. Provide your child with an alphabet strip with letters of the same size as he/she is to use.

7. Write the letters on your child's paper and have him/her trace them.

8. Make certain your child is instructed in each letter formation, giving your child oral as well as physical descriptions and demonstrations.

9. Provide your child with physical prompts by moving your child's hand, giving him/her a feeling of directionality.

10. Use arrows to show your child directionality when tracing or using dot-to-dot to form letters.

11. Use color cues for lines (e.g., red for the top line, yellow for the middle line, green for the bottom line) to indicate where letters are to be made.

12. Draw simple shapes and lines for your child to practice forming on lined paper.

13. Highlight the base line or top line on the paper in order to help your child stay within the given spaces.

14. Write the complete letters and have your child trace them. Gradually provide less of the letters for your child to trace (e.g., dashes, then dots) as he/she is successful.

15. Identify those letters your child does not form correctly. Have your child practice the correct form of one or more of the letters each day.

16. To facilitate appropriate holding of a pencil, put colored tape on parts of the pencil to correspond to finger positions. Then put colored tape on your child's fingernails and have your child match colors.

17. Reduce the emphasis on competition. Competitive activities may cause your child to hurry and fail to form letters correctly.

18. Have a brother/sister or a friend act as a model for your child by working daily on drill activities involving letter formation, ending and connecting strokes, spacing, and slant.

19. Have your child practice forming letters correctly using writing activities which are most likely to cause your child to want to be successful (e.g., writing a letter to a friend, rock star or famous athlete; filling out a job application or contest form; etc.).

20. Recognize quality work (e.g., display your child's work, congratulate your child, etc.).

21. Provide your child with quality materials to perform the assignment (e.g., pencil with eraser, paper, handwriting sample, etc.). Be certain that your child has only the necessary materials.

22. Make certain your child has mastery of handwriting concepts at each level before introducing a new skill level.

23. Check your child's handwriting work at various points throughout a handwriting activity to make certain that your child is forming letters correctly.

24. Make certain your child is not required to learn more information than he/she is capable of at any one time.

25. Have your child practice forming letters correctly by tracing over a series of dots.

26. Make certain your child has an alphabet strip to use as a reference.

27. Require your child to proofread all written work. Reinforce your child for each correction made.

185 Uses inappropriate letter size when writing

1. Make certain your child's vision has been checked recently.

2. Reward your child for using appropriate letter size when writing. Possible rewards include verbal praise (e.g., "Your handwriting is beautiful."), a kiss on the cheek, a hug, having a friend over to play, staying up late, watching a favorite TV show, and playing a game with a parent. (See Appendix for Reward Menu.)

3. Evaluate the appropriateness of the task to determine: (a) if the task is too difficult and (b) if the length of the time scheduled to complete the task is appropriate.

4. Check your child's posture. Have your child sit erect in an appropriate sized chair with feet touching the floor, his/her back pressed against the back of the chair, shoulders slightly inclined, arms resting comfortably on the desk, and elbows just off the lower edge of the desk.

5. Check your child's paper position. A right-handed person writing in cursive should tilt the paper to the left so the lower left-hand corner points toward the midsection. As writing progresses the paper should shift, not the writing arm.

6. Check your child's grasp. The pencil should be between the thumb and first two fingers, holding the instrument one inch from its tip.

7. Use paper that has a midline and a descender space.

8. Have your child identify maximum letters (b, d, f, h, k, l,), intermediate letters (t), and minimum letters (a, c, e, g, i, j, m, n, o, p, q, r, s, u, v, w, x, y, z) in order to help your child locate the correct placement of each group.

9. Make certain your child is shifting his/her paper as writing progresses.

10. Provide your child with quality materials to perform the assignment (e.g., pencil with eraser, paper, dictionary, handwriting sample, etc.). Be certain that your child has only the necessary materials.

11. Evaluate writing for alignment by drawing a horizontal line across the tops of the letters that are to be of the same size.

12. Highlight lines on the paper as a reminder for your child in making correct letter size.

13. Have a brother/sister or a friend act as a model for your child to imitate making letters the appropriate size when writing.

14. Be certain your child has samples of letters of the appropriate size for his/her activities requiring letters.

15. Provide your child with an alphabet strip with letters the same size as he/she is to use.

16. Write letters on your child's paper and have him/her trace them.

17. Write letters on your child's paper in a broken line and have your child connect the lines.

18. Darken the lines on your child's paper which are used for correct letter size.

19. Have your child correct mistakes involving inappropriate letter size.

20. Draw boxes to indicate the size on specific letters in relationship to the line.

21. Using examples written on grid paper, have your child copy the examples beneath them.

22. Using tracing paper, have your child trace over specific letters or words.

23. Using a series of dots, have your child trace words or sentences.

24. Provide your child with clearly stated criteria for acceptable work (e.g., neatness, appropriately sized letters, etc.).

25. Recognize quality work (e.g., display your child's work, congratulate your child, etc.).

26. Make certain your child has mastery of handwriting concepts at each level before introducing a new skill level.

27. Check your child's work at various points throughout the assignment to make certain that your child is making letters the appropriate size.

28. Make certain your child an alphabet strip as a reference.

29. Use vertical lines or graph paper to help your child space letters correctly.

30. Provide your child with a different sized pencil or pencil grip.

186 Reverses letters and numbers when writing

1. Reward your child for making letters and numbers correctly when writing. Possible rewards include verbal praise (e.g., ''Your handwriting homework looks wonderful.''), a kiss on the cheek, a hug, having a friend over to play, staying up late, watching a favorite TV show, and playing a game with a parent. (See Appendix for Reward Menu.)

2. Make certain that your child's formation of letters is appropriate and consistently correct. In manuscript writing, all strokes use a forward circle (e.g., circling to the right) for letters that begin with a line (e.g., *b*), and a backward circle (e.g., circling to the left) for letters in which the circle is written before the line (e.g., *d*).

3. Use poster board activities (e.g., drawing lines, circles, etc.) to teach your child proper directionality for each letter or numeral.

4. Physically guide your child's hand, providing a feeling of directionality.

5. Have your child trace letters and numbers in magazines, newspapers, etc., which he/she typically reverses when writing.

6. Use direction arrows to remind your child of correct directionality.

7. Identify the letters and numbers your child reverses and have your child practice making one or more of the letters correctly each day.

8. Make certain your child recognizes the correct form of the letters and numbers when he/she writes them (e.g., *b, d, 2, 5,* etc.).

9. Make certain your child checks all his/her work for those letters and numbers typically reversed. Reinforce your child for correcting any reversed letters and numbers.

10. Provide your child with letters and numbers to trace which he/she typically reverses.

11. Given letters and numbers on separate cards, have your child match the letters and numbers that are the same.

12. Have your child keep a card with the word *bed* to serve as a reminder of the correct form of *b* and *d* in a word he/she knows.

13. Have your child keep a list of the most commonly used words which contain letters he/she reverses. This list can be used as a reference when your child is writing.

14. After identifying those letters and numbers your child reverses, have your child highlight or underline those letters and numbers in a magazine, newspaper, etc.

15. Point out the subtle differences between letters and numbers that your child reverses. Have your child scan five typewritten lines containing only the letters or numbers that are confusing (e.g., nnhnhhnn). Have your child circle the ''n's'' and the ''h's'' with different colors.

16. Cursive handwriting may prevent reversals and may be used as an alternative to manuscript.

17. Make certain your child has a number line and alphabet strip to use as a reference to make the correct forms of letters and numbers.

18. Reduce the emphasis on competition. Competitive activities may cause your child to hurry and reverse numbers and letters when writing.

19. Recognize quality work (e.g., display your child's work, congratulate your child, etc.).

20. Have your child practice writing letters, words, and sentences by tracing over a series of dots.

21. Require your child to proofread all written work. Reinforce your child for each correction made.

22. Have your child engage in writing activities designed to cause your child to want to be successful in writing (e.g., writing a letter to a friend, rock star, famous athlete, etc.).

187 Fails to write within a given space

1. Make certain your child's vision has been recently checked.

2. Reward your child for each word and/or sentence that is appropriately spaced. Possible rewards include verbal praise (e.g., "You did a nice job of spacing your words and letters in your writing assignment."), a kiss on the cheek, a hug, having a friend over to play, staying up late, watching a favorite TV show, or playing a game with a parent. (See Appendix for Reward Menu.)

3. Have your child perform a "practice page" before beginning the actual homework assignment.

4. Have your child look at correctly written material to serve as a model for him/her to imitate.

5. Have your child sit erect in an appropriate sized chair with feet touching the floor, back pressed against the back of the chair, shoulders slightly inclined, arms resting on the desk, and with elbows just off the lower edge of the desk.

6. Check your child's paper position. A right-handed person writing in cursive should tilt the paper to the left so the lower left-hand corner points toward the midsection. As writing progresses the paper should shift, not the writing arm.

7. Place dots between letters and have your child use fingers as a spacer between words.

8. Make certain your child is shifting his/her paper when writing.

9. Using appropriate spacing, print or write words or sentences. Have your child trace what is written.

10. Provide your child with samples of hand-written words and sentences he/she can use as a reference for correct spacing.

11. Reduce the emphasis on competition. Competitive activities may cause your child to hurry and fail to use correct spacing when writing words and sentences.

12. Draw vertical lines for your child to use to space letters and words (e.g., | | | |).

13. Teach your child to always look at the next word to determine if there is enough space to the margin.

14. Provide your child with graph paper, instructing him/her to write letters in each block, while skipping a block between words and sentences.

15. Recognize quality work (e.g., display your child's work, congratulate your child, etc.).

16. Provide your child with quality materials to perform the assignment (e.g., pencil with eraser, paper, dictionary, handwriting sample, etc.). Be certain that your child has only the necessary materials.

17. Check your child's work at various points throughout a writing assignment in order to make certain that your child is writing within a given space.

18. Give your child one handwriting task to perform at a time. Introduce the next task only when your child has successfully completed the previous task.

19. Assign your child shorter writing assignments and gradually increase the length of the assignments as your child demonstrates success.

20. Have your child engage in writing activities designed to cause your child to want to be successful in writing (e.g., writing a letter to a friend, rock star, famous athlete, etc.).

188 Does not copy letters, words, sentences, and numbers from a book, work sheet, etc.

1. Make certain your child's vision has been recently checked.

2. Reward your child for copying letters, words, sentences, and numbers from work sheets, textbooks, etc. Possible rewards include verbal praise (e.g., "I like the way you copied your math problems so neatly."), a kiss on the cheek, a hug, having a friend over to play, watching a favorite TV show, and playing a game with a parent. (See Appendix for Reward Menu.)

3. Evaluate the appropriateness of the task to determine: (a) if the task is too difficult and (b) if the length of time scheduled to complete the task is appropriate.

4. Have your child question any directions, explanations, or instructions not understood.

5. Reduce distracting stimuli (e.g., noise and motion around your child, pictures in the textbook, etc.) in order to enhance your child's ability to copy letters, words, sentences, and numbers.

6. Enlarge the print from which your child is copying.

7. Talk to your child's teacher about changing the format of the material from which your child copies (e.g., have less material to a page, remove or cover pictures on pages, enlarge the print, etc.).

8. Highlight or underline the material your child is to copy.

9. Use a frame or window to cover all material except that which your child is to copy.

10. Have your child copy small amounts of material (e.g., one sentence or line) at a time.

11. Make certain your child's work area is free of all materials except that from which he/she is copying.

12. Provide your child with a private place to work (e.g., a private "office," a quiet desk, etc.). This is used as a means of reducing distracting stimuli and not as a form of punishment.

13. Provide a variety of ways for your child to obtain information without copying it (e.g., commercially produced material, photocopy of the material, self-made material, etc.).

14. Have a brother/sister or a friend assist your child in copying material (e.g., to read the material aloud as your child copies it, copy the material for the student, etc.).

15. Maintain consistency of the format from which your child copies.

16. Identify any particular letters or numbers your child has difficulty copying and have your child practice copying those letters or numbers.

17. Have your child practice writing letters, words, and sentences by tracing over a series of dots.

18. Make certain your child has a number line and alphabet strip to use as a reference for the correct form of letters and numbers in order to reduce errors.

19. Require your child to proofread all written work. Reinforce your child for each correction made.

20. Recognize quality work (e.g., display your child's work, congratulate your child, etc.).

21. Provide your child with quality materials to perform assignments (e.g., pencil with eraser, paper, dictionary, handwriting sample, etc.). Be certain that your child has only the necessary materials on the desk.

22. Reduce the emphasis on competition. Competitive activities may cause your child to hurry and commit any number of errors.

IV. Appendix

IDENTIFYING BEHAVIORS TO BE CHANGED:

CONSIDER...

1. THE BEHAVIOR THAT OCCURS MOST FREQUENTLY.

2. THE BEHAVIOR THAT IS MOST INAPPROPRIATE.

3. THE BEHAVIOR THAT IS THE CAUSE OF OTHER RELATED BEHAVIORS.

One or all of the above approaches may be used to assist you in selecting behaviors to help your child increase appropriate behavior (e.g., doing chores) or decrease inappropriate behavior (e.g., going to bed too late). Your child's perfection need not be the goal, but helping your child become more successful should be the goal.

POSTED RULES

- BE ON TIME FOR DINNER

- PUT AWAY ALL PLAYTHINGS

- BE IN BED BY 9:00 P.M.

- BE READY FOR SCHOOL BY 8:00 A.M.

"Posted Rules" are those behaviors that are of primary importance or are a primary problem. If a behavior is not a problem, such as "Running in the House," then it does not have to be a "Posted Rule." Keep the list of rules short, refer to them often, and "reinforce" the child for following the rules. The "posting" of the rules is as much a reminder for the adults as it is for the child. Find a conspicuous place to post the rules where they can be seen easily and often (e.g., the refrigerator is a good place if it is not already overcrowded with other information).

SAMPLE LIST

1. PUT DIRTY CLOTHES IN CLOTHES HAMPER

2. TAKE A BATH BEFORE BEDTIME

3. BRUSH TEETH

4. GET CLOTHES READY FOR NEXT DAY

5. LISTEN TO A STORY READ BY MOM OR DAD

For those behaviors for which the child needs "reminders," a list such as the one above is developed and placed in the child's room, by the mirror in the bathroom, on the refrigerator or any place where it will easily and frequently be seen by the child. If a behavior like "Putting Dirty Clothes in the Clothes Hamper" is not a problem, then it will not be on the "List."

WEEKDAY SCHEDULE

7:00 AM-	GET UP, WASH FACE, DRESS, MAKE BED
7:25 AM-	EAT BREAKFAST
7:40 AM-	BRUSH TEETH AND HAIR
7:50 AM-	LEAVE FOR BUS STOP
8:30 AM-	BE AT SCHOOL
4:00 PM-	GET HOME AND PLAY OUTSIDE
4:30 PM-	SET TABLE FOR DINNER AND WASH UP
5:00 PM-	EAT DINNER
5:30 PM-	CLEAN UP KITCHEN
6:00 PM-	HOMEWORK
7:00 PM-	WATCH T.V.
7:30 PM-	TAKE BATH AND BRUSH TEETH
8:00 PM-	CHOOSE CLOTHES FOR NEXT DAY AND ORGANIZE BOOKS AND MATERIALS TO TAKE TO SCHOOL
8:30 PM-	BEDTIME

The "Weekday Schedule" is used when "Getting Up on Time," "Catching the Bus," "Doing Homework," "Watching TV," etc., at the appropriate times is a problem. The schedule increases the likelihood that behaviors will occur on time and that "other things" will not destroy the routine that is required for individual and family success. The schedule may be less specific than the sample provided and can be somewhat flexible, but it should improve "getting things done."

SATURDAY SCHEDULE

SATURDAY

7:00 AM –	WAKE UP AND GET DRESSED
7:30 AM –	BREAKFAST
8:00 AM –	CARTOONS
9:30 AM –	SHOPPING
11:45 AM –	LUNCH
12:15 PM –	PLAY WITH FRIENDS
2:45 PM –	SWIMMING CLASS
4:00 PM –	CLEAN-UP CHORES
5:00 PM –	HELP WITH DINNER
5:45 PM –	FAMILY DINNER
6:30 PM –	FAMILY TIME
9:00 PM –	BEDTIME

The "Saturday Schedule" or "Weekend Schedule" is used for the child when "being ready" and "getting things done" on a Saturday or weekend is a problem. By establishing a "schedule" the child, as well as everyone else, knows what is expected; and it increases the likelihood that "must" activities (e.g., meals, shopping, etc.) will take place on time. There is still a lot of time to "have fun." The schedule can be less specific or more specific that the sample and can be as flexible as necessary.

LIST OF CHORES

DAILY

- MAKE YOUR BED
- TAKE DISHES AND SILVERWARE TO THE SINK
- FEED SPOT

WEEKLY

- CLEAN YOUR ROOM
- HELP MOM CLEAN THE HOUSE
  OR
- HELP DAD CLEAN THE GARAGE
- HELP WITH THE LAUNDRY
  - FOLDING
  - PUTTING IN DRAWERS AND CLOSETS

A "List of Chores" is posted as a reminder of what is expected. This assures that everyone "knows" exactly what is to be done, there are not surprises, and other activities can be scheduled.

POINT RECORD

MY BEST BEHAVIOR IS...

_____

DATE	HOW WELL I DID	DATE	HOW WELL I DID

The "Point Record" provides a means of recording the appropriate behavior (e.g., going to bed on time, doing chores, completing homework, etc.) the child accomplishes. The "Point Record" is posted on the refrigerator, kept in a file, or placed wherever is most convenient. The child should be able to see the "Point Record" and know how well he/she is doing. Points are "turned in" for rewards which are determined by the child's preference. (See Reinforcer Survey in this Appendix.)

SAMPLE POINT RECORD

MY BEST BEHAVIOR IS...

GOING TO BED ON TIME

DATE	HOW WELL I DID	DATE	HOW WELL I DID
JAN. 10	OK ✶		
JAN. 11	A LITTLE LATE		
JAN. 12	OK ✶		
JAN. 13	OK ✶		

This sample "Point Record" represents the behavior "Going to Bed on Time." When the child "earns" a reinforcer for which he/she has been working, a new "Point Record" is started for the same behavior. When "Going to Bed on Time" is no longer a problem, a new behavior, such as "Doing Chores," can be substituted.

BEHAVIOR CONTRACT

_____ AGREES TO

_____

_____

EXPECTATION: EVERY TIME _____

_____

_____ WILL EARN 1 POINT.

REINFORCEMENT: WHEN _____

EARNS _____ POINTS HE WILL BE ABLE

TO CHOOSE A REWARD FROM THE REWARD

MENU.

The "Behavior Contract" is one of the most individualized, personalized, and direct strategies designed to increase appropriate behavior and decrease inappropriate behavior.

The "Behavior Contract" should specify:
- Who is involved in the contract
- What behavior is expected (e.g., chores, homework, etc.)
- The amount of behavior that is expected
- How reinforcement is earned
- When reinforcement is earned
- What reinforcement is available

BEHAVIOR CONTRACT

_____William_____ AGREES TO

_____Pick up clothes in his_____

_____room each day_____

EXPECTATION: EVERY TIME _____that_____

_____clothes are picked up_____

_____William_____ WILL EARN 1 POINT.

REINFORCEMENT: WHEN _____William_____

EARNS ___3___ POINTS HE WILL BE ABLE

TO CHOOSE A REWARD FROM THE REWARD

MENU.

The ''Completed Behavior Contract'' represents:
● Who is being reinforced
● What behavior is to be performed
● When the child earns reinforcement
● What reinforcement is available

REWARD MENU

REWARD	COST
• MODEL AIRPLANE	100
• TOY BOAT	90
• MOVIE	80
• HAVE A FRIEND STAY OVER	70
• PLAY MONOPOLY	60
• GO SHOPPING SATURDAY	50
• CANDY BAR	40
• GUM	30
• MAGIC MARKER	20

This sample "Reward Menu" is compiled from information gathered from the child responding to the "Reinforcer Survey" or otherwise indicating what the child would like to earn for improved appropriate behavior. The value of a reward is determined by its importance, size, cost, etc. Be certain to include lower cost as well as higher cost rewards in order that your child can work for a long-range goal, but also have smaller rewards for those times when a lot of points have not been earned.

REINFORCER SURVEY

1. MY FAVORITE THINGS TO DO AROUND THE HOUSE ARE _____

    _____

2. MY FAVORITE TV PROGRAMS ARE_____

    _____

3. MY FAVORITE FOODS ARE _____

    _____

4. IF I HAD $10.00 I'D _____

    _____

5. MY BEST FRIENDS ARE _____

    _____

6. MY FAVORITE THINGS TO DO WITH THE FAMILY ARE _____

    _____

7. IF I COULD HAVE A NEW RECORD, IT WOULD BE _____

    _____

8. THE THINGS I LIKE TO DO AFTER SCHOOL ARE _____

    _____

9. MY FAVORITE SPORTS ARE _____

    _____

10. IF I COULD BUY THREE GAMES THEY WOULD BE _____

    _____

The ''Reinforcer Survey'' is a must in order to know what the child would like to earn for hard work and appropriate behavior. There is no better way to stay in touch with the changing preferences children and youth have for favorite activities, games, and material things that are popular for their age group. The ''Reinforcer Survey'' should be read to the young child for his/her responses and filled in by the older child. The ''results'' of the survey then provide the basis for the reward to be earned. The ''Reinforcer Survey'' can be ''conducted'' once every month, six weeks, etc.

Assignment Sheet

ASSIGNMENT SHEET		DATE _____	
SUBJECT	**ASSIGNMENT**	**DUE DATE**	**TEACHER SIGNATURE**
Math			
History			
Science			
English			
Fine Arts/ Practical Arts			
Other			

_____

PARENT SIGNATURE

Comments:

ASSIGNMENT SHEET		DATE _____	
SUBJECT	**ASSIGNMENT**	**DUE DATE**	**TEACHER SIGNATURE**
Math			
History			
Science			
English			
Fine Arts/ Practical Arts			
Other			

_____

PARENT SIGNATURE

Comments:

Schedule of Daily Events

SCHEDULE OF DAILY EVENTS

NAME _____

	#1	#2	#3	#4	#5	#6	#7	#8	#9	#10
Monday										
Tuesday										
Wednesday										
Thursday										
Friday										

SCHEDULE OF DAILY EVENTS

NAME _____

	#1	#2	#3	#4	#5	#6	#7	#8	#9	#10
Tuesday										

Each individual student's Schedule of Daily Events is developed for him/her and attached to his/her desk for a week at a time or for one day at a time. This schedule identifies each activity/task the student is assigned for the day, and the schedule is filled in by the teacher one day at a time. Students tend to know what they are to do next when the schedule is provided, and teachers can expect fewer interruptions for directions when students refer to their schedules.

Schedule of Daily Events Sample

SCHEDULE OF DAILY EVENTS

NAME _____

	#1	#2	#3	#4	#5	#6	#7	#8	#9	#10
Monday	Reading	Art (Clay)	Math	Art (Paint)	Science	Creative Writing	Social Studies	Listening	Music	P.E.
Tuesday										
Wednesday										
Thursday										
Friday										

Flash Card Study Aid

Questions   **Topic:** _____

Who:

What:

Where:

When:

How:

Why:

      Topic:_____

Who:

What:

Where:

When:

How:

Why:

Flash Card Study Aid Sample

Questions   Topic: __Pilgrims_____

Who: were the first settlers of North America?

What: did the first settlers do upon arrival?

Where: did the first settlers establish a colony?

When: did the first settlers come to North America?

How: did the first settlers survive?

Why: did the first settlers come to North America?

Topic: __Pilgrims_____

Who: Pilgrims

What: Built longhouses

Where: Plymouth, Mass.

When: 1620's

How: Learned from Indians

Why: Religious freedom

Selected Abbreviations and Symbols

ab.	about	$	money
add.	addition	mo.	month
&	and	natl.	national
bk.	book	no.	number
bldg.	building	#	number
cap.	capital	oz.	ounce
c/o	care of	p., pg.	page
cm.	centimeter	pd.	paid
cent.	century	par.	paragraph
ch., chap.	chapter	pop.	population
co.	company	lb.	pound
cont.	continent	pres.	president
cont.	continued	qt.	quart
corp.	corporation	rd.	road
dept.	department	rep.	representative
dict.	dictionary	Rev.	Reverend
educ.	education	sch.	school
enc.	encyclopedia	sc.	science
Eng.	English	sig.	signature
fig.	figure	s.s.	social studies
geog.	geography	sp.	spelling
govt.	government	sq.	square
gr.	gram	subj.	subject
ht.	height	subt.	subtraction
hist.	history	syn.	synonym
ill., illus.	illustration	temp.	temperature
in.	inch	t.	ton
intro.	introduction	treas.	treasurer
lab.	laboratory	U.S.A.	United States of America
lang.	language	univ.	university
lat.	latitude	v.	verb
leg.	legislature	vs.	versus
lib.	library	v.p.	vice-president
liq.	liquid	wk.	week
max.	maximum	wt.	weight
meas.	measure	w/	with
mi.	mile	yd.	yard
min.	minute	yr.	year
misc.	miscellaneous		

The above list only serves as an example. The
student should further develop his/her own list.

Outline Form

SUBJECT: _____

Topic: _____

General   Specific

Who:

What:

Where:

When:

How:

Why:

Vocabulary:

DO NOT
X
TOUCH

DO NOT
X
TOUCH

DO NOT
X
TOUCH

DO NOT
X
TOUCH

DO NOT
X
TOUCH

DO NOT
X
TOUCH

DO NOT
X
TOUCH

DO NOT
X
TOUCH

DO NOT
X
TOUCH

DO NOT
X
TOUCH

POISON POISON

POISON POISON

POISON POISON

POISON POISON

POISON POISON

IV. Index